BEYOND TECHNIQUE

The Hidden Dimensions of Bodywork

Ronan M. Kisch, Ph.D.

Foreword by Deane Juhan

BLHY Growth Publications
Dayton

Copyright © 1998 by BLHY Growth Publications, Inc.

BLHY Growth Publications, Inc.
2521 Far Hills Avenue
Dayton, Ohio   45419

Printed in the United States of America

Last digit is print number: 9 8 7 6 5 4 3 2 1

ISBN 0-9664761-0-7 (hard)

Library of Congress Catalogue Card Number   98-72933

Every effort has been made to trace and contact copyright holders prior to publication. In some instances, this has proved to be impossible. If notified, the publisher will be pleased to rectify any omissions in the next edition of this book.

ACKNOWLEDGMENTS

In addition to the twenty-five bodyworkers who shared their stories with me there are several other people to whom I would like to express my appreciation. I would like to thank Drs. Melvin Lerner and Robert Straus. Their confidence, encouragement, and investment in me over twenty-five years ago provided me with a graduate education. Innumerable people have been touched and supported as a result of their trust in my abilities and potential. Dr. Yvonne Dalton and Carol Curtis provided their encouragement for this project from the very beginning.

A lot of reading and rereading goes into producing a book. Nancy Laurel Peterson made helpful editorial suggestions in early drafts of this manuscript. My wife, Elizabeth, has participated in editing the manuscript to turn my Brooklynese into readable, understandable, English. Her heartfelt support has helped me bring this project to completion. Linda Edwards, herself a bodyworker, edited the final manuscript. She told me that, like pruning her rose garden, she went through it twice. After the first editing she went back to provide balance. Thank you Linda for a well-balanced job. Linda Wothington proofread the final draft. Her meticulous eye for detail is greatly appreciated. Many of my clients and students have had an opportunity to read selected chapters from this book. Their encouragement has been invaluable. As much as anything else, by allowing me to participate in their life-struggles they have helped in the production of this book.

FOREWARD

Here is a book that sheds real, practical light upon one of the most exciting and yet often one of the most challenging aspects of bodywork of all kinds: the array of personal psychological issues under which practitioners themselves labor—personal challenges that can lead either toward positive professional development or toward intractable difficulties, frustration, and burnout. And much of this same light falls as well upon the sudden, powerful, and potentially cathartic emotional reactions of clients to the work.

The primary focus in most training programs for a wide variety of effective massage and movement therapies is—quite understandably—tactile, physical, biomechanical. Obvious concerns are the development of the quality of touch, the anatomical and physiological background necessary to effectively and responsibly manipulate the human body, proficiency in assessing muscular tensions, ranges of joint motion, and dysfunctional postures, and the successful use of manipulative techniques to improve them. These are the indispensable nuts and bolts of professional bodywork.

But among the most frequently asked questions by virtually all of my own students have been, "What do I do when my client has a powerful emotional response during a session, when the physical work has apparently opened up painful memories or important personal issues for them? And what do I do when I find myself reacting too emotionally to a client, to a situation, or to my work in general?"

Ronan Kisch's book has provided me, my students, and my colleagues with a well thought out and responsibly presented source of experienced observation. Ronan is both a practicing psychotherapist and a bodyworker, and is in a unique position to appreciate both the strengths and shortfalls that each of these disciplines offers. He has also obviously attended to his own psychological development so that he brings focus and clarity to the particular problems that can arise between professional and client, psyche and soma, established patterns and future development.

What all bodyworkers discover is that the structure and functional fusion of the body and the mind guarantees that psychological responses will be inevitable, not unusual, in any bodywork practice. Indeed, an intimation of these deep interconnections between body and mind is more often than not the very thing that has attracted both client and practitioner to the experience of bodywork.

The stimulation of coming to actual grips with both the pathological and therapeutic potentials of this mind-body interaction is one of the principal reasons why bodywork in its various forms is currently the fastest-growing sector of the health care industry. But there are often some jarring surprises in store for those fresh and optimistic practitioners who are too complacently expecting a new, sensually pleasurable, and richly rewarding job of helping people to feel good. To be sure, the rewards are immense. But most of the significant ones, as usual, do not come with unconscious ease.

Touch is pleasing, nurturing, healing, and an inexhaustible source of human contact, comfort, and useful information between individuals. Without an adequate measure of it—and this adequate measure turns out to be rather large—we simply cannot successfully develop and thrive. It is critically absent in our culture, and is I believe one of the primary missing ingredients in our approaches to relationships, child-rearing, education, health care, and many other social contexts.

However, this clear lack and crying need do not necessarily translate into a simple and happy touchy-feely solution. Our need for touch is such that in its absence we suffer, develop anxieties, withdraw or act out in compensatory behaviors, even fail to complete certain levels of our physical and psychological development. Touch is one of the main catalysts of our successful organization both within ourselves and within the world around us, and after we have been without it for too long we are often no longer organized enough to easily give or receive it. Its absence can create the very problems that make its therapeutic assimilation difficult. This is to say that providing pleasurable and revitalizing touch will often run smack into the painful issues created by our lack of it. And this commonly happens for client and practitioner alike.

In many ways our culture is mistrustful of touch, and this mistrust has been both created and reinforced by a long history of philosophical, religious, and social beliefs and conventions. It is largely because of these negative associations and taboos around touch that we have become starved for it, and developmentally compromised by its absence. Many of us have suffered cruelly from one or another abusive form of touch—or abusive denial of touch. All of this leaves most of us deeply confused about touch, filled in equal measure with neediness and fearful misgivings, unable even to distinguish between comforting contact and intrusiveness, pleasant stimulation and arousal. In the very process of "relaxing" and "de-stressing," a whole host of memories, associations, beliefs, compensations, projections, and defensive strategies may well come unbundled, leaving the client—and the practitioner—in the midst of these reactions wondering what on earth went "wrong."

Most bodyworkers have little or no training or licensure in psychological assessment or intervention, and have nothing more than the fortuitous depth or paucity of their own prior life experience to fall back upon when these issues arise. Dr. Kisch reports that few of the practitioners he interviewed "perceived their massage school instructors as conscious of or knowledgeable about psychological phenomena... Experiences of a psychological nature that were encountered in massage school training classes were often ignored or trivialized by instructors. Simplistic answers were provided, instructing students to ignore any psychological material. Little or no explanation of the issues behind these rules was provided... Such professional training practices were reported to leave the student unprepared to deal with the psychosocial realities of everyday practice."

Dr. Kisch's contribution in this book is emphatically not to offer the bodyworker a crash course in psychotherapy, degrading complex issues with simplistic solutions and arming practitioners with a little bit of knowledge that would unquestionably prove to be a dangerous thing. What he does offer is a great deal of clarity concerning the difference between practicing professional psychology and the responsible handling of a range of psychological issues that are likely to emerge in the course of any bodywork practice.

In all of these circumstances, Dr. Kisch's emphasis is never upon "psychologizing" the client, but upon defining the boundaries between intelligent, compassionate support on the part of the bodyworker and the recognition of the need for further discussion, clarification, and possible referral to various other forms of therapy.

Nor are the ethical and emotional interests of the client and the merely legal protection of the bodyworker his only concerns. For practitioners, the inability to recognize and deal successfully with their clients' and their own emotional and interpersonal issues is undoubtedly the major factor in professional burnout—potentially far more taxing and damaging than the physical exertion. These problems inevitably sap the work of its spontaneity, its fascination, and its rewards. They render the bodyworker far less effective, and greatly increase the likelihood that he or she will simply give it up.

On the other hand, there are also continual opportunities for practitioners to develop personally and improve their effectiveness as
therapists and their potency as individuals. "What I came to appreciate
during each interview," Kisch observes, "is that work encounters are
not simple, singular events, but rather a multiplicity of events.
Practitioner and client meet on economic, somatic, social, psychological, medical, religious, spiritual, and perhaps even psychic realms. And
these realms exist within as well as between each bodyworker and
client." This is an enormously rich field for interaction and learning for
both parties, and indeed it is one of the chief joys of the profession of
bodywork that it continually offers the opportunities and makes the
demands for endless personal growth and refinement.

One final note: Bodyworkers have not only a personal interest but
also a large collective responsibility for coming to grips with these
boundaries between the somatic and the psychological. This domain of
the bodymind, and the development of more and more effective therapies that will come from it, are unlikely to be explored extensively
anytime soon by the strictly psychological disciplines, since for the
most part their legal and ethical protocols specifically prohibit or profoundly limit touching. This book, and the active addressing of its
concerns and conclusions, will be an important part of the bridgework
across the chasms of abuse and repression, and the painful distance
between our flesh and the touch that would make it whole. Ronan
Kisch extends a psychotherapist's hand to us, beckoning toward a
future where clearer heads and more open hearts, and better therapists, will prevail. But we will have to do our work.

Deane Juhan
September 20, 1996
Mill Valley, California

PREFACE

As I completed this book, several thoughts came to me that I wanted to share with my readers. I incorporated bodywork into my life long before I began bodywork training. It helped me to manage stress. Later, bodywork provided an invaluable tool in releasing my own longstanding, chronic, psychological holding patterns. Bodywork has become an integral part of my practice of clinical psychology. It is no longer possible for me to listen to a client's concerns without being aware of body posture, breathing patterns, stereotypic positions of their hands and feet, holding patterns and movements, as well as their aches and pains.

Bodywork permeates every aspect of my life. It feels so significant, so important that I am privileged and blessed to possess the knowledge and skills it provides me. Until his death, bodywork offered me a somatic language to communicate with my father who had been deprived of verbal language by Alzheimer's Disease.

This research project began following a divorce, and has been with me through the decline of my parent's health, and the death of both of my parents. It also has been an underlying support for my wife Elizabeth and myself after the tragic and senseless death of her son at the hands of a drunken driver. Beyond any question, undertaking this project has been of immeasurable support for me over the last seven years of my life.

In contrast, writing has always been traumatic for me. I flunked the third grade, struggled with spelling, and passed high school English by only two points. Many times along the way of writing this book, I doubted whether or not I had the skills and the stamina to finish this project, or the courage to put my work out for public scrutiny.

During those times I listened to the bodyworkers I met with at trainings and in informal meetings. As I heard them talk of their experiences and their concerns, I felt a renewed conviction to continue. Later in the project, as I lived with the struggles of my interviewees, as I read my notes, listened to my tape recordings, wrote on my word processor, or reviewed things in my memory, the need to finish this project became an imperative. I felt and believed that the material entrusted to me needed to be shared with its future readers. There were people waiting to be supported, comforted, and educated by this information.

Undertaking this project allowed me to meet and become enriched by many talented, caring individuals. I hope this material will allow me to reach out from behind the cloister of my office and share with people whom I would never otherwise have had an opportunity to make contact. Hopefully by writing about my own psychological perspective on bodywork, I will have the opportunity to pass on some of the aspects of this gift that have been such a blessing for me.

Ultimately what I wish to convey to bodyworkers, health care providers, educators, administrators, and managers is that you do not merely possess the tools of your trade. You embody those tools. You are the tools of your trade. The quality of your intervention with your clients is a function of the quality of your presence with them. To the degree you invest in your own personal development, you perfect the tools of your trade.

R.M.K.
Dayton, Ohio
3 October, 1996

TABLE OF CONTENTS

INTRODUCTION

This study explores the experiences of twenty-five bodyworkers, people who work with their hands, their intuition, and often their hearts. It began one morning when I received a long distance phone call from a bodyworker friend. My friend explained that she had just had an encounter with a client that left her feeling shaken and upset. She shared this experience with me and afterward reported feeling greatly relieved. We also discussed how she could approach this client, should the client return. That would have been the end of the phone call incident except...just for a lark, I decided to write down the telephone conversation.

A month or so later I received another call from my friend. Guess what! The client returned...and my friend was now prepared. The second session went smoothly, leaving my bodyworker friend feeling good about the session and herself as well. I wrote this episode down, also.

Later the thoughts occurred to me, "My friend had a personal and professional growth experience. This experience and similar experiences could be made available to others, and perhaps they too could learn and grow from them." The troubling symptoms of stressful life circumstances can often be relieved merely by understanding and appreciating their normality. My hopes were, and still are, to share these events so that novices to the bodywork field might understand certain emotional reactions are the natural consequences of life stress and be spared similar struggles in their development of a professional stance in these situations. Those already in the field would have an opportunity to normalize some of their disturbing experiences. They would see how some of their colleagues have dealt with a variety of personal-professional challenges and compare and contrast how they would deal, or had dealt, with similar encounters.

I further thought that in addition to the stories, key psychological issues could be highlighted and discussed. This would provide for the further depth of understanding and potential growth of the readers.

With these thoughts in mind, I began collecting and transcribing the professional experiences of bodyworkers.

As I gathered and recorded the stories, I discovered that certain themes were pertinent to some of my psychotherapy clients. I offered the particular manuscripts to these individuals to read. They reported that the stories were both interesting and clarifying and they were readily able to identify with the situations of the bodyworkers. The stories helped them to gain insight into their own issues of personality development and the dynamics of their interpersonal relationships. At that point, I realized the material could be of benefit not just to bodyworkers but anyone interested in personal growth. It could be particularly helpful for those in positions of leadership, health care, education, management, or administration.

As the collection of stories grew and my analysis of the stories deepened, I realized I was defining my own beliefs and underlying philosophies. While this collection of stories would be far from an exhaustive psychological treatise of human behavior or the full range of possible experiences that a bodyworker could encounter, I hoped they would demonstrate the rich source of information and growth potential that could be derived from everyday work/life experiences. Another belief I maintain is that learning from experiences is particularly important to bodyworkers because many of those who enter the profession are not simply exploring a means of financial support; they are seeking personal life-meaning from their vocational choice. Additionally, they are concerned with supporting their clients in their ability to live fulfilling lives.

Should bodyworkers choose to identify and utilize the potential growth that emerges from their professional encounters, this growth will have a ripple effect beyond the immediate experience. Consequently, the quality of the practitioners' work will enrich their selves, their clients, and the community that is being supported by them.

The purpose of this book is not to train counselors or psychotherapists. It is intended to help people working in the healing professions, specifically bodyworkers, become more aware of some of the psychological phenomena that may arise as they are working with others. Moreover, anyone in a position of authority may benefit from exploring the potential of everyday professional encounters.

Every individual is unique and each situation must be assessed on its own merits. This work is not meant to provide a prescription for solving or fixing specific work situations; it is not intended to provide solutions to the personal dilemmas of bodyworkers in their practices. Nor is this material intended to provide "advice" to bodyworkers' clients should they face similar situations. This work is an attempt to bring issues to the practitioner's awareness. Through this awareness, hopefully, bodyworkers will be able to improve self-knowledge, enhance self-acceptance, heighten self-respect, and make better decisions. As readers wrestle with this material, they may begin to define more clearly their personal and professional identities, and their sense of values and ethics. From positions of ever-increasing clarity of self-definition, these practitioners will then be able to be more fully present with their clients in a more grounded, integrated, and supportive way. The quality of the bodyworkers' integrity and their touch sends a nurturing message that may be as important as, if not more important than, the actual physical manipulations performed.

While this work is specifically not meant to be a "How To" book, from time to time I offer what I term, "Problem-Solving Strategies." They are designed to be helpful tools for clarifying the salient features in the particular situation and may then help the practitioner in drawing more precise conclusions and in creating their own unique solutions.

Life experiences are important events in the development of one's personal and professional identities. Thankfully, it is not necessary to have every experience in order to acquire a fully developed sense of identity. Many facets of one's identity can be fleshed out through vicarious learning, that is, learning from the experiences of others, thus saving a lot of personal wear and tear. This study has gathered professional experiences that have helped bodyworkers to develop and define their own sense-of-self and their professional boundaries. Hopefully, these stories provide a sense of the many paths that can lead to growth.

This author believes that the psychophysiological grounding bodyworkers bring to their work is derived from the technical skills they perform and from the integration of life experiences. Awareness of these experiences, when, and even after they occur, may exist on a continuum which ranges from beneath the limit of awareness; to a fuzzy, pre-verbal awareness; to an intuition; to a clear realization. When these situations are beyond awareness, the bodyworker has little or no command of the unperceived situation. However, as a bodyworker becomes cognizant of these experiences, a window begins to open into the opportunity of a new realm of potential growth. Those who choose to grasp this opportunity take command of their lives. The result of this step of awareness and the choice to respond is the building and reinforcing of the individual's character. If the action taken is effective, the bodyworkers become more professionally successful. In a spiral effect, this is also character-building. The two grow upon each other: personal growth lends to building professional growth; professional growth lends to building personal growth.

Sometimes these growth situations present themselves once, and we call them a fluke. Sometimes they occur over and over again; then they are termed recurring themes. Whether they are flukes or recurring themes, it is advantageous for the bodyworker to recognize the situation as a potential growth event and then take action upon it. The situation might be written down, contemplated, discussed with colleagues, and/or explored with a consultant.

Sometimes these experiences present themselves, and there is plenty of opportunity to mull them over and deliberate upon both their significance and the direction to be taken. At other times, the bodyworker may be abruptly confronted by these experiences. Then the immediacy demanded by these confrontations may leave the bodyworker feeling overwhelmed and unprepared to respond effectively. When this demand outstrips the ability to respond, such a case is called a "crisis." This crisis may evoke feelings of anxiety, frustration, fear, anger, rage, resentment, or abandonment. The list can go on and on. However, as soon as the bodyworker recognizes that something is happening and chooses to respond, she or he is back in command.

Though a growth experience may be perceived as a crisis, with sufficient internal or external support, the event can alternately be an invitation for self-exploration and growth—a friend in disguise—or the client as teacher. The type of outcome which emerges depends upon the perspective from which the bodyworker chooses to view this event.

Identity achievement is a process. It happens as a result of our interaction with our environment. We do not come into the world with a perfectly formed sense of identity. It develops as we interact with our environment, as we live and learn. This process may either be growth-driven or fear-driven. We have a choice over how the process is motivated. We can allow our fears to direct us onto a path of avoidance or denial. This path results in "foreclosure," a shallow unexamined life, or "identity diffusion," a fuzzy sense of self. Although punitiveness and self-blame may stop an undesired behavior, punitive reactions leave a scar of lowered self-esteem in the psychological core of an individual and usually do not lead to paths of growth and improvement. The alternative is to face and grapple with imperfection without judgment or shame and to strive for a more complete sense of self-realization. This is "identity achievement."

The naïve reader may think that the interviewees soon to be encountered are somehow weak because they talk about childhood wounds, professional stumbling blocks, or apparently unresolved lifestyle dilemmas. The truth is that the stark awareness of and confrontation with one's growth areas requires great courage and strength. This growth process is a journey which is taken by few.

Self-awareness, self-confrontation, and self-growth may not be as commonly practiced as denial, suppression, or blaming. In the short run, introspection may feel uncomfortable or even punishing. As we turn our psychological eyes inward, pain, inadequacy, imperfection, insult, doubt, avoidance, loss, trauma, and regret may emerge. Certainly such awarenesses are no fun to encounter. However, failing to turn inward, perceiving, and becoming aware is to maintain the status quo. In the long run this creates its own pains, inadequacies, imperfections, insults, doubts, avoidances, traumas, and illnesses. Healthy or not, maintaining the familiar, the status quo, is the norm.

The opposite of maintaining the status quo is to engage in one's life-growth. It is a courageous journey because, in the process, the voyager is subject to some of the most heinous and frightening of obstacles. People may face what they consider to be their own repulsive imperfections. They run the risk that others will see and be revulsed by what they believe are unacceptable inner characteristics. Furthermore, they risk the loss of control of their sense of reality by letting go of the familiar as they open themselves and become vulnerable to the unknown. Many people do not undertake such a growth journey. "If it ain't broke ...," they do not attempt to improve upon it. If they are unable to perceive "what the fuss is all about" for others, they tend to deny the significance of the event. They then become callous to another person's pain. This is the norm. Growth is undertaken by those who possess the insight, integrity, strength, and courage to transcend the norm.

Bodywork is not a panacea. However, those who are familiar with bodywork have long known the significance and power of touch. They experientially, as well as intellectually, understand and appreciate the factors of body weight, temperature, constriction, pulse, vitality of the flesh, range of motion, body awareness, unconscious somatic internalization, as well as, release. They know that these physical pulses are also a measure of emotional well being. They know that the same modality, touch, which allows them to access their clients' well being, also allows them to provide a cathartic release, and measure the success of their intervention. These factors are virtually invisible to, and experientially unknown by, the strictly verbal therapist. Allowing their touch to be guided by these variables, and a theoretical framework of healing, the bodywork practitioner can provide profound releases of symptoms due to conditions such as: anxiety, panic, depression, aches and pains, post traumatic stress, TMJ, migraine, sexual and physical abuse, somatization, arthritis, and fibromyalgia. To the degree that these conditions effect other illnesses, injuries, or diseases they may even have additional healing effects. Also taught is the feeling of nurturing, non-invasive, non-sexualized touch. It can help those who have become alienated from their bodies by trauma, illness, familial rigidity, or abuse, to reclaim and appreciate their bodies.

Bodyworkers like psychotherapists come from different theoretical orientations. Neuromuscular therapists work with the muscles to release spasm. Craniosacral therapists focus on bones not muscles. Trager practitioners are concerned with the quality of their touch rather than the specific techniques used. Healing Touch practitioners do not actually touch the body. Mainstream psychology which has no specific knowledge base of a discipline for the release of somatic stress, struggles with the issue of whether or not to touch at all. For psychologists touch usually means: shaking hands, providing a comforting hand to a client's arm, shoulder, or back, or perhaps a reassuring confirming hug as a client walks out the door. Sometimes it might even involve cradling a client who is reliving some terrifying life event. While these techniques lack the sophistication of the bodyworker's, they can have profound therapeutic or cathartic value.

Unfortunately, for many of those who possess only an intellectual knowledge of the mindbody connection, touch is still suspect. For some, there is a dogmatic, authoritarian disapproval of any form of touch, an almost phobic avoidance of physical contact, and a concern for the professional and economic consequences of malpractice suits. Others are in a theoretical deadlock as to what constitutes healing and what if any role touch should play in the process. Psychologists in general are concerned over those who might be frivolous or would flagrantly violate either the personal or sexual boundaries of their clients.

In many realms in which abuse can exist, we recognize that there is also a healthy and productive middle ground. This is true in the realm of touch. To achieve that stance one must appreciate the potency of this intervention, the vulnerability it creates for both the practitioner and the client, and the deliberate integrity one must bring to its use. When such respect is brought to bear, touch has the potential for physical and psychological confirmation, comfort, catharsis, healing, and self-confirmation. If not from earnest, knowing, trained professionals from where would such information come?

Ken Dychtwald in his book, *Bodymind*, explores the dynamic relationships between the parts of the anatomical body, their function in relationship to the physical environment, and their psychological significance. Dychtwald suggests that the realm of the body and its functions are integral with the mind and not separate. By hyphenating the term body-mind *(or mind-body)*, a separation or duality is created and maintained. By omitting the hyphen, the conceptualization of bodymind or *mindbody* preserves an integral, functional unity. In a similar context, Dean Juhan, in his book, *Job's Body*, discusses the contraction of the words "body" and "work" into a single term "body-work." Bodywork conceptually implies a meaning that surpasses a simple physical intervention performed on a body. Bodywork specifically connotes an intervention upon the person touched which intentionally impacts the psyche and is not separate from but integral with the soma. Both Dychtwald's and Juhan's conceptualizations are essential to the appreciation of the themes explored in this book.

Arbitrarily, I decided to collect twenty-five stories for this project. The majority of practitioners in the bodywork field are women. To represent the gender difference, twenty of these stories are from women; five are from men. Most of the stories were drawn from bodyworkers who were engaged in some type of advanced professional training. They agreed to share a story which they understood would be used to better prepare novices and professionals alike for the experiences that might arise in a bodywork career. Their stories might help to normalize some of the experiences that others in the field had encountered but never had the opportunity to share. Further, these stories may provide an opportunity for other bodyworkers to compare their responses in similar situations.

The participants were asked to relate the first story which came to their minds that was indicative of a critical or problematic professionally related experience, one which caused them to wrestle with themselves in order to clarify, change, or establish some understanding, policy, or procedure. From time to time questions were asked to help clarify answers. Finally, an epilogue was added for some stories when, as a result of telling the story, a bodyworker had an awareness or insight which led her or him to go back to a client, to re-address an issue, or to respond differently at a later time.

To obtain the twenty-five stories in the study, twenty-five women and fourteen men were approached. Of the women, three declined to participate. Of the men, five declined to participate. Of the women, two stories did not meet the criteria for the collection because they did not clearly present both a sense of crisis for the bodyworker and a struggle for clarification and commitment. Of the men, four did not meet the criteria.

For example, one bodyworker spoke of crying for a week after receiving work from a chiropractor. She reported being frightened because she was unable to understand where all her sadness was coming from. After a week or so, she decided that the chiropractor must have been working on some emotional trigger-point. Having come to this conclusion, she dropped the incident—end of story. Clearly, there was an emotional crisis for this woman, but, she did not feel moved to identify, understand, confront, or change anything. A second example is that of a man who spoke of a friend who came to him complaining of leg pain. This practitioner reported having a bad feeling about his friend's pain and was reticent to work on him. He suggested the friend seek medical care. However, his macho buddy insisted that he be worked upon. The bodyworker complied. The man's pain worsened. The buddy then went to a physician who took x-rays which revealed bone spurs—end of story. In this case while there was some indecision as to what to do, there was no personal-professional struggle, self-examination, resolution, or addressing of professional policy or practice.

Some of the participants tended not to be analytical or verbal. As a result, self-expression was a struggle for them. Their dialogue was choppy, marked by long pauses, shifts in thought, "ums," "ya knows," and "I means," and did not necessarily lend to paragraph format. For the benefit of readability, this author took the liberty of editing idiosyncrasies in speech. In addition, the names and identities of the bodyworkers have been altered in order to provide for privacy. Otherwise, every attempt has been made to maintain the integrity of the bodyworkers' stories.

Each story is followed by a discussion which emerged from an examination of the interview which began by asking the questions: What are the central issues that confronted the bodyworker in her or his experience? What is the psychological nature of the issues that were experienced? What happened to the bodyworker as a result of this experience? What decision emerged for the bodyworker as a result of this encounter? What would have made this or a similar case easier to cope with, respond to, or understand?

The twenty-five stories have been divided into six sections. The reader will discover that there are multiple themes in each story. In the sections, stories that were characterized by a specific decision were placed together. The first section reflects a variety of situations that either brought a person to the bodywork field or marked a beginning of a new way of perceiving and practicing bodywork. The second section explores challenging situations with clients that forced the bodyworkers to recognize their own beliefs and to take a stand with a client. The third section is comprised of stories relating to the special problems presented by clients who suffer from psychologically clinical syndromes. The fourth section relates to bodyworkers who had a desire to help, give advice, rescue, or heal their client. The fifth section is devoted to the experiences of the five male bodyworkers. The final section is comprised of stories told by bodyworkers who identified themselves as being "in recovery" or having been sexually wounded in childhood or adolescence.

I would like to share a final concern I have regarding the material in this book. This material, like any personal growth stimulus, may act for some readers as an emotional trigger for troubling life memories or issues. Should this occur, it is my hope those readers will demonstrate the strength, wisdom, and courage to seek appropriate consultation or professional support to cope with and resolve their issues.

Part I

BEGINNINGS

1

RESTRAINED FROM INSIDE

Pam is a serious, emotionally flat, 36 year old, divorced flight attendant.

I was flying a Transatlantic flight from New York when a man several years younger than myself caught my eye. He requested a magazine which I gave to him. But, then, two or three minutes later he handed it back. This seemed somewhat peculiar. I quickly let this pass as I had other passengers to attend to. Then meal service began. During the meal service, I became aware of a commotion. Someone fainted. I was busy serving meals, but out of the corner of my eye, I saw approximately where in the plane this incident occurred. The head stewardess took care of it.

I later saw the person who fainted. It was the same man I gave and took the magazine from. He appeared to be a young, healthy man. I thought, "People do faint in flight and require oxygen, but they are not usually young, healthy people." This was puzzling to me. The head stewardess later came to the kitchen area where the stewardesses were still handling the meal service. She informed us, "You will have to talk to him. I can't handle this anymore. He just lost his wife in a car crash." With this she walked away. I immediately felt as if I had to cry.

After I finished delivering drinks and blankets to the passengers I saw none of the other stewardesses had approached the man. I decided I would respond to him. Before I did, I immediately began to pray that I would have the courage and strength to console him. I sat down with the distraught, rocking, man. He began to ramble. I knew that this man was desperately in need of support. I also recognized that

I was limited in what I could do for him. I was limited by my own community, family, and marital background.

In my home town everyone knows everyone else's business. Showing feelings is a sign of weakness and vulnerability. But they can't know your feelings if you hold them down. There is no community counseling service or private psychotherapy other than alcohol abuse treatment or the psychiatric treatment at the community hospital. Going to a treatment center or a psychotherapist would be stigmatizing even if there was such a service. There is a spiritualist in town who provides consultation, but, she is usually booked-up, so it's hard to get an appointment with her. The community encourages pushing down feelings and I learned not to be open with mine.

At home, my parents were constantly in conflict over financial matters. There was constant tension and little expression of warmth. I am the oldest of four children and received the least amount of attention from my mother. I felt unlovable and not as important as my brothers. As the oldest, it was my job to care for my younger siblings.

My husband's father died in his childhood. His mother then withheld her physical closeness from him. My husband was a "jock." He would neither touch nor allow himself to be touched lest he look like a "sissy." He was possessive. He would mimic and mock me if we were together and I would say "hello" to another man. I learned not to touch after eleven years of a touch deprived marriage. I was afraid to reach out and touch others and thought if I did I would be rejected. "Better to suffer from deprivation than rejection." From early in my life I learned to insulate my feelings and to deal with the outside world as best I could.

Suddenly, I was confronted with an emoting passenger. I was torn between wanting to help and wanting to avoid what this was demanding from me. As I talked to this passenger, I learned that he had long feared he would lose his wife in an accident. I tried to console him as best I could. I wanted to somehow touch him. However, after three decades of holding myself back, I felt as if my parents and my ex-husband were restraining me from inside. After a lot of soul searching and struggling I was able to reach through my own barrier. I gently touched and stroked his back. He then quieted and began to speak more coherently of his plans and expectations for himself and his wife. I began to cry without knowing exactly why. I quickly apologized with a chuckle, "I'm supposed to be making you feel better and here I am getting upset. I am not helping you at all." Spontaneously, he pulled himself together and said, "Oh, But it helps! You are the first person who has shown any compassion. Eighteen hours ago I was contacted about the accident. My wife was to join me in The States. Since then, en route home to Europe, I have told people of my loss. They tell me they are sorry and promptly turn away. Your crying has been healing for me."

A week later, I received a phone call from Europe. It was the man and he just returned from the funeral. He told me that his wife had committed suicide. Months later, I called to inquire how he was doing. He was not in. I spoke with his roommate. I never heard from the passenger again. I realized, I must have been a painful reminder of the past and let go of my contact with him.

(As Pam spoke of this event, her face became flushed and red patches like a dam burst of capillaries broke out over her neck. Tears started to roll from her eyes. She whispered.) I can't talk. *(Then regaining her composure)* I'm grateful because I was chosen to be there. I did not recognize that there were four stewardesses available to support this man. Only I chose to respond.

At first I felt for this passenger. I felt really bad for what he had to go through. *(As she reflected on the situation she cried more.)* Then my thoughts went from my passenger to the man's dead wife. I remembered my own pain in marriage. I remembered how I felt better about myself and my life when my husband went away on long business trips. I remember heavy feelings like dark clouds coming over me when he returned. Then like a fresh breeze clearing the air, the feelings would lift again when he left. The wounds would not heal from his indiscretions. I remember being unable to receive comfort from my priest. He told me that I was not deserving because it was my duty to forgive. I felt the pain all over again. I can't forgive.

I didn't believe that my "macho" husband's ego could tolerate my asking him for a divorce. I remember my life of praying that he would ask me for a divorce so my torment in the marriage would be ended. I remembered my own thoughts and plans of suicide. That would have been another way out. *(Sobs then came from deep in Pam's belly.)* I remember feeling despair as a child. It's unfair being a girl. It is like you are not on the Earth. You *had* to take care of others, but you don't have a right to be yourself. You are only here to take care of men.

I had a friend who, the day after my flight, was to attend a reflexology workshop. I never would have done this before, but after the struggle I had with touching on the flight the day before, I decided to do it. I didn't sign up for the class to practice reflexology. I wanted to overcome my discomfort with touch. I took the class for personal growth. Later I signed up to study two other forms of body contact therapy though I didn't do it to become a bodyworker. My aim was to overcome my own blockages with touch. Ultimately I want to teach what I learned to others.

DISCUSSION

AGITATED DEPRESSION   Pam's passenger took a magazine and then turned around and gave it back. She recognized this man's behavior[1] was peculiar, but she was unable to understand it. Some people get depressed and become lethargic. Others get depressed and become agitated. Pam, though unable to identify an agitated depression, was sufficiently sensitive and intuitive to suspect something was very wrong with the passenger.

CATHARSIS   Pam's agitated passenger told her that she was the only one to "show any compassion." As she struggled over what to do, she opened her own earnestness to him. That compassion quieted the passenger. As she opened to his loss, she simultaneously opened herself to her own losses. Opening to any loss often has the effect of getting a person to realize other unresolved losses. The act of active grieving has the effect of providing a catharsis[2] for loss.

CULTURAL INFLUENCES   While cultural influences are often subtle, their effect on the development of personality is extremely powerful as can be seen in Pam's story. Exactly what those influences are can be difficult to identify unless one leaves the context of her or his cultural rules or breaks those rules as Pam did in her work as a stewardess by putting her in contact with people from various backgrounds. As a professional woman, Pam commanded a different kind of respect than she did as a daughter, wife, or community member. Pam's alternative perspective sensitized her to the norms of her own community, as well as, those of different communities.

NEGLECT   Pam's reaction to her peculiar passenger was also influenced by a subtle form of child abuse which Pam experienced in her youth. Child abuse is usually recognized when it comes in the form of severe, habitual, physical punishment. It is easily recognized in the form of sexual involvement with other children, adolescents, family members, or other adults. Sexual abuse may even be seen when a parent does not protect a child from the acting out of other children, family members, or friends. And, child abuse may also articulate itself in the form of neglect, which is often more subtle and unfortunately, often unrecognized.

Neglect may present itself in a physical way when a child does not receive proper supervision, food, adequate clothing, bathing, shelter, medical attention, access to education, or sufficient physical stimulation. All these can lead to growth impairment, or failure to thrive. More subtle and also damaging is psychological neglect. Pam's psychological neglect was the result of sex role discrimination by her parents, husband, and community. Non-verbally Pam was taught that she had little personal value outside of serving her brothers. She received less attention from her mother than did her brothers. In her marriage, she acted as a servant to her husband. In her career as a stewardess, Pam served airline passengers even though she was compensated for her work. If serving as a stewardess was actually what Pam wanted to do and she had made a conscious decision to enter this field, then her work would leave her feeling fulfilled. But, Pam may not have been provided the awareness and opportunity of alternative vocations from which to choose. Her choice to be a stewardess may not have been a totally free one. Furthermore, early life experiences led Pam to feel inferior and unworthy of pursuing her aspirations just because she was a female. The brothers' childhood experiences and expectations were not dominated by caretaking. Though it was not stated overtly, Pam was taught to abandon herself.

ALIENATION   Pam spoke of her community's lack of psychological support for its members and of an attitude which fostered the repression of its members' self-expression. "Normal" behavior involved "holding down" feelings in order to have a sense of integrity and an image of strength. These left Pam feeling lonely and insecure rather than whole and strong. Having an image of strength is not the same as being strong. Pam's community did not teach her to be strong. It taught her how to be stoic and depressed.

Pam's family reflected its community's values. She learned from her parents that her sole value in life was gained from the role that she played. As a female and the oldest of four children, it was her task to cater to the needs of her younger brothers. For decades Pam would remain unaware that her personality was shaped in a different way and in certain ways remained underdeveloped because she was a female. She experienced herself as inferior, inconsequential, and irrelevant as compared to males. Her feelings of inferiority would make it relatively easy for her husband to exploit and dominate her.

Pam's family also taught her not to expect or demand warmth, attention, love, respect, or physical comfort from a marital partner. Her choice in a husband reflected her family values. His punishment of Pam by mimicking her attempts to make friendly social contact further reinforced the conditioning she had already received at home.

In turn, Pam's priest reinforced her role to accept her husband's "indiscretions" and "forgive." He failed to recognize those indiscretions were gnawing away at Pam's will to live. He also failed to reinforce in Pam, her right to have her needs for love, warmth, affection, appreciation, encouragement, and sexuality be fulfilled. The entire issue of Pam being recognized, appreciated, and reinforced for being the person she was and receiving external support to actualize her own potential was neglected by the significant members of her social arena. Even within the Church, forgiveness is announced following contrition, confession and repentance. Yet this representative of the Church expected such forgiveness to come from Pam to her former husband without genuine signs of his contrition, confession and repentance.

From a young age, social reinforcement taught Pam to abandon her feelings for herself, her needs, her desires, and her frustrations. She felt as if there was "no place on the Earth" for her. This loss of self is the nature of alienation. Thankfully, Pam was to be brought out of her alienation by the crisis she faced over touching her passenger.

JOCK Just as Pam was victimized by her family background and community norms so was her former husband. At the very same time that he was internally embracing community-determined norms and externally sporting the image of "macho jock," he was depriving himself of the richness of mutually expressed love as well as intimate warmth, understanding, confirmation, and heart-felt touching from his wife. As the ex-husband succeeded in achieving his image, he lost contact with his core personality and genuine feelings.

The former husband's facade is clearly that of "he-man." What are the underlying issues that would motivate an intelligent man to emotionally abandon his wife, while jealously maintaining her as a possession? Pam explained that her former husband's mother withdrew her emotional support from her children after the death of her husband. Very likely she became depressed after the loss. In a community that had no available psychological services and a norm of internalizing feelings, she may have had insufficient emotional help to deal with her loss, and depression became part of her life style. As a result, it is possible that early on Pam's husband learned from his maternal role model that love from a married woman was not overtly expressed. He expected that his wife would not express her affection. They would both have it and know it, but not act upon it. A second possibility might be that the ex-husband, not having observed loving interaction between his parents lacked an appropriate role model, and overcompensated for what he believed it was to be a man. A third explanation suggests the former husband may have been angry at his mother for withholding her affection from him. In the family of origin, he may have played the role of "dutiful son" and internalized his angry feelings toward his mother. These hostile feelings were then displaced onto his wife. Another possibility is that the ex-husband may have learned rather provincial roles for husband and wife. The wife would have been perceived as a "Madonna." As a "Madonna" she was to be treated as if she were beyond carnal experience or desire. Consequently, to meet his needs he would have to seek gratification outside of the marriage. Complicating the ex-husband's touch issue was the additional factor of his extramarital relationships. He might have been suffering from feelings of guilt over his "indiscretions." Not dealing with his own impropriety, he then may have projected his impropriety onto his wife and became hypersensitive to her contact with other men. All along he was suppressing his own guilt.

It is also possible that Pam, angry at men, was unwilling to be emotionally and physically present for her husband. What mitigates against this last explanation is that both during and after the marriage Pam was interested in having emotionally intimate contact. In all likelihood, some issue, either conscious or unconscious, existed in the former husband making him unwilling or unable to confront either himself or Pam.

Whatever the psychological reason for the husband's behavior, he was willing to take care of his own needs while he oppressed hers. After eleven years of touch-deprivation she learned not to ask for what she believed would not be forthcoming. Pam internalized her feelings from the rest of the world. The husband's core feelings were also internalized from the rest of the world. The two were in a marriage, but physically and emotionally insulated from each other.

The family and the community created roles for both Pam and her husband. For many years they dutifully played their roles at their own expense. Legitimate societal representatives who could have helped to bring health to the relationship instead reinforced its pathology. Perhaps, if the husband were truly his own man and able to perceive how external forces influenced him to withdraw his affections from his loving wife, he could have resolved these issues for himself. He then could have known intimacy in his marriage and would not have subjected his wife to the emotional torture that brought her to the brink of suicide.

CONFLICT: A PROBLEM-SOLVING STRATEGY   With emotional maturity certain psychological qualities can be discerned that at earlier stages were not perceivable. With this vision one can look through the available partner pool and more clearly identify who is, and who is not, a viable partner.

However, even this partner may not provide a perfect fit. As a result, it is essential that partners be willing to problem-solve. At a more mature point in life it is easier to build a problem-solving mechanism into a relationship and it is best incorporated as early as possible. Future issues can then be resolved as they arise. The problem-solving process helps create closeness, compatibility, and bonding. The longer the relationship exists without a mutually satisfying problem-solving mechanism, the harder it is to double back and build one into the contract. If the perspective partner is unwilling to problem solve, she or he may be defining herself or himself out of the category of attractive, viable partners. If either partner is unwilling to problem-solve, she or he is already building disharmony and emotional distance into the relationship.

Usually in the initial or romantic phase of a relationship, conflicts, disagreements, or fights are avoided at all cost. This creates a romantic and false picture of what the relationship is actually like. A better indicator than first impressions of the viability of a relationship is the couple's ability to problem-solve. Precisely because most relationships are not perfect, there will always be differences. How these differences are handled will provide an excellent predictor of things to come. Consequently, rather than fearing conflict, a couple would do well to eagerly look forward to it. It is here that they will discover their capacity to work through their issues and their willingness to build a realistic, constructive problem-solving mechanism into the relationship.

IDENTITY CRISIS   The internal emotional turmoil created within this stewardess after being confronted by her needy passenger was immense. Two value systems and two levels of truth would have a Transatlantic midair collision. Pam experienced the crash between her intuitive wisdom and the prohibition of decades of internalized social and psychological oppression within herself. After all, who was she to go against the values of family, the man she had married, her church, and her community? Somewhere above the Atlantic Ocean, at a moment in time, all of these unconscious, internalized forces were welling up, piercing into her consciousness, bringing cognitive, emotional, and somatic awareness into unity.

Pam's decision to touch broke the social taboos of her past. It also broke through another layer of her depression. In order for Pam to hold herself in by not making contact, she had to reject something that was of greater value to her—touch.

LETTING GO RATHER THAN BREAKING DOWN   Pam had an emotional explosion. She too, like her passenger found herself in uncontrolled sobbing. One could perceive Pam's response as breaking down. She could also be seen as choosing to let go. Decades of painful emotions which had been pushed from her awareness came gushing out. This 36 year old woman was able to allow herself to experience the emotions that prompted her divorce. She could start grieving her losses. Pam was on her own and outside of the context of her repressive family, former husband, and community. She had her own financial security and no longer had to fear her dependence upon another person being threatened by her self expression. In this free air space, her repressed energy was liberated.

IDENTIFICATION   As her emotions migrated from her unconscious to her conscious, Pam began to grasp the idea that her emotional identification was not with her passenger, but with his wife. She realized only too well that she could have been the deceased wife of a traveling husband. She might have ended her years of deprivation and suffering at her own hands. Pam recognized all of the emotional trauma and pain that a person must go through before she or he makes such a final break with life. Her emotions began to flow as she became one with her experiences and thoughts.

Pam recalled her long, enduring struggle to come to her own truth about her marriage. It was only by listening and trusting her feelings that she was able to plot a new life course. There were often doubts along the way, and even the "guidance" she received from clergy served to make her feel less deserving as a person and more self-effacing as a wife. The lack of support and viable alternatives within her own command led Pam to suicidal desperation.

SUICIDE   Pam identified strongly with the solution of her passenger's wife. If not for her "macho" husband's asking for a divorce, that same brutally final solution might have been her own. She would have turned the explosion of the anger she felt toward her husband, her parents, her community, and her inferior female identity status back on herself. She would have been released from the unending internal pain deep within her psychological core. Thankfully, Pam was spared that choice.

There are many reasons that people contemplate suicide. It can be an indirect way of lashing out with one's anger when other alternatives do not seem to exist. Sometimes it is an attempt to get attention. Often it is a way of seeking relief from chronic pain or terminal illness. Sometimes it is an attempt to stop an interminable emotional pain with a terminal physical pain. The latter would have been true in Pam's case. Pam felt trapped in a marriage[3] that did not provide for her needs. Yet a more benign solution was offered by her husband's desire to move on in his romantic life.

A LIFE CHANGING DECISION   Ultimately, Pam's Transatlantic flight freed her from her unresolved depression, the suicidal feelings, her alienation, and the internal restraint that prohibited her from touching or feeling. The serendipitous encounter with the depressed passenger provided the catalyst for Pam's own catharsis. Personal growth follows self-examination, as well as, motivation to change one's lifestyle, and taking action on that decision.

Pam faced a crisis on her flight. She acted to emotionally and physically support her passenger. This, however, was not the final resolution to her identity struggle. The action that Pam took with her passenger created a momentum which would extend to her own life. Pam would seek the quality that had been missing for her—touch. She would do this by taking a reflexology class that a friend had mentioned to her. She did not go to learn new skills to serve others but because she recognized that there was something missing within herself. This hiatus was no longer acceptable. Pam decided to go to the reflexology class "to overcome my own blockages with touch," to fill the void within herself. It was as if she were reparenting herself by making the statements: "I do not know very much about it." "I want to bring touch into my life." "I want to find people who can responsibly provide me with information about touch." "I am mature enough, wise enough, and strong enough to act on my own behalf." "This is the action that I need to take."

Hopefully, Pam also learned that touch was not just another way for her to provide for others. Caring touch was also for her to receive. To be in a healthy relationship Pam needs to have a partner who appreciates the meaning of supporting her and providing her with quality touch as much as it is for her to be able to provide touch for her partner.

Pam pursued other forms of "body contact therapy" to continue her "personal growth." She had made a decision and developed a new criterion for how to live her life. She would no longer focus on what she would do for others. Instead, Pam's new course would be plotted on the coordinates of who she was and what she needed to do to provide her own life with meaning. Learning the skills of bodywork would help her to establish that meaningful course.

SUMMARY

The confrontation of a troublesome work experience presented Pam with the awareness of a blockage in her personality. As a result of this encounter, Pam traveled in her awareness to the emotional spot of self-loss in her marriage. Pam recognized her inability to freely and flexibly provide meaningful touch. In the form of a cry, she allowed for a release of feelings that had been pent up for most of her life. This emotional discharge transported Pam further back in time. Her final destination, deep in her belly, was the despair from childhood: "It's unfair to be a girl," "It is like you are not on Earth," " You are only here to take care of men." Pam knew and resented the inequity between the sexes from the time of her childhood. In childhood, she was unaware that there were alternative paths she could take. Furthermore, as a child if she had been aware of these paths, Pam had neither the freedom nor the power to choose them. Pam's midair "identity collision" provided her with the opportunity to decide for herself exactly what the focus of her life would be. With this new awareness she chose to begin a course of developing bodywork skills. Pam would undertake three different bodywork disciplines in order to overcome her "blockage." She realized that this learning was not just for herself. What Pam first gained from a professional encounter with her passenger, she then took to a personal level to overcome her own obstruction with touch. Ultimately, Pam wanted to be able to give back to others her personal discoveries by teaching them what she had learned—to be and feel free.

END NOTES

[1] **Depression**   Depression is one of the most common ailments from which psychiatric patients suffer. It is a psychological defense against some other more painful or terrifying feeling, usually an emotional reaction to loss. In the case of the passenger, the man's wife was lost to death. Any kind of loss can trigger a depression: a divorce, the sale of a home, the marriage of a child, a misplaced or broken sentimental gift. Subtle losses can trigger depression. The many signs of aging for example, a man's growing baldness or the sagging of a woman's skin can be perceived as losses. Retirement can trigger depression. Even the anniversary of a loss can trigger a depression. Being around a depressed person can trigger depression. Depressed people feel helpless and hopeless. Sometimes, a depressed person is unable to grasp hold of any comfort that might be provided. Being unable to alter a person's depression can become depressing.

In the case of loss, depression numbs a person to the anticipated sense of overwhelming grief. Depression may also numb other feelings such as anger. When a person feels hurt, an immediate reaction is to protect the wound by getting angry, but a person is likely to turn her or his anger inward if she or he does not feel that it is acceptable or safe to express this anger. This internalized anger then takes the form of depression.

Often depression is a brief reaction to loss. It is characterized by disturbances in any or all of the normal patterns of sleep, energy, appetite, self-esteem, productivity, concentration, social contact, sexual activities, and by continuous sadness or crying spells. If the wound is not healed, the symptoms can persist and become part of a life-style. Indeed, symptoms are likely to persist and intensify as the condition continues. If a person is already in a depressed state or does not have sufficient support to handle the insult of loss, the emotional reaction can take life and death proportions. Many severely depressed people turn to suicide as an alternative to coping with their overwhelming pain.

In the case of internalized anger, "conscious" physical activity is helpful in releasing pent-up feelings, but the movement must be monitored. Too much movement may release stored emotions too quickly. Movement alone, like medication alone, is not a complete solution. There is usually a wound beneath the levels of depression and anger. Or there may be a threat or a perceived threat that caused the individual to internalize her or his feelings in the first place. In any case, the underlying wound or threat must be addressed. Attempting to remove the structures of internalization and muscle tension in such cases can be unwise and very dangerous. Before the removal of such defenses, the individual needs to feel assured that there is an effective alternative means of protecting her or himself. This is the work of psychotherapy.

At times antidepressant medication is helpful. While medication can help to reduce uncomfortable and incapacitating feelings, it does not in and of itself resolve the underlying issue of the emotional loss. Consequently, a person may best be able to resolve the causal issue if medication is used in conjunction with psychotherapy.

2   **Catharsis**   In the case of loss, grieving usually is a catharsis for the numbing process. Grieving involves not merely expressing, but sharing feelings, whatever they may be with someone who is capable of empathizing. An adjunct to dealing with feelings is any type of physical movement such as: walking, gardening, or writing. The movement must be in keeping with what the individual is capable of performing at the particular time. If one finds a level of activity is inappropriate, she or he must find another level of involvement that is appropriate. Unresolved feelings of grief do not go away with time, but are internalized and compromise an individual's full range of functioning.

3   **A Contract**   Marriage is a contract. Each of two parties contracts to remain faithful to each other for the rest of their lives. It is probably the only contract that people regularly sign (by saying, "I do,") without any of the specifics spelled out. If one buys a car, one specifies the model. If the wrong model is delivered, the goods do not have to be accepted. One may even change the decision to do business with that dealer. Not so with marriage. You do not fully know what is in the package until after the ink dries. Even if you live with the person, you may not know significant information about who she or he is in critical situations. Certain psychological information may not be revealed until after the formal condition of being married is met. Then it may be like living with an entirely different person.

The task of finding the right partner to fulfill the desired contract is exceedingly difficult. The norm is to marry at a young age when neither partner has had sufficient life experience to know who she or he is psychologically. At a young age, neither possesses the sophistication to discriminate who in the available pool of partners is a viable mate.

Mature healthy couples recognize that with the passage of different stages of their lives they grow, mature, and clarify their senses of self. As a result of these changes, they must change their expectations for one another, the roles they play in the relationship and their agreements of how to respond to their partners. When the marital contracts do not keep pace with development of its members the relationship is ripe for misunderstanding, conflict, and resentments. When marriages allow for such adjustments of their contracts, the bonds of the relationship deepen and the love between the couple grows.

While marriage is a contract, it is not a business contract. It is a contract of the heart. When one signs on the dotted line, this signature must come from a loving place where giving is not performed as a necessary requirement but as a gift, not to placate, but to enhance. The other's individuality is to be protected as much as one's own, as is the integrity of the partnership. This kind of bond allows for the individual growth of the partners and provides for the longevity of the union. One has a bad contract if one of the partners is either unwilling to sign or deliver from this spiritual place.

While life experience can be a painful teacher, a terminated marriage need not be considered a failure. Indeed, it may provide the very curriculum which if carefully studied will reveal the answers to the questions, "Who am I?" "Am I happy with who I am?" "If I am not happy with who I am, what do I have to change in order to be happy with myself?" as well as, "What are the desirable and essential characteristics a partner need possess for me to be willing to commit the rest of my life with her or him?" If this information can be gleaned from a terminated marriage, then the relationship may have been infinitely valuable.

2

BEGINNING A JOURNEY

As Leigh, a massage therapist in her mid-forties, begins to share, her speech is rapid and emotionally flat.

At a course I went to, I learned that massage can really put you in touch with yourself. We were working on the psoas muscle on the right side…and, it was just like I had a flashback to the time when I had my appendix attack. I was on the massage table and I wasn't expecting anything! I would have never imagined it. Suddenly, oh my gosh, I was nauseated. It was just exactly the way I felt when I was having my appendix attack - exactly. When the psoas on the other side was worked on, it felt like the pain I had when I was in labor with my son. Isn't that amazing?

I wasn't prepared for this experience. The instructor didn't tell us very much. It was like, "Well, that's okay." But he didn't go on to explain about the memories that the tissue holds. There were other people who had flashbacks. But, he really never explained it to us. That left us in the dark. It was like, "So it happened." He didn't really explain that there could be any memory.

This experience marked the beginning of a life journey of self-discovery and liberation for me. From that time on I began to clean out my psoas and get well, because, I knew there were lots of things in there. I never had any more of those memories after the first time that the psoas was worked on…only pain. Every time I had it worked on, it was painful. And we would keep going back and for some reason it would get tied up constantly…constantly.

Then I went to this somatoemotional class where the scar tissue from surgery released. I had some female problems stuffed in my psoas, too. I learned that my psoas was a stuffing place for me…for my emotions. I put that together. That was my place for holding feelings all the way back to my childhood…I didn't know it then, but I've put it together since. But, as I was doing it, I wasn't trying to put it together. I was just trying to clean out the pain.

As I did the neuromuscular work, I wanted to know why I repeatedly kept having the pain. Because I would exercise, I would get massage regularly. I really tried. And, I was eating better, too. *(Leigh took on a teaching voice.)* You have to realize, you don't eat junk. That's a contributing factor also. So, there are all kinds of contributing factors to pain. But, the main thing is, that if I get upset in my life or something happened…that would make the pain even worse.

I did weekly trades with my friend, another massotherapist. The two of us worked on the problem of my chronically tight psoas. But we couldn't get it to release. We said, "Why won't this release?" "Why can't we get this out?" We'd kick it around ourselves. Then I realized, "There has to be something else." I also learned in the somatoemotional class that there are certain laws about the body and feelings it might hold. For example, something in my life could have upset me and I held onto the pain. Or, for some reason, I could be drawing that kind of pain to myself. While I learned this in class, I just couldn't apply it, like, "I did this event back then and then this body thing happened!"

Yet at times something will come up and I will be able to apply it. There was so much that he gave us in that class. But we were so green. We didn't realize what he was giving us. Even though I was already out of massage school, I had just started in massage…and he was giving us so much, it was a lot to learn.

Every time I get some kind of different work I always have it in my mind that I will have some kind of release. Maybe, if I keep repeating it the effects will be so subtle I won't be aware of it. But, at least the first time I really felt the difference. I had the biggest release in my somatoemotional class. I felt the emotion in my body.

The instructor planted the idea in my mind in that class. After I told about my psoas, I told about the memory I had of the appendectomy, and I told about the pain that was there. He then asked, "Did you release it emotionally?" I thought, "No, I didn't. That is something I have to do." So, when I came back home my partner and I addressed that issue. Then as my friend worked on me, I even remembered the birth of my son…I had him C section.

(Leigh's speech began to slow and break. Her feelings deepened as she went from talking about the general events of her discoveries in class to expressing her personal experience. However, she kept halting as if it were too much for her to deal with.) There was an

emotional thing, there…there was an emotional thing there. That, I, I,…*(This thought seemed to disappear from Leigh's awareness. The life drained from her face. Then as if someone turned up the current on a power switch, Leigh's facial expression, color, eye contact, and vital presence returned. She again began to talk as if teaching a lesson.)* When things happen to us, we cause it. That is something else I learned. It's from…it started in our childhood or as we grew up. It started way back there and we help add on to it. And, we kind of don't want to let it go. And, then things can happen to us because of it. *(Leigh's eyes dulled and then developed a crystal clarity as she turned from teaching a lesson to talking about herself.)* What I mean by that is that when I let go of it emotionally…I had stuffed…when I was young…my dad would hit me. And,…ah…I mean, he wouldn't beat me, but…still…I was a young kid,…ah…I mean I was probably about three or so…but, I knew he did it.

(Leigh's demeanor totally changed. Her fumbling for words stopped. Her attention was totally present. Her insecurity was gone.) It happened when I was about three. There was this one incident, I was afraid to go upstairs in the dark. I wanted my mom to go upstairs with me to the bathroom. My dad said, "Oh, no! Go by yourself." Instead of going by myself, I didn't go. I hid and went to sleep. Then it got later and they were looking for me. But, they couldn't find me. So my dad went out looking for me. My mom found me. She told me that my dad was going to whip me…because he couldn't find me. I was so afraid…and, that got tied to my having to go to the bathroom…and, when my dad came home, he took off his belt and whipped me. I peed in my pants. That was the connection! There was a connection there all the time between that event and the stored memories in my psoas.

Now, I guess, they would call it abuse. And it was abuse, because you don't have to whip a child like that. You don't need to. And so I had a fear of him. You never knew how to act. You never knew what was right or wrong to him. When I got a whipping it was because of silly stuff…mainly. I hadn't done anything that bad. That is why I was confused. I never knew what was right or wrong.

I grew up not liking my dad. I never understood how a person could whip up on a child and love you at the same time. I was told he came back from the Army changed. I was so confused. All through my life…I have…it has been a chain reaction. *(Leigh's eyes became dull. She seemed to have a troubling thought, a painful awareness, but she was not prepared to share it out loud. Then she did.)* My son is a good boy. But, there is something that stops me from fully giving him my love. I think it has something to do with the way my father was with me.

All of this started to come to me after I started working on my psoas, it brought me back to the childhood...the little girl that got whipped...and...she couldn't understand why she got a whipping. Physically, every time I woke up in the morning...I mean as soon as I woke up in the morning, I had to go to the bathroom. That was a physical thing. But after I realized that connection between having to go to the bathroom and my father whipping me, I have not had that urgency to go to the bathroom again. I was amazed that that awareness changed something in me physically. And, that was just six months ago.

There are still some things left that I have to work on. I don't want to look inside anymore. *(Leigh spoke as if she knew what was in the interviewer's mind and she believed or projected that he was disapproving of her reluctance to pursue her own growth. She continued with a laugh.)* Yup, I know, I know, it is disgusting, but I have to know. I have to keep looking inside.

Now, when I work with clients, I know that there are different parts that have to be addressed. Before, I knew there could be an emotional part in there, I just addressed the muscle. Now, I know that there could be a memory in there if the muscle is really tied up.

People ask me, "Well, why am I this way and why am I that way?" Well, it's what you do in your life and how you look at things. If I hadn't seen it and experienced it, I couldn't give it to my customers. I couldn't open any doors for them. So, it is important that I keep opening doors for me. Even if I feel that I don't need it. I'm on a journey to seek out what else can happen. Everyone is so different...and, you have to have different ways for different people. So, you try this and if it works, fine. If it doesn't, you know someone they can go to...and, you are putting them on a road...and they keep on journeying.

DISCUSSION

LEFT IN THE DARK   Leigh's "flashbacks" in her training classes appeared bizarre and frightening to her. She would have benefited from some preparation for what was about to unfold regarding her own personal growth, her repressed memories, and the role that her bodywork training was playing in bringing to her awareness certain traumatic themes. She wanted someone in authority, her neuromuscular instructor, to reassure her that her experiences were not abnormal. Leigh was dismayed at how fixed her instructor was on the mechanics of bodywork and how unresponsive he was to both her emotional need for support and that of others in her class who were experiencing similar releases and memories. She felt that she and her classmates were "left in the dark."

The theme of a male in a position of authority failing to respond to her affective needs had even greater significance for Leigh than merely what happened in the classroom. While her instructor's neglectful behavior was different than her father's physically abusive behavior, the two experiences were similar in that they involved men in positions of authority who failed to provide legitimate preparation, protection, and support for a dependent's emotional needs.

SOMATICALLY STORED MEMORIES Involuntary, unconscious, internalized, muscular holding patterns occur from bracing or protecting against fear and/or pain. Chronic fear or pain leads to chronic muscular holding patterns. These chronic holding patterns in turn lead to numbing and forgetting. Muscular holding patterns are the somatic equivalent to psychological repression. They are like placing a painful memory into a rigid muscular time capsule. When the time capsule is upset by movement or massage then the memory may break out. This is what Leigh experientially discovered as she began to restore normal movement to her psoas muscle.

Like a well-traveled path in the snow, the more the path is traveled, the more it encourages traveling and ingrains the path. Once Leigh established a psychomuscular holding pattern to cope with the terror of living in a home with an unpredictable abusive father and a unprotective mother, other fears and pains were directed to this same holding pattern. The pattern then became more and more ingrained.

The first time the holding pattern is broken it may be accompanied by a somatoemotional explosion. This somatoemotional explosion is know as the psychological abreaction phenomenon. An abreaction is a psychological release of formerly repressed memories. With this explosion, the stores of emotional energy are released. The psychomuscular holding pattern is diminished to the extent the internalized holding has been released. After a splinter is pulled out there may be some general discomfort in the area until healing takes place. While the discomfort is nothing like the pain when the splinter was first picked at or rubbed upon, if the wound is continually prodded a person may continue to feel the pain even though the initial event of the wounding is over and the splinter has been removed.

Leigh returned home to work on her psoas muscle with her friend. This work only led to pain without emotional release. Leigh needed to be instructed that after her psychological splinter was removed and the wound was cleansed she needed to physically leave it alone for a while to allow it to heal.

OVERCOMING DENIAL   Leigh seemed to be circuitous and rambling in sharing her story as she slowly worked her way toward the point that she needed to make. It appeared to be too frightening for her to simply jump right into it.

This woman was a physically abused child. Initially, she denied her father's whippings were abusive, "I mean, he didn't beat me." Eventually, she came to realize and accept that whipping a three year old with a belt is abusive. In recognizing that she was abused, Leigh had to accept that her father[1] was a child abuser. Previously, without sufficient emotional support, this may have been too frightening for her to accept.

Leigh was told that her father went off to war and came back changed. Whatever insult he may have experienced, he chose to cope with his distress by turning his innocent, toddler daughter into a scapegoat. In the process of punishing his daughter he may have set the stage for her to become involved with a romantic partner who might also act out his anger in an abusive way. On the other hand, the daughter of such a man might rebel against this model and find someone who is the opposite; inadequate and dependent. While this type of person would be too threatened to act out his anger, he would also be unable to recognize and initiate the support, recognition, and love that his spouse would need. In either case this father did not teach his daughter that she was lovable and deserving[2]. He did not provide his daughter with a role model of what a healthy romantic partner would look like. Nor did he teach his daughter how to cope with inner fear and frustration in a healthy manner. In all likelihood, he too suffered from the lack of a thoughtful, caring, parental model to help him understand and deal with the unknowns in life. He was unable to teach his daughter what he did not know. Likewise, Leigh's mother may have believed that she successfully undertook her responsibility to prepare her daughter to deal with an unjust, senseless and often cruel world by telling her in advance that her father would beat her. This kind of behavior was a far cry from the motherly love and protection that Leigh needed.

INSTRUCTORS AND TEACHERS   Instructors and teachers, like parents, are merely people. While they may be the ultimate authority in their classroom, they may be lacking in life wisdom. Their expertise is in a specific content area, but in other areas, they may be wanting. They may not be talented as teachers. Leigh's first instructor may have had technical knowledge of anatomy and physiology. Yet, like her parents, he failed to prepare Leigh or to support her through the experiences that she had as a result of his training. Nevertheless, Leigh had the courage to share her experience in class. Unfortunately, in addition to lacking the expertise to guide Leigh through the process she was undergoing, he also failed to provide an appropriate referral to help her deal with her experience.

A STUDENT'S RESPONSIBILITY Finding instructors, professors, doctors, politicians, and even psychotherapists who are unable to fulfill their role as instructional leaders in life is not uncommon, though it is indeed frustrating, disheartening, and unfortunate. In addition to learning a content area and relating it to her or his life, a student must also be able to recognize when her or his needs in a classroom are not being met. The student then needs to search out the type of teacher she or he desires. A growth journey may begin when one discovers certain courses are taught by instructors who are lacking in a desired area of knowledge. The path of the journey is then to find a teacher who can provide the missing information.

Leigh's formal education, like most people's, did not include a pragmatic education in psychology, but she had the intuitive sense to know that something was missing for her. She also had the courage to pursue her curiosity with her mind, feelings and actions. Leigh demonstrated the strength of character to search out the information that she believed would make her a stronger, better integrated, more spiritual and giving person.

PERSONAL INTEGRATION Leigh's search took her to a holding pattern within the strata of her psoas muscle. There, as if on an archeological dig, she found layered the artifacts of earlier life experiences. Leigh unearthed psychophysical and psychosocial trauma. First, the most recent were uncovered, then the deeper childhood traumas. She concluded that the psoas region of her anatomy was a storage place or burial ground for emotional wounds which had been too painful at the time for her to confront.

This woman's holdings were in the muscles closely connected to where her traumas physically occurred. These insults included: an extended bladder, the trauma of her father's belt lashes, loss of control of sphincter muscles, a Cesarean section, an appendix attack, and an appendectomy. Leigh discovered that mechanical interventions alone, in the form of neuromuscular therapy, were insufficient to release these traumatic, repressed, psychological fossils, and their accompanying pain. She actually felt more pain with further mechanical digging. However, Leigh experienced immediate, permanent muscular release with each cognitive connection of the emotional/physical experience with psychological memory and emotional expression.

REPRESSION There is a twofold nature to repressed information. First, specific information of a troubling or traumatic event is pushed out of awareness. The second part is a forgetting that this painful information was pushed out of awareness. These painful memories are deeply buried in the muscular holding patterns. Leigh's childhood experience was overwhelmingly painful when it occurred. She did not want to be consciously reminded of it and at some point locked the door of her memory and threw away the key.

Leigh was puzzled by her partner's inability to release the pain in her psoas muscle. Leigh's body was actively working to keep her from getting in touch with memories that were too painful to recall. This is the definition of resistance. It is a strategy, a contract, that a person signs with her or himself which allows the forgetting of something too troubling to remember. Resistance provides for forgetting through the holding and numbing of musculature. The more Leigh and her friend tried to knead, the tighter Leigh's muscles became in order to honor the contract. The physical intervention became iatrogenic or counter-productive; it created its own pain.

Another "law" of emotional release is that emotional support is necessary for a safe emotional release. The support needed to overcome the holding pattern has to be equal to or greater than the fear or pain that generated the holding in the first place. Mechanically working a muscle system is insufficient support to permanently release a somatoemotional holding pattern. Sometimes however, just providing intentional emotional or spiritual support can be effective in providing somatic release without physical intervention.

SERENDIPITY At earlier times of her life, Leigh may not have been strong enough to confront the memory of her fears of going upstairs alone; the pain of physical beatings; or the pain and confusion of not feeling loved by her parents. For some reason, Leigh felt sufficiently supported at the time of her neuromuscular training to begin to confront her past. The energy that had been directed to holding her psoas in spasm was liberated, and the release of the somatoemotional holding allowed catharsis of the past trauma. As a result, this emotional release provided for greater support in her present day life. That is one of the values of therapeutic release and working through past traumas.

PAIN AS A SYMPTOM Pain brings an important message if one is wise enough to listen to it. It tells us that something is wrong, something is too fast, something is too much. Wisdom cautions a person to back away from the action that causes the pain. In our macho, do-more-with-less culture, we often equate or confuse endurance of pain with strength, bravery, and leadership. But, repressed information does not jump into our awareness just because we further stress the holding pattern. More likely than not, repressed information will be pushed deeper into our unconscious, or a new line of defense in the form of anger, rage, or shock will be generated. Best a person's pain be respected rather than contorted by the belief, "No pain, no gain."

The distinction can be made between "Pain received" and "Pain relieved." Pain received is the pain that one experiences when one gets hurt, such as Leigh's pain when she was whipped, shamed by wetting her pants, birthing her son, or had her appendectomy. "Pain relieved" is the cathartic pain of massaging a sore muscle, or the smarting discomfort of pulling out a splinter, or the nauseous feeling that Leigh had in her neuromuscular class when she first discovered how massage could place her in touch with her forgotten memories. It is essential that therapists provide their clients with the experience of releasing pain, rather than inflicting pain.

The experience of pain itself is a complex phenomenon. Psychological variables can intensify the experience of pain. The feelings that accompany physical injury become part of the complex experienced as pain. Consequently, a snap-slap of a branch as one walks through the woods on a fun outing can be totally disregarded, but a slap of equal or lesser intensity delivered by a punitive parent, a bullying peer, or a rejecting partner can be bitterly stinging. A portion of the pain felt is psychological rather than physiological. As a result, healing must address the emotional as well as the physical injury.

RESPONSIBILITY VS. BLAME   Leigh spoke of "drawing pain to herself." Apparently, Leigh subscribed to the philosophy "if something happens to you it is because you caused it." Perhaps in one manner of speaking this is accurate. The holding pattern in her psoas muscle that began early in her life probably did contribute to the pain of childbirth, and to her appendectomy. The tension she internalized in childhood contributed to, if not caused, the immediacy problem that she had with urination.

Yet, it would be simplistic and unfortunate if Leigh held herself responsible for and blamed herself for her misfortune and pain. There were factors within Leigh's environment which were beyond her awareness and command. Leigh's childhood holding patterns were reflexive. They were neither consciously nor deliberately chosen. She was a three year old, too frightened to go upstairs to the bathroom on her own in the dark. She was beaten with a belt, wet her pants, and felt humiliated. What then developed as a holding pattern in her psoas muscle was a learned trait not a character flaw. It would indeed be tragic if Leigh were to further place blame, repulsion, and rejection onto the child that she was. She has suffered long enough from shame and years of physical and psychological punishment.

Leigh was not responsible for making her father a bitter, punitive man. Assuming emotional responsibility for her father may have been an attempt to maintain a sense of his stability and truth. This would leave her the hope of being eligible for his acceptance and love. Likewise, an appendicitis attack and surgery are frightening, life-threatening events. These are not issues of fault. Without emotional support and specific training in how to respond psychologically to such traumatic emergencies people naturally brace against their fear and hold onto that protective posture even after the event is over.

There is a limit to what Leigh can hold herself responsible. It would be unfortunate if Leigh held herself responsible for things which were beyond her awareness. As a child, adolescent, and even as a young adult, Leigh could not have known the extent of the psychological damage inflicted by her home environment. She could not hold herself responsible for what her home life was like and the patterns it traced on her personality. And, Leigh must give herself credit for what she consciously achieved. As she became aware of her psychosocial past, she rejected the negative paths that many follow. Intuitively she knew there was a healthier alternative. This is the intrinsic strength that Leigh chose to embrace in order to embark on her life journey.

Leigh stated, "My son is a good boy. But, there is something that stops me from fully giving him my love." In making this observation, Leigh assumes responsibility for her actions. She may also recognize, whether it is intentional or not, that this withholding can be hurtful to a child. From a position of acceptance and responsibility for her actions Leigh can choose how she would like to address the situation. There are many actions that she can take which would deepen the bond and the understanding in their relationship. She could share her concern with her son; apologize for her omission; and/or ask him for his forgiveness. She could also decide how she wants to treat her son from this day forward and then put that plan into action. All of these interventions would promote healing.

In contrast, Leigh could also get defensive and deny responsibility for her actions. This would create even more distance. She could also blame herself for her failure which would also create more tension between herself and her son. To blame is to find fault; it is to disapprove. Blaming is judgmental. Leigh is already wounded by the way she was reared as a child. If, in addition to this wounding, she were to blame herself for her omission, she would further lock herself into an emotional position where it would be impossible to express her love. In general, blaming, whether it is blaming oneself or another is an ineffective, if not futile means for resolving conflict and healing wounds. Another ineffective way to respond to the past wounding would be to attempt to compensate by buying lots of gifts or providing lax rules. Overcompensation is not contactful and does not build strong loving bonds between a child and a parent. It tends to produce a spoiled, overindulged child who does not know how to be appreciative, loving or responsible, a child who believes that she or he is entitled and does not have to share or take responsibility in a relationship. An additional tragedy[3] of child abuse is that it often sets a chain reaction into place that is passed on to the generations to follow.

Leigh is troubled by the scars left by her relationship with her father. She fears it has tainted her own relationship with her son. She confesses that it has compromised her ability to openly share her love with him. Nevertheless, this confession of inadequacy need not be taken as a damning statement of her replicating either her father's inadequate, punitive parental pattern or her mother's ineffectual parental pattern. Instead, it may represent the harbinger of new strength, transcendence, and an ability to share fully the love that she truly has for her son. It may also mark the beginning of her ability to receive more deeply, the love her son has for her. In the same way that denial marks the beginning of stagnation, self-recognition and acceptance of one's weakness marks the beginning of growth. The awareness of her unhealthy patterns gives Leigh the clarity of knowing what to change. While Leigh does not discuss her husband, the most effective changes come about from parents working together[4] as a team.

NOTE OF CAUTION By definition, children of abusive parents did not have healthy role models to demonstrate how to set caring, protective limits. Consequently, they did not learn how to set realistic and caring limits. Violation of boundaries and abusiveness were the norm. Such children, even in adulthood, may treat themselves as they were treated by their parents. They may punish themselves, though ever so subtly, as their parents did. Furthermore, what they do to themselves, they may unknowingly do to others. Leigh often pushes herself in her own attempts at personal growth. Her pursuits may even be at the expense of her physical pain.

This raises a special note of caution for bodyworkers from abusive backgrounds. It is extremely important in cases like these for a bodyworker to be conscious of pacing her or himself in this personal development, and not push too far, too fast. Likewise, it is essential to pace her or himself with a client. For the bodyworker to push for too much, too fast may only replicate a past wound within the client and serve to slow, arrest, or even set back the growth process.

UNFINISHED BUSINESS Leigh had some very important insights regarding her physical holding patterns and certain somatoemotional events in her life. She recognized that by giving emotional as well as physical support to her chronically tight muscles, those holding patterns and symptoms of those holding patterns could be released.

What Leigh did not know is that certain psychological holding patterns cannot be released just by relaxing tight muscles. The issues themselves must be identified and resolved. Leigh realized there was a problem between herself and her willingness to express her love for her son. Just being aware that this issue exists helps to overcome the block. But, Leigh must do something with her awareness to provide for the desired change. Leigh's neuromuscular instructor presented the model, "If it is beyond the scope of our practice, ignore it." He did not teach in his training that when a student reaches the limits of her or his practice, it is appropriate to seek consultation. Because she did not recognize that she was facing a choice point, and even if she had realized she was at a choice point, she may not have known the appropriate action to take.

When Leigh wanted to share her love with her son, she might have encountered the obstacle of unresolved past anger leaving her unable to express those feelings. The same psychological defense mechanism that protected her from incoming psychological assault would have interfered with outgoing emotional expression. This protective mechanism, at least in part, would prevent Leigh from sharing all the love she felt toward her son. She would have to change her self-perception and the message that somehow she was responsible for her ill fate. Leigh had unfinished business with herself.

HEART-TO-HEART TALK: A PROBLEM-SOLVING INTERVENTION The role model provided by her parents was immediately and experientially familiar as the way to treat children. It was a neglectful model which lacked understanding, protection, and support. Leigh learned from her parents that she was to be treated as the recipient of neglect and abuse. To the extent that she normatively accepted this about herself she might logically transfer this same message to her son, who was, after all an extension of herself. Leigh was cruelly punished by the hands of a male. Even though her son did not beat her with a belt, he was a male and Leigh could easily transfer her feelings of resentment from an abusive male onto all males.

To intervene, Leigh needs to have a heart-to-heart talk with her inner emotional child. She may need to do this many times, until she herself believes what she is saying, in body as well as in mind. She needs to find a quiet time and a safe place and imagine talking with her childhood self. She could even use a childhood photograph of herself.

In her conversation she needs to tell that child that she, the adult Leigh, understands that the child Leigh is confused about how loving parents could treat their daughter in such a harsh manner. There is nothing wrong with her, in fact, she is a lovable little girl. Then Leigh must tell this little girl how she was supposed to be treated by her parents. She is entitled to warmth, recognition, appreciation, support, understanding, help, kindness, and all the hugs and kisses she wants. As a result of this strategy, Leigh will learn to genuinely love herself. In the process, as her emotionally wounded heart heals, she will also learn how to open her loving heart to her son.

SUMMARY

Leigh tells of her encounters in her massage classes. She was unprepared for what she experienced. She was reliving memories as if they were happening in the here and now. As her muscular holding patterns were being released Leigh was experiencing somatoemotional fossils of past traumatic life events. Leigh would have liked some preparation and support so that she did not feel so blind-sided by her experience. She would have liked guidance as to what to do with her experiences. This information was not immediately forthcoming.

What Leigh experientially discovered in class she was not about to abandon. She chose to use at home the tools that seemed to work in class. Leigh wanted to uncover all of the artifacts that were buried in her psoas muscle. As she dug through the strata, she finally unearthed the beginning of this holding pattern. The template for her somatic internalization of stress began with a childhood trauma of being whipped with a belt by her father because she was too frightened to go to the bathroom upstairs alone in the dark.

Being able to retrieve these memories helped Leigh to overcome physical pain and an immediacy problem, and also helped her to grapple with the troubling emotional relationship she had with her son. Though Leigh was not physically abusive to her son, by withholding full expression of her love for him, she was replicating at least, in part, the treatment she received as a child. In order for her to overcome her withholding, Leigh would have to change the perceptual filter that she maintained within herself. This perceptual filter held that the little child that Leigh was, was somehow deserving of the abusive treatment that she received. As a result, she had to maintain a certain defended posture to protect herself from the abuse that she feared receiving. Both Leigh's perceptual system and the assumed defensive posture would stop her from freely articulating the feelings she experienced toward others.

Leigh recognized that the struggle she had in opening her feelings to her son related to the abusive relationship she had with her father. She also realized that if there were important buried material in her muscles, there must also be important buried material in the muscles of her clients. Leigh wanted to be able to provide them the same opportunity that she had experienced. Leigh recognized that there might be some clients she would not be able to help in her practice. Unlike the inadequate models provided by her parents and her instructor, she would direct them to someone who could help.

END NOTES

1 **Parents As People** Making negative statements about their parents can be extremely hard for many people. Children of all ages have a difficult time perceiving their parents as ordinary people as opposed to some sort of perfect, adult, authority figure. Parents are the gatekeepers of their children's reality. Children want their parents and the world their parents made for them to be perfect, right and just. This motive is so intensely desired that children are often willing to bend their own perceptual reality and the facts in order to make themselves wrong and their parents right even when the converse is true. This distortion provides a false sense that the parents are the guardians of truth and all is well in the world. To believe the contrary, that parents could be wrong and all might not be well in the world, is too threatening for most children, to say nothing of many adults to contemplate.

If parents are not seen for who they are as people, and the dynamics of their personalities are not recognized, their children may either replicate the parental patterns, rebel against them, or both. Ultimately to become a mature adult one must be able to perceive her or his parents as people with their own personalities, strengths and weaknesses. And, it is our adult selves that must confirm our lovability and our deservability. Precisely because of who our parents were they may not have had the willingness or ability to provide this confirmation upon us. No matter how long we wait, protest, demand, rebel, or cry, that will not change.

2 **Lovable and Deserving** The idea that our parents' perception of reality is the correct and only view of reality is one adolescents must reckon with as they move into adulthood. The theme of being lovable and deserving is perhaps even more difficult to address. Feeling okay and lovable are absolutely essential for a child to build a healthy self-concept, a strong sense of self-esteem, and the courage to stand up for her or himself in an often hostile, indifferent, and under-emotionally-nourishing world.

More children than are normally recognized, grow up in families where they do not receive the support, recognition, confirmation, appreciation, celebration, and love that they need and deserve. This love is not showered upon their children because the parents do not know how to express their love, and the parents' own defenses may prohibit them from sharing their feelings. Other parents may simply not love their children at all. In some cases, parents themselves are insecure or are self-punitive. They are unable to give something to their children that they deny to themselves. Some children are "unwanted," "accidents," the result of an undesired pregnancy. The birth of a child may also be the unfortunate consequence of someone's sense of duty, fulfilling a spouse's expectations, or may be the only way for two youths to leave their parents' homes. There are many painful reasons why people have children.

One of the results of bringing an unwanted, unloved child into the world is the creation of an emotionally wounded child. Children are not as resilient as people often believe. The scars of childhood wounds linger to influence and shape adolescents and adult self-perception, self-esteem, and life choices.

As explored earlier, children of inadequate parents routinely tell themselves that their parents are okay and they are the ones who are wrong or bad. In the short run it is easier to say, "I am bad, dumb, or ugly." "I am unlovable," than to recognize and say, "I am unloved by my parents. And without this key element of esteem and strength, I must go out into the world, learn, compete, and fend for myself."

This fallacious self-distortion of believing one is unlovable and undeserving then ripples from one generation onto the next. The distortions are passed on unless someone has the courage to confront one's self and stop the pattern. She or he must be able to know for her or himself, "I wasn't loved by my parents. But, I am lovable. I am deserving. Furthermore, I love myself and I will back myself up. I'll share my love and support for my own children as it should have been shared with me."

3   **Cycle**   One of the many tragedies of child abuse is that it ignites a chain reaction that reaches across the generations. Not only did Leigh's father's abusive behavior directly hurt his daughter, this man indirectly set the stage to wound his grandson.

The grandson could be hurt in several ways: he might be hurt by his mother's inability to express fully her love for him, and Leigh, unconsciously, might have transferred vestiges of her fear and anger toward her father onto males in general. She also might have transferred her belief in men being authority figures who capriciously act out their rage. This transference onto all males might have included her son which would leave her in fear of her child, and she might have been subject to regression in the presence of this child, "male authority figure." A regressed mother, herself feeling like a child in the presence of her son, might look for acceptance from him as she might have from her father. The son would be perceived as a powerful figure even though he was just a child. A mother in such an emotionally regressed state would then have difficulty setting limits and guidelines lest the boy disapprove of her or reject her. This young, authority figure substitute would have emotionally devastating power over his wounded mother. This is another way the son might have been hurt. He would suffer not only from the loss of expression of his mother's love, but also by the loss of learning reasonable, healthy, behavioral limits from her.

Adolescents may become oppositional or rebellious. This behavior can be an attempt to elicit genuine contact from parents who have been emotionally unavailable. If the mother feels unable to take a loving and firm stance with the child's testy behavior, she is likely to become resentful in addition to being fearful of the child. This growing resentment further complicates the expression of love and concern which she may feel toward her son.

Adolescents do not like limits being set upon them. Yet they become disrespectful and out of control without external limits. Therefore to be an effective parent one must tolerate being disliked from time to time. It might be overwhelming for a mother in a regressed state to set limits and run the risk of being disliked or hated by her child. Although she may know that limit-setting is appropriate, she might lack the necessary internal emotional strength to enforce those limits with a male child.

4   **A Consistent Parental Team**   Two parents sending the identical message to a child is a powerful child-rearing approach. In the situation where the integrity of the message of one parent is compromised by the other parent, the message becomes nullified. There is nothing to counter the oppositional or rebellious qualities of the adolescent when a healthy, mature father is not present or available to support the mother in setting caring and firm guidelines. The child or adolescent cripples her or himself through acting out behavior which prohibits development of legitimate adult skills and attitudes.

In such circumstances outside support is essential. Psychotherapeutic support often can place perspective on the original abuse so that the past trauma no longer interferes with present function. It can help the mother to identify her own reasonable and acceptable limits. It can provide role playing to learn what to do and what to say in order to perform this adult task. Finally, it provides ongoing support to the mother to reinforce limits when a child or adolescent engages in limit-testing behavior. In such cases, the earlier the intervention the better the potential outcome.

If two parents do not work together, the rebellious adolescent may identify with an aggressive male. He may resent his abused, victimized, and ineffectual mother. He may then transfer his resentment onto females in general. Perhaps, some day he may transfer his resentment to his wife and daughter. Then the cycle continues.

3

JUST SAY THE WORD

Judi is a vivacious bodyworker in her mid-thirties.

When I first got started it was odd to work with men. Maybe, it was just my own little hang-up thing...my own personal issues of touching men in a non-sexual way. Before I got into massage I did not touch. I was not comfortable doing that. I was always concerned over how someone else would take it. Well, maybe they would think I was coming on or something like that. In real life, not in massage...in normal real life would someone think that?

Dad worked in the trades. I didn't get a lot of touching in my home...from my dad. Okay! I didn't see him touch mother either. They didn't touch much...I don't think, not around me. Actually, we all got touched. But when adolescence came with me, I don't think my dad touched me too much anymore. When I started getting boobs, my father had to start dealing with his issue of male-female attraction...son, daughter, mother...all that kind of stuff. I think he flipped out. He blew some stuff my way which wasn't too cool. Nothing physical. But I think he abused me emotionally, a little bit...sexually just a little bit. He would accuse me of things that I never thought of. He'd say that I was going to do stuff that I didn't even know what it was. He was telling me right there what it was.

At seventeen I had my first child. So his wish came true; his fear came true. I can see that now. Then it was like, ooooowwwww! That's life!

I guess in a way, my mother was uptight, too. But I didn't receive as much from her as him. She wasn't accusing of me. I think because when my mom and dad would be hugging or kissing in the kitchen and they would see me, they would quit. So, it wasn't cool to do. When it came time to learn about menstruation and all that kind of stuff, they gave me a book to read. And I couldn't go out of the house until I read it. For anything else they never grounded me and stayed with it. But, they stayed with this. So it was like...I'm not going to read that book! They really didn't know how to handle things real well. To learn about periods, they took me to the doctor, so the doctor could tell me. But mom's mother probably didn't tell her anything. But unlike dad, mom never blew anything my way. I didn't really have a problem with her.

So I think that with having to deal with men...massage—touching was really a good thing for me to have to do because I had to learn to deal with that. I think that I had to learn that men were not just over there wanting to have sex with me all the time—like my dad would tell me. Ya know? So I learned how to do that. So I think that's what I had to deal with...*(laughing)*...It's pretty strange.

Dad is now in his sixties. He is diabetic. His health is declining rapidly. I think about his condition, and maybe him being gone...*(Judi becomes distraught.)* I don't want to think about this!

I think the reason I don't stop, I am so intense, I keep on going, having to get something done, always got something to do, it is as if I stop and have to think about any of this...it will flip me out. I'll start crying. *(Defiantly, Judi insists.)* I don't want to feel it! That's what happens to me at night. I'll wake up. And it is like a train hit me in the face...because I finally relaxed. Well, fuck this! Get Up! Get something to eat. Go drink something. You're not going to think about this! *(Judi was silent. She began to cry, then stopped.)*

(Judi looked calm after her cry. Her face was soft and full of color. Her voice soft and mellow) My dad is probably not going to be around for that long. I can see it. I don't like to admit that. I argue with him. Dad is macho. He wouldn't be open if I would want to share my sadness and grief with him. It may be an avoidance of feeling, his and my pain—it's corny, but we have never talked. It would be like I would have to laugh afterwards. I see him more; but, we haven't gotten to talk.

I don't know how I could just talk with my husband either. He is not there to give me support with my pain over dad. I was not there to give him support when his father died. I think he will be distant with me over this issue.

There was not much training about touching in school. We only had one man in our class. I don't think I even worked on that one guy. Maybe I worked on his leg or something, but never when I had to deal with sheets and all this other kind of stuff...where there might have been any suggestion that I was probably going to see genitals. Goofy!

I might have avoided it. Yeah, I think I would have avoided anything where I might have had to deal with…genitals, ya know? I think I might have had to work with his butt!

So you didn't get to deal with men very often in school. You did women all the time. You didn't develop being comfortable with…men, until you went out and started to practice. At least, I didn't. Now, I prefer to work on women. They are lighter and easier to work with.

When I first started in practice, I found that I was getting weird phone calls. And I had to deal with a couple clients who could have been a little bit inappropriate. I had to deal with and handle those. But as soon as I dealt with and handled it…I was okay. And it didn't come my way anymore.

In those events there was a suggestion that I would go out with them. Or, "just what do you do for forty dollars?" I mean they would ask with a wink in their eye and a suggestion in their voice. Inside I was pissed. I wanted say, "Fuck you!" However, I was aware I had to handle this in a professional manner to turn it around. I was proud of myself for being able to handle these situations professionally. I kind of deflated that balloon. Once I handled it and I became comfortable with that, I didn't have those people coming to me anymore and I didn't have to deal with it anymore.

The way I handled these situations was to be up front. When asked what I did for forty dollars, I'd say, "Full body massage…I don't do genitals." That just kind of deflated people real quick. When I found that worked, it did real fine for me. I said, "Great!"

I did have a gentleman friend of mine. He was a massage therapist I met in class. He helped me a lot with that. In class he asked me if I wanted to do an exchange. And I thought to myself, "Nnnnnnnnnnnn, I don't know!" This is a great big guy, ya know. I said, "Yes, I need to learn this." So we did.

Then I mentioned that I hadn't worked on many men and he took it from there. He said, "This might happen to you; and this might happen to you…da, da, da, da, da, da." So I got a little prepared that way. He just pretty much…he is just that way. Hey, this is the way it is. He just embarrassed me kinda almost to where I had to deal with it. He just threw it into my face.

He'd say, "Ya gotta do this, and that, and the other. You have to do this. You just have to completely deflate anything that you might think." Ya know, what am I going to do if this guy gets an erection? He told me, "If that happens, just go about your business." And I have had guys ask me before…you can tell they kind of hem and haw around, "What if I get an erection?" And I just say, "Hey, that's normal for men. I just go about my business. I don't know if it is happening. It doesn't bother me, if it doesn't bother you." And I just go ahead and do my massage. And that is the only thing for me to do.

Usually after a massage or two, they don't do that any more. I find that when a lot of men find out that there are other parts of their body that can feel good besides their penis they settle down. There are a lot of men who think, "This is the only place that is going to feel good." When they discover that other parts of their body can feel good, it is like a light goes on. They quit thinking about "Penis." They start getting along with the massage pretty good.

All men don't do that. Others, when they think about it, they get it...ya know. But when they get comfortable, they don't have one. So it's okay. No big deal anymore. You just have to give them all the privacy...all the privacy they need and still be able to do your work. Answer their questions. If you think they are thinking...and trying...ya know...maybe try to help them out a little bit. "Are you talking about having an erection?" "Yeah!" And, that eased it. I guess just saying the word...works. Saying, "I do not do genitals," made it easier.

I am not without my own sexual feelings. Occasionally, I am aware of these feelings at work. When I got comfortable with the issue of "I might see genitals" or "Someone might have an erection" or something like that...um, when I go to work, I just see muscles; and I stay with that. Ya know? But there is one man who is really neat. He's um...he's a hunk. I just really like working with him a lot because he is neat as a person. We have become good friends and I like him. And it is easy to get to him, ya know? But he doesn't know about these feelings, because I have never told him.

How do I keep my sexual feelings separated from my work? It's just a habit. I guess becoming more familiar with the person, ya know? Then those edgy little feelings of, "Gosh, he turns me on!" kinda soften and kinda go away a little bit.

(After a long pause Judi continues.) I find that I am at a standstill with a bunch of my clients. I think that it is because I am at a standstill with several personal things within myself. Until I work with them, I'm going to be stuck.

I am at a standstill with a marriage that I am not sure I need to be in or out of. I don't know where I need to be with it. I am teeter-tottering. As I don't make a decision, I am hanging in limbo. This seems to go ahead and spill into my bodywork with people. Somehow I am aware that I am not able to give as much release with them as I know that I can. I do everything that I can, yet something is missing. I need to know something else to take this person a little further.

I am just relating this to where I am personally. I need another piece of a puzzle before I can take this relationship in or out. I need another piece of a puzzle before I can take my client further. I think that I know what the piece is that is missing. I went to a workshop...a muscle-energy workshop. And I thought I would come back with all these tools and be able to deal with all of this. But it isn't going to be that way. I am going to have to work really hard at it! To make it happen...I know this is the thing that these people need.

The same thing with this marriage relationship. I am going to work hard at finding out what I need to do. And I have been doing nothing. I thought that I did enough. So in both cases I know what I need to do.

In massage, I thought that I had all the answers with my deep tissue work. That was all I needed to know to take care of a person...along with maybe some adjustments from a chiropractor, but no, that's not all. With my marriage, I thought that I did everything that I needed to do and could do. But now I see that there are other things that I need to do to get answers. There is more I can do.

(Judi's eyes began to glass up as she spoke.) It's not real painful, I don't think. No, as a matter of fact, I just came from a counseling session, and it was okay. It's time to get off of the fence. It is time to do something. I've been waiting for it to do something itself. I thought that I had the answers until I was shown another depth...that I needed to go into with my work to find out whether or not this is good for me. This depth is a matter of developing my spirituality a little more...a lot more. I don't know. I have to communicate a little better. I need to just start looking within...sorting stuff. I need to trust God more in both aspects. I need to have faith that things are working out for the best. When I get in my head and doubt, things get all messed up.

So it's kind of neat in a way. I have some answers. I just have to do some work to get it. That's better than not knowing. I've married for the second time; I've been in this marriage for eleven years. We have just lost communication. Though I don't know if we had a lot. We have gone separate ways. I don't like that. He doesn't like that. We are just like roommates, and it isn't much fun. I could have a roommate and not have the hassles of marriage.

I went through a period of bitterness and anger and all that kind of stuff. I am sure I will go through more of that. But I don't think that either one of us feel mad-angry at the other. We just want to say, "Well, how many more years do we have to live? Well, let's go...do the best we can." I am ready to find some answers, put some things to rest. I don't like things scattered and unsure.

He is not involved in counseling with me. He says he is too busy. "I'm working on paying the bills." He is just like my dad. He was not there either. This is the mother and father thing. I am doing what my parents did.

It's okay. I feel okay. I know at this point in life it is going to all be all right. It's just going through the crap to get to the "all right" part. Everything always turns out for the best. And that's because I've seen it. I wouldn't have believed it years ago.

My clients feel fine with my work, but there is something missing for me. When I work with my clients, I question my faith in myself. I question things when they happen rather than going with the faith of it all. So at this point I am looking at my faith a lot. I look at my clients, me, and The Man Upstairs as one...my work. I think that there are certain things that I can do that will trigger their growth...just trigger it. Then they will make it happen.

There is something more I could do, particularly with my long-standing clients, but I've not got it down yet. But it's not going to come from my deep tissue stuff. Some of it may come from dealing with them psychologically, which I am not real super comfortable with what to do with them. I am not real interested in doing that with my work...a whole lot. A little bit, but not to delve real far, because I don't want to, at this point, anyway.

Even my business is going down the same avenue. My practice is not going very, very well. However, I need to have someone in with me at the place that I rent in order to make a profit. I have had two different people and neither one of them has been able to make a go of it. The second lady is leaving in a month. Financially, that will leave me in a spot. So, I'm looking at another change. I may move my business to a more populated area. Maybe what is going on is a way of me creating something new to accomplish because things are getting just a little bit, uh...boring.

DISCUSSION

SELF-FULFILLING PROPHECY OF DOOM Judi spoke of her "little hang-up thing" with touch. Actually this is not such a "little thing." It should come as no surprise that a parent would find her or his own child attractive. After all, half of the child's genes came from a person that the parent found attractive enough to marry. The other half of those genes came from themselves! It is like finding attractive aspects of the unity between a special other person and yourself. Our cultural taboo prohibits a parent from taking action upon the sexual elements of this attraction. What sometimes happens is that parents not only withhold their sexual feelings toward an offspring, but they totally deny their loving feelings for that child. The feelings are present. They are simply withheld, or they are pushed into unconscious awareness. Then the fact that they have been pushed down is forgotten. This is somewhat like locking away one's memory to the feelings, and then swallowing the key. This is the process of repression.

Repression of sexual feelings for one's own child removes such feelings from troubling conscious awareness, but does not make those feelings go away. As Judi entered adolescence and began to develop secondary sexual characteristics, "boobs," her father began to repress his sexual feelings for his daughter.

The father's feelings toward his attractive daughter, however, did not disappear. They simply erupted indirectly. The father began to project his unacceptable, lustful feelings onto his naïve, adolescent daughter. To some degree, his thoughts about what some adolescent boys were thinking regarding his attractive daughter were probably accurate. Ironically, what Judi was sexually naïve to, her father taught her with his constant innuendoes and accusations. The sexual preoccupation did not belong to her. It belonged to him.

On the one hand, Judi received the unacceptable sexual feelings that her father felt for her. On the other hand, she was denied his healthy emotional-physical support and love. This father failed to teach her how to differentiate between lust and love. By example, he failed to teach Judi how to share the many levels of love and intimacy that can exist in a marriage. Judi was accurate; her father set her up to act out his denied wishes—his fear of her becoming sexually involved. This is sometimes referred to as a self-fulfilling prophecy of doom.

The tragedy of this scenario was that this man was not an uncaring, unloving father. His harassment and abuse arose out of his naiveté, ignorance, and unwillingness to learn how to deal with his powerful feelings toward the daughter he loved and about whom he cared deeply. Not only did this father and daughter miss out on a full and rich sharing of her adolescence, but they lost out on fully sharing the later developmental stages in both of their lives.

EMOTIONAL CONFUSION Judi's parents were uncomfortable with expressions of their sexuality and affection. They modeled the behavior that one should be secretive and hide expressions of affection, loving, and caring—except to prepubescent children. The parents sent their adolescent daughter to a physician to learn about menstruation, and they made reading a book about sexuality a punishment. Furthermore, Judi's father kept accusing her of his projections—what he himself wanted, and then accused her of wanting. Ultimately, the whole family had to deal with the consequences of his actions.

Judi's parents were unable to teach her healthy attitudes regarding touch, affection, love, and sexuality because they had discomfort and confusion around issues of sexuality. When feelings are not understood or appreciated, one feeling is easily confused or engulfed by another. On some level, Judi's father knew that sexual feelings toward his daughter were unacceptable. And, he was unable to differentiate pure sexual attraction from healthy feelings such as love, caring, delight, enjoyment, appreciation, and many many others. Judi's father pushed down the feelings that would have allowed for healthy closeness and non-sexual intimacy. His emotional confusion left him without a means to share lovingly with his attractive daughter. So he became fixated and irritated over her sexuality. In the process, the father taught his daughter his own emotional confusion. For him, all touching was equivalent to sexual touching which was unacceptable.

As an adolescent, because she was lacking in healthy role-modeling, Judi did not know how to deal with her sexual energy. She had difficulty differentiating between having a feeling and appreciating and acting upon the feeling. Her father denied his feelings. Her mother hid her feelings. So how could Judi have learned what do with her feelings? Judi was vulnerable to sexual advances because she may have interpreted them to be the love and confirmation she lacked at home.

Rejection, threat, and punishment are ineffectual deterrents of adolescent sexual behavior. This is especially true when a parent is continuously bombarding his adolescent daughter with the theme of sexual promiscuity and then withholding legitimate love and affection. The messages from parental modeling and the association of her father's negativism regarding sex and teenage pregnancy lent powerful reinforcement for Judi not to touch males, not to share feeling, and not to be open to emotional-spiritual intimacy. And it just left her vulnerable to her sexuality.

SEXUALIZING Sexualizing happens when a person reduces another solely to the sexual component of her or his identity. Usually this narrowing of perceptual focus inhibits the viewer from perceiving, appreciating, and interacting with the entirety of another person. And, it is far more damaging when that other is a susceptible dependent. In a case like Judi's, perceptual reduction could inhibit her from recognizing and appreciating the entirety of her personal attributes, talents, and strengths. She may then view herself as only having value as a sexual being—and that value is a negative one.

Judi found herself being confronted early in her practice by new sexist male clients. These men would ask with a wink in their eye and a suggestion in their voice, "Just what do you do for forty dollars?" Judi found herself becoming angry and wanting to explode at them, "Fuck you!" This explosion that Judi did not allow herself to express was her defense. Underneath the anger was a wound caused by callous, demeaning, and insulting remarks. In Judi's case there were actually two wounds. The first was the immediate wound of being reduced by her client into a unidimensional sexual object. It is the wound of not being seen for the person she is, the accomplishments she has achieved and the highly skilled talents that she has developed. The second wound was an old one created by similar treatment from her father.

These men may have perceived themselves as being flattering of their massage therapist. They may have been self-aggrandizing by fantasizing themselves a sexual partner for this attractive woman. They may also have been psychologically hostile toward women, needing to devalue them so that they could feel better about themselves. Whatever their motivation, their behavior was hurtful and demeaning. As Judi became more skilled she learned how not to personalize these messages, and to confront and deflect their callousness. This psychosocial skill should also serve as a point of pride for Judi and help to reinforce her sense of integrity.

Another issue that reflected sexualizing was Judi's own "edgy little feeling" reactions to some of her clients. She had learned to deal with her own sexual feelings toward her clients by putting her attention onto her work rather than the shapes of their bodies. She also noted that as she learned more about her clients and perceived them for the people that they were, those "edgy feelings kinda go away."

DECLARATION OF BOUNDARIES: A PROBLEM-SOLVING STRATEGY Before Judi went to massage school, she was chronically worried about how she was perceived by men. "Well,…maybe they would think I was coming-on, or something like that." Judi suffered from her own emotional confusion. As a result, she became externally dependent for a sense of confirmation. If she was unclear as to where she was coming from and others were not clear about where she was coming from, any kind of touching could compromise her integrity. Judi did not know as an adolescent that she could defend herself against her male peer group's misperceptions. Even if she had wanted to she would have been unable to because her parents had never taught her how.

What Judi needed to know was that she could have established her boundaries with her male peers by stating her limits. These statements would be a declaration of her boundaries. If a young man were unable to differentiate between Judi's friendly touch and a sexual advance, she could simply say, "That was a friendly touch; not a sexual advance." Or, "You are not hearing where I am coming from." Or, "I may have sexual feelings, but I am not willing to act on them."

Judi's massage school friend provided her with similar declarative statements that would help her to maintain her boundaries in her business practice. These statements clarified her personal boundaries with men who were unclear themselves, who perceived women through sexualized lenses, or who tested her sexual limits. Armed with a set of simple statements, adolescent Judi could have reduced her anxiety around members of the opposite sex. She could have felt stronger about herself and could have better enjoyed her contacts with males.

ERECTION Judi discussed the occupational issue of dealing with some of her male clients who had concerns over becoming sexually aroused during a session and developing an erection. Erections, like many other reflexive responses, are highly affected by anxiety. The more clients feel uncomfortable and anxious over the prospect of having an erection the more this issue may become figural for them and the greater the likelihood of this dreaded occurrence.

The best thing that Judi could have done for her clients was to help allay their anxiety. She talked with them about the issue. When she sensed that they were having a difficult time articulating the issue themselves, she put it out in the open herself, "Are you talking about having an erection?" Then she normalized the issue, "Hey that's normal for men. I just go about my business." What Judi's experience taught her was that this may be an issue early on, but after several sessions when her clients see that this is not an issue for her, it ceased to be an issue for them.

AVOIDANCE Judi avoided dealing with the issue of touching a male when it presented itself in her massage class. According to her report, on one occasion, she may "even have had to touch the one male in my massage class—probably his 'butt'." That was such an uncomfortable experience, she pushed those thoughts out of her conscious awareness. Only with probing did these memories return. Avoidance was a major issue in this bodyworker's family and in her own personality.

This central issue was also excluded in the curriculum of her massage school. Perhaps out of a similar discomfort, the school staff avoided this unmistakably central issue of bodywork. Judi undoubtedly would have been helped if this issue had been maturely and professionally addressed.

The theme of avoidance of touching males and making genuine contact recurs in Judi's professional work, her relationship with her father, and in her relationship with her husband. Judi is beginning to recognize that there is something missing in her bodywork. New mechanical techniques are disappointing. They do not hold the hoped-for answer to what has been missing with her longer standing clients. Judi later considers that the missing piece has to do with "psychology," with which she is uncomfortable. Judi may discover that unless she opens to her emotional core, even psychology provides just another conglomeration of techniques. One can hide in the realm of psychological concepts as easily as one can hide in the realm of behavior.

ANTICIPATORY GRIEF With each developmental life stage Judi encountered, she struggled with the issues of her repressed emotions. She learned very well not to feel or express her true inner emotions. At the prospect of experiencing powerful emotions, Judi felt unable to control her feelings and she panicked, "I don't want to think about this!" Experiencing her deeper feelings was so upsetting that Judi had developed a life style of staying highly active and so busy so that she did not have to be with her true self. This created a particular problem in the dead of night when there was no external activity to divert her attention. When she was confronted with her truth, "like a train hitting me in the face," Judi manufactured artificial activities such as eating or drinking to camouflage and hide her experience.

Just as a dying patient faces the grief stages that accompany death, so do relatives and friends as they come to grips with their losses. The father's failing health triggered what is often referred to as an anticipatory grief reaction for Judi. Death does not always occur instantaneously. Often it occurs in steps. In this respect, there are many mini-deaths. A person's activity level may deteriorate, sense of humor dry up, or memory fail. Each one of these events is a mini-death and can trigger a grief reaction. The overwhelming pain of death often may be mitigated by those who actively grieve over the many mini-losses as they occur.

Dealing with the issue of her dad's dying is almost insurmountable for Judi. Since she has repressed core feelings for decades, it will be difficult for her to open them up. If Judi wants to resolve the distance in her relationship with her father while he is still alive, not only must she confront her own discomfort, but she must do this in the face of his discomfort. This makes the task of working through the painful loss even more difficult. Indeed, Judi's high activity level during this time of pending loss may also be indicative of an agitated depression regarding this loss.

In most societies the pain of loss due to death is usually shared as a family and community. Adding to Judi's anxiety is the possibility of facing the loss of her father alone. She does not expect her husband to be available in her time of emotional need. She was "… not there to give him support when his father died."

Judi was probably unavailable for her husband, not out of a sense of malice or a lack of caring, she simply was trained to avoid intimacy. She had no emotional-behavioral skill repertoire to fall back upon during those times of emotional need to provide her husband with support.

EMOTIONAL VITALITY   Feeling is an essential ingredient in developing and maintaining the vitality of a relationship. The avoidance of intimacy must surely have placed a powerful drain on the emotional energy of Judi's marriage. Common interests and physical attraction may have originally drawn the couple together, but over time, as the couple failed to recognize and share each other's emotional life episodes, they twisted a tourniquet around the flow of their marriage's life blood.

To revitalize the marriage's spiritual blood, both parties will have to recognize old wounds and provide heartfelt forgiveness to each other. This will allow for the healing required. Then the couple will have to begin to oxygenate each other with the freshness of their unrepressed, liberated love, otherwise, the two will either continue to cohabit as roommates, or they will part.

Conceivably, the couple might find new partners who would be attractive and "safe" because she or he would be uninterested in sharing intimate feelings. Then the old pattern would replicate itself in a new relationship and the old complex would have a new chapter.

COMPLEX   Early in Judi's professional career she had difficulty dealing with male clients. A classmate provided her with suggestions for dealing with her discomfort with men, especially with regard to their sexuality and inappropriateness. These suggestions helped with the initial issue, but Judi's concerns were rooted deeper in her psychological history. Judi's discomfort over how she would be perceived by others and how to respond to inappropriate requests were only part of a greater complex. The foundations of her insecurity and the deeper issues regarding her own sexuality, as well as her relationships with men, were bypassed when only the overt issues were addressed rather than the entire complex.

A psychological issue is said to be a complex when it is comprised of multiple, interacting factors, some of which may be unconscious. Judi was confronting a complex that began in her adolescence. This complex included: her father's discomfort and abusive rejection of her originating in his anxiety toward her developing sexuality; a lack of healthy role models from whom Judi could have derived the skills to help her choose a nourishing mate; her parents' failure to teach both communication and problem-solving skills that would have allowed their daughter to confront and resolve the intimate issues that were bound to arise in any relationship; low self-esteem because Judi felt denied, rejected, and tainted by her father's accusations and ineffectual support by her mother. This complex may have influenced Judi's choice to become sexually active at a young age because of the message from her father that this was the only female aspect desired by men. Her low self-esteem was likely reinforced with the complication of pregnancy.

The complex that created distance between Judi and her father in her youth, again complicated Judi's relationship with him later in her life. It may have influenced her choice of a mate and also may have drained her marriage of its emotional vitality. In addition, the complex may have been responsible for compromising her work performance.

Judi's clients found her work to be "fine." However, she had recognized that something was missing in her work. She came to the conclusion that after pursuing many advanced training sessions the missing ingredient would probably not come in the form of another massage technique. Judi recognized that in both personal and professional levels she was at a "standstill." In order to move "a little further," with either her clients or her marriage, she would have to find "another piece to her puzzle." In fact, this missing ingredient may also be related to the complex.

RESISTANCE When working with clients, Judi is aware that there is a potential depth that she is unable to reach. Something stops her. Judi recognizes that this is a missing piece to the puzzle of her work. In actuality, there may be a number of pieces that are missing. Judi's passive waiting for something to fall into place or doing more of the same thing will not produce the desired change. When she suspected the missing piece may come in the form of developing a spiritual presence, she may be moving in the right direction. If Judi can bring a non-judgmental, accepting, loving presence to her touch, her clients may feel sufficiently supported and safe to release their deeper, chronic holding patterns. It is here that the complex of her family's discomfort with closeness may effect her performance.

To perform deeper work involves opening one's self to the contact. And Judi learned early on in her family to brace against closeness. This bracing is antithetical to opening chronic psychophysical holding patterns. It is difficult if not impossible, for a bodyworker to convey to a client the message of releasing a chronic holding pattern, if the bodyworker tightens her or his own musculature to combat fears of contact. This complicating factor, which is the underlying element of the complex, is the issue of resistance.

Resistance is an unconscious mechanism which protects an individual from painful memories, thoughts, or awarenesses. Judi may inhibit herself from releasing her own muscular stress when she works with her clients for two reasons. First, by releasing her own muscular tension she may get in touch with the painful emotional awarenesses that accompany her physical release. The resistance Judi experiences is the reluctance to reopen painful, old internalized messages. Second, if she experiences direct contact with another, she will have violated the family taboo equating any kind of contact with forbidden sexual contact. For whatever reason Judi may be holding herself back, she must choose to release those holding patterns. Otherwise, her defenses maintain her "standstill" in both her personal growth and her work with her clients.

In this case, the key to deeper work with her clients will require Judi to do deeper work with herself. She needs to set the emotional record straight within herself. She will have to recognize that there was nothing wrong with her as an adolescent and appreciate that the problems in her relationship with her father belonged to his unresolved issues about sexuality. The physical and emotional distance, the name calling and sexual accusations belonged to her father's unresolved feelings for his daughter. As Judi absolves herself of feelings of guilt and shame, she may clarify for herself what kinds of contacts and feelings are acceptable and which are not. With a clear sense of her own boundaries she can decide how to resolve her conflicts with her father, her husband, and her work.

SUMMARY

Judi presented two related dilemmas that she encountered in her practice. The first, she had early on in her career. The second was current. Judi's first issue related to her discomfort working with men as she began her career as a massage therapist. She called this dilemma her "little hang-up thing." Judi, who was in counseling, provided ample psychosocial history to readily recognize the link between early familial experiences and present conflicts, including her frustration with taking her work to deeper levels. Though Judi did not formally learn how to resolve her problem in massage school, a classmate provided her with effective suggestions. Learning to speak bluntly of sexual matters helped Judi to overcome her inhibitions. This lesson was essential to her professional growth. As a result of entering the massage profession Judi began to deal with and confront her discomfort with men. Through Judi's work in massage she learned that all men were not as her father described. Whether or not they found her attractive, all males would not violate her sexual boundaries. Furthermore, when she clearly stated her limits, they were respected.

Deeper levels of this same issue later emerged as Judi intuitively recognized that she was reaching arbitrary limits in her bodywork. New, different, more powerful physical techniques failed to help her overcome her impasse. She was also at an impasse in her ability to communicate with her husband. She was uncertain where her marriage was going, or whether or not she wanted to be in it. Judi was aware, too, of an emotional chasm between herself and her father. As he was aging and his health was poor, she felt an internal pressure to be able to overcome this distance before his death.

In addition, Judi was beginning to recognize the importance of opening to her deeper feelings. She was beginning to recognize and struggle with the spiritual void in her life. To open to her spiritual relationship with her Higher Power, however, she would have to overcome her reluctance to open to feelings within herself. A spiritual connection can only come through feeling.

Judi had brought herself to counseling. Hopefully, this potentially liberating relationship will provide her the support and direction that she needs, enabling her to overcome the complex created when her father denied her his acceptance, confirmation, and love. As Judi both opens her heart to her feelings and allows herself expression, the growth process will begin to destructure the self-limiting complex and create a firm foundation upon which a healthy, true, and nourishing identity can emerge. From this new self she can experience a releasing in her own musculature which will signal the way for her clients to safely release their own chronic holding patterns.

4

PASSING IT ON

Margaret is a good humored, pleasant, soft spoken, optimistic woman in her mid-forties.

When I tell people of my past, they don't believe a word of it. I came from an abusive background. I was born in 1945 and my father returned from the war crazy, alcoholic, and abusive. I remember when I was four he held my mother and me at gun point. I turned around and went to get help.

After four marriages and four divorces, my mom finally left my father. The man provided no financial support for our family...and, so my mother had to go to work. My mother was bitter over her life circumstances. She was disappointed, frustrated, and physically vented her anger at me. I also had an abusive step-father for four years. *(With a sense of relief)* He was a traveling salesman and was not home much.

I was married twice. Both husbands were alcoholic. The second husband was polydrug addicted. I also became a heavy drinker and smoker. In spite of my personal and domestic problems and having only a high school education, I successfully maintained myself at a thirty thousand dollar a year job at an advertising agency. At forty-two years of age, I was in counseling working on giving up my addictions. Then I began "Rebirthing."

My life was changed. I was instantly released from drugs and alcohol. I developed a new sense of myself and a wall developed between myself and my abusive past. As I became sober, stronger, and self-respecting, my chemically addicted husband announced to me that I was "no fun." He developed a relationship with another woman and then left me.

The emotional-physical trauma in my life left me with little self-confidence or self-esteem. I was always doing...like all good little girls, I was a hard worker ready to please. However, now I am excited about life. I am not sure where I am headed, but I am having fun. I am sturdy. As for relationships, sometimes I feel loneliness and wonder what I would do if there was someone in my life. But I am real clear they will need to be on my path. I'm not willing to walk a spiritual path alone within a relationship. So I imagine if that piece happens, it will happen in God's time.

I was forty-six at this turning point when I went to an advanced training session in my third bodywork discipline. I just left my job at the advertising firm where I was continually confronted with deadlines. It was high stress work. I worked 9 or 10 hours a day, six days a week. I hardly took vacations. I was determined not to allow my bodywork business to be the taskmaster of my life the way advertising had been.

I also had had an auto accident twenty-five years earlier. My car had been struck in the rear by a reckless motorist. He had hit his brakes, continued to slide for 75 feet and then smashed the rear bumper of my car all the way into the back seat. I suffered whiplash from the impact which left me in chronic pain. I was at the chiropractor all the time, for at least 12 years! Then I had three Trager® sessions and the pain began to diminish.

I went to a bodywork training session knowing sure enough I would have to work on someone's neck. By accident I paired-up with a man just about my age. I then timidly began to work on his neck. I had to perform a "neck lift," but something inside me stopped me from doing to someone else what would have been excruciatingly painful to me. I reflexively tightened my muscles. I was providing very little flexion in spite of all the muscular tension and pressure that I was experiencing in my own hands, wrists, forearms, shoulders and neck. My partner was unaware of the conflict going on inside me. He didn't know how important it was for me to be acceptable to others and how frightened I was of anticipating making pain on him.

Without being aware of what was going on inside of me he said, "You can lift more." I told him, "I'm afraid I'll hurt you." Then I heard him say, "I am confident in you!" "You will do fine." That freaked me out! Whether no one had ever said that to me before or I was just unable to accept it, I don't know, but I had never heard that before. I never had anyone confident in me about anything. I not only heard what he said, I took in both his words and his feeling of confidence. I was really touched by this. My self-confidence was boosted by the confidence he felt in me. My muscular holding released. Suddenly, I was aware of feeling the sensations of this man's neck resting in my hands. It was as if someone had suddenly turned on an electric switch. I suddenly could feel the flexibility of his muscles as they arched in my cupped hands and I watched his head tilt back. I could feel the weight; I could feel the skin. I continued to lift his neck muscles, reaching the full extent of their range. Then I just stopped lifting. I not only understood how to do the technique safely, but I had the confidence to perform it.

But this is not the end of the story. I returned home after the training, and wouldn't you know, my first client was a chronically glum looking, 30 year old, woman. Ellen suffered from spina bifida. I was told that this woman's parents were informed by her physician that she was mentally impaired. She was also told that she would live a short life.

Ellen was not mentally impaired at all—but brilliant. But the stigma of what her physician communicated stayed with her. She felt intellectually as well as physically impaired. Physiologically, she had almost no neck. Three of her cervical vertebra were missing. As a result of the pinching, she continually suffered from shoulder pain.

As I began to work with Ellen, I could hardly get one of my fingers behind the woman's neck to do the "neck lift," so I stopped. As I began to work with my client I was filled with my old fear. I thought to myself, "This woman is fragile. I could make the wrong move with her and she will be paralyzed for life. She'll be a cripple."

I was aware, "This is the beginning of the session. If I don't have confidence in myself now, what will that say for the rest of the session?" As soon as I recognized, "This is a confidence issue," I remembered my experience at the training. I remembered the confidence that my partner had in my skill, my listening to what his muscles were telling me, and my muscle tension let go. I was doing it again!

I completed a full circle and finished my session the way I began it—with a "neck lift." Ellen told me her chronic shoulder pain disappeared by the time I worked my way back to her neck. But what struck me the most was the fact I could fit three fingers behind Ellen's neck as I did the lift. After the session, I looked back at my table as I left the room to wash my hands. That deep ingrained gloom in Ellen's face had turned into a broad, beaming, smile. Ellen had truly been touched by the session, and she was not the same. The two of us cried in joy.

DISCUSSION

MINDBODY   Margaret was in counseling to overcome her addictions, but it was not until she incorporated bodywork into her therapeutic regimen that she was able to achieve a behavioral release from her addictive life-style. After Margaret participated in rebirthing sessions, she experienced a letting go that allowed for a profound release of her past destructive behaviors. She explained, "My life was changed. I was instantly released from drugs and alcohol. I developed a new sense of myself and a wall developed between myself and my abusive past."

Verbal therapies are often powerful interventions allowing for the development of clear understandings, insights, new perspectives, problem solving, and planning. Growthful changes can occur on numerous levels in the process of this work. Internalized feelings may be catharted, behavioral holding patterns may be released, and life-style patterns may be changed. Sometimes these benefits do not occur, that is, a person may gain greater and greater intellectual understanding of her or his problems and remain just as emotionally, somatically, and behaviorally imprisoned. Bodywork may provide the catalyst which can unlock that mindbody holding pattern which constitutes that prison.

MARITAL DISHARMONY The health and well-being of one's spouse is not always a value or priority for both members of a marriage. One partner may become threatened by the other's clarity, strength, awareness, or independence. As Margaret explained, "As I became sober, stronger, and self-respecting, my chemically addicted husband announced to me that I was no fun." When the husband's chemically dependent life-style was no longer reinforced by his wife, he took his romantic energy out of the relationship. Faced with the prospect of growth and the integrity of his marriage or a life-style of chemical dependence, the husband chose the familiar route. With this choice he psychologically, spiritually, and eventually, legally, ended his marriage.

For a relationship to thrive when one of a couple is involved in counseling or psychotherapy, it is essential that the other partner be actively supportive of the growth process. It is helpful if the other partner can be informed of the process and progress, and even be included in it. But, when one partner is interested in growth and the other is not, strain is placed upon the relationship and the prognosis for the relationship is poor.

Though Margaret's second marriage ended in divorce, Margaret moved on to a new awareness, rather than to a new "fun" relationship as her husband did. Margaret wanted to have fun, but she wanted more than that from a relationship. Margaret became clearer about who she was and the meaning that she wanted to derive from a relationship. She gained a new sense of what she needed from a partner to support her integrity. She said, "As for relationships, sometimes I feel loneliness and wonder what I would do if there was someone in my life. But I am real clear they will need to be on my path. I'm not willing to walk a spiritual path alone within a relationship." Margaret determined that the pain of being with herself, though alone, was a better alternative than to be with someone and feel alone on her spiritual path.

CAREER CHANGE   At the age of forty-six, Margaret was at a turning point in her life. This courageous woman had just left a well-paying job at an advertising firm. She gave up a way of life in which she was constantly confronted with deadlines, high stress work, long work days, and long work weeks. Work was so much the focus of her life that she hardly took vacations.

Margaret made an identity statement, "I was determined not to allow my bodywork business to be the taskmaster of my life, the way advertising had been." She then made bodywork her full-time career. Eventually, Margaret invested in learning a third bodywork discipline; one that gave her relief from her own neck pain.

POST TRAUMATIC STRESS   Margaret had had an auto accident early in her adulthood. She remained in pain resulting from the whiplash she sustained in that accident, in spite of years of chiropractic treatment. After two decades of suffering, she assumed that her pain was just one of those life circumstances with which she would have to live. She was amazed and delighted when after three Trager® sessions her pain significantly diminished.

Pain is an experiential phenomena that is comprised of multiple components. Some of these components are directly related to the injury and the body's attempt to protect itself while healing takes place. Other components of the pain may be related to holding patterns created by one's emotional state at the time of the accident.

For example, a person is likely to be frightened, angry, or guilty as a result of an accident. These feelings may be locked into the musculature along with the messages of physical pain as the body's automatic protective holding pattern engages. In addition to these reactions directly related to the accident, indirect feelings dealing with other present or past life circumstances may be locked into the musculature. These indirect reactions may be related to the intensity of Margaret's work load or her troublesome marriage. Both direct and indirect emotional components may then inhibit the recovery and exacerbate the pain.

Margaret continued to experience physical pain years after the physical healing process had ended. This residual pain may have resulted from emotional holding patterns that sustained the message to the brain of physical injury. Chiropractic intervention may have provided for a temporary realignment of bones and joints, but it did not release the holding patterns in the muscles or reach the psychological levels of the holding pattern.

The Trager® intervention that Margaret received, like Rebirthing, is a gentle technique which subtly encourages release of the organism rather than attempting to impose release. Perhaps because of the gentle nature of her bodyworker, Margaret was able to release the holding pattern which had caused her pain for over two decades.

PSYCHOPHYSICAL EXPLORATION: A PROBLEM-SOLVING STRATEGY

Margaret reported that she remained in chronic pain for 12 years after her auto accident, then, "I had three Trager® sessions and the pain began to diminish." There may be additional components to Margaret's pain which are related more specifically to psychological holding. She may achieve further release of her pain by a combination of psychological catharsis and physical release. This psychophysical intervention may release holding patterns related to the accident and the general emotional climate of that period of her life. In addition, it may release holding patterns that possibly predated the accident, such as patterns from her abusive childhood or her marriage.

Psychophysical exploration could follow three possible routes. In the first case Margaret might be able to achieve further release of her holding and pain by reliving her accident through role play. Another option is writing, which, like role play, is a psychophysical activity, and can also provide for psychophysical release. When exploring emotional releases of traumatic events, it is important, and sometimes necessary, to have professional support available. Margaret might choose to process her accident with a psychotherapist who is familiar with psychophysical release techniques or who can work in conjunction with a bodyworker who is familiar with clients with post traumatic stress. In any of the above approaches, Margaret would need to pay particular attention to the emotional as well as the physical factors related to her memories of the accident.

INTERDISCIPLINARY TEAM Professional rivalries, economic expedience, and lack of knowledge may stop a professional from working with an interdisciplinary team. This is most unfortunate as a combination of therapeutic interventions may be necessary to receive the full benefit from a therapeutic regimen. Because of this lack of interdisciplinary cooperation, it may fall upon the accident victim, medical patient, or psychotherapy client to create her or his own health care team.

HYPNOTIC SUGGESTION Many people in the presence of an authority figure such as a physician, immediately assume an altered right brain state of consciousness. This shift can occur in any situation involving anticipation, anxiety, or emotional intensity. In such a state, people are open and susceptible to hearing not merely the content of what is being said, but to being hypnotically programmed by what is being presented. People who are susceptible to hypnotic suggestion are just as vulnerable to negative suggestions as they are amenable to positive ones.

Margaret explains of her thirty year old client, "...the stigma of what her physician communicated stayed with her. She felt intellectually as well as physically impaired." Ellen's parents probably believed and acted according to what they were told and accepted from their physician. Ellen then lived up or down to her parents' expectations.

The cause of Ellen's inability to find relief from her neck tension, which contributed to her shoulder pain is unknown. It may have been due to the limits of medical knowledge at the time, the specific limits of the physician's knowledge, or her physician's professional prejudice toward health care workers to whom he would refer his patient. Whatever the reason, Ellen was imprisoned with a 30 year sentence of continual shoulder pain, low self-esteem, and chronic glumness.

What any person in a position of authority, including a bodyworker, pronounces about a patient or client in her or his presence is exceedingly critical. This is especially true if that patient or client is in an altered, right brain, emotional state. What is being pronounced, whether accurate or inaccurate, may become a lifetime sentence for that person.

Intuitively, Margaret used a positive right brain state of being to undo the consequences of a negative right brain state of being. While working on Ellen's neck, "I remembered my experience at the training. I remembered the confidence that my partner had in my skills, my listening to what his muscles were telling me. Then I began to feel myself fill from a spirit deep within me. My muscle tension let go." Margaret, through the use of imagery, placed herself back in the right brain state of being that she experienced at her training. She made contact with her client from this altered state of being. It is not surprising that Ellen's chronically tight neck muscles would entrain with the soft, relaxed muscles of her bodyworker, resulting in Ellen's release from her psychophysical, hypnotic prison sentence of thirty years duration.

CONTACT Margaret was first the recipient of contact before she had the opportunity to pass it on. Margaret experienced this when she heard her training partner say to her, "I am confident in you. You will do fine."

We know that she was changed by this event because she described being freaked-out. "Whether no one had ever said that to me before or I was just unable to accept t, I don't know, but I had never heard that before. I never had anyone confident in me about anything. I not only heard what he said, I took in both his words and his feelings of confidence. I was really touched by this. My self-confidence was boosted by the confidence he felt in me. My muscular holding released. Suddenly I was aware of feeling the sensations of this man's neck resting in my hands. It was as if someone had suddenly turned on an electric switch. I could feel the flexibility of his muscles as they arched in my cupped hands and I watched his head tilt back. I could feel the weight; I could feel the skin. I continued to lift his neck until my fingers could feel those flexible muscles reaching the full extent of their range."

Contact, used in the context of Margaret's performing bodywork on Ellen, means more than merely physically touching with hands, it infers more than just manipulating Ellen's tissues, muscles, and bones. Margaret's contact indicates that she brought her entire psychophysical and spiritual self to the limits of her being. She genuinely encountered her client at the frontiers of that boundary.

Sometimes, to differentiate this form of contact, it is referred to as "high contact" or "Gestalt contact." This type of encounter is extremely powerful. In and of itself, "high contact" can produce profound changes for the parties involved. Margaret clearly described such a contact event when she told of her training experience. She had her partner's head resting in her hands when he expressed confidence that she could perform the move accurately. His head and neck were draped in her hands when he expressed his assurance in her. Margaret had never before heard such belief and confidence in her abilities. Margaret's partner had touched her deeply by the words and trust he placed in her.

After Margaret's session with Ellen, looking back at the table as she left the room, Margaret saw that the deep ingrained gloom in Ellen's face had transformed itself into a broad, beaming, smile. The two women glanced at each other and nonverbally confirmed the truth of what had just taken place as a result of the session. This glance, also, was a contact event. They shared a cry of joy.

SELF-ESTEEM   One may have a sense of self-confidence because her or his parents provided recognition, appreciation, and celebration of who she or he was. It was just the opposite for Margaret. Margaret recognized, "The emotional and physical trauma in my life left me with little self-confidence or self-esteem." To make up for the negative internal feelings she had, Margaret was always working and driving herself to impress others and live up to their expectations, "I was always doing. Like all good little girls, I was a hard worker ready to please." Margaret's other-directedness, her attempts to please others at her own expense further diminished her self-esteem. These actions confirmed for her that she was only worthy of conditional acceptance.

This does not mean that Margaret must be condemned to a life of self-doubt because her parents failed to provide external validation, confidence, and love. Self-esteem is something that is built up. It is developed as one runs the risks of learning and implementing new skills. Additionally, one must recognize, appreciate, and celebrate her or his own accomplishments and achievements. In the past, Margaret performed for others. In this other-orientation, she lost a sense of herself. As a result of her life scars she learned to identify and meet her own needs. This is one of the tasks of adulthood, to provide oneself with validation. This self-recognition of one's achievements provides additional energy for continued growth.

Intuitively, one knows when growth occurs. Margaret recognized this truth, "...now I am having fun. I am sturdy." Growth does not always happen in a straight line, like learning to ride a bicycle or learning a new bodywork discipline. New behaviors are often internalized gradually, over time. Sometimes there are even temporary or partial setbacks in the growth process. These setbacks are not significant. What is essential, is that the individual continues to learn from these setbacks. This is the process of building self-confidence and self-esteem. Margaret may have gained some excellent skills from her bodywork training session, but it was the act of practicing those skills that made them part of her professional and personal identity.

GROUNDING AN INTERVENTION: A PROBLEM-SOLVING STRATEGY
Margaret began the relationship with her new client accompanied by her old neck pain anxiety. She knew how delicate necks could be from her own auto accident experience and did not want to cause further trauma to her client's fragile neck. Margaret's creative use of imagery helped her to overcome her anxiety. Another way of handling this situation could have been to consult with her client.

Rather than deciding for her client, Margaret could have grounded her intervention by bringing her client into the decision making process. She could have asked her client what was safe, acceptable, and comfortable for her and what was not. Should Ellen have not known her own limits, it would have been helpful for Margaret to have a medical consultant with whom she could have conferred regarding this issue. If Margaret did not know of anyone with whom to confer, she might even have contacted Ellen's present physician. When in doubt, one can always ask.

SUMMARY

Margaret went to a training session to learn a new bodywork discipline. While working with her partner, she discovered that she received more from the exchange than a set of new techniques. Her partner was able to perceive something in her that allowed him to both trust her work and express that trust to her. The result of this exchange was that Margaret received his confidence in a way that she had never before experienced. From this contact she was able to release the fear she had of working on someone's neck and hurting them. Having experienced a neck injury from a car accident more than two decades earlier, Margaret had a profound appreciation for how an injured, painful neck could effect a person's life. After psychologically and physically releasing the fear she was holding, this bodyworker, "not only understood how to do the technique safely," but had the confidence to perform it. That was not the end of Margaret's story.

She was not a person to just learn from her experiences. She was someone who passed on her growth to those with whom she worked. Margaret's first client after returning from her training was a woman who suffered from spina bifida. At first, she feared working with her client lest she do permanent damage to someone who already suffered from a disability. Then as she faced her professional task, Margaret remembered the training experience that she had just completed. She recalled her experience with her partner and the confidence that it had instilled in her. As she did this right brain exercise, Margaret felt her own holding pattern release. She experienced her confidence return. She performed the "neck lift" as it was meant to be done.

When Margaret was finished with her session, both she and her client cried as they recognized the release of a thirty year old emotional and physical holding pattern. From her contact in her training, Margaret experienced a healing of her low self-esteem. As a result of her own healing, she was able to actualize what "passing it on" can mean.

People usually imply physical touch when they refer to contact. "High contact" goes beyond physical touch, it is emotional and spiritual in nature. Consequently, anyone who opens her or himself to being touched by a contact event, can be changed. Anyone who chooses to open her or his heart to Margaret's sharing, can be transformed by the contact.

Part II

SETTING LIMITS

5

AN INDIGESTIBLE EVENT

Sandy is a massage therapist in her mid-forties. She spoke rapidly with anxiety and agitation. The following is a phone conversation the day after Sandy gave a massage to Joyce.

Joyce was forty-seven years old. She recently had a mastectomy. She was a friend of a friend. So even though I see new clients at my office, I didn't have any concerns over working with her at home. But later that night, I couldn't stop thinking about what happened that morning. Joyce pulled off the sheet as I worked on her. When that happened, I didn't think anything about it, but then she grabbed my wrists and slid my hands onto her breasts!

It all happened so fast and unexpectedly. I was really uncomfortable with what was happening, and I was trying to make sense for myself out of what was going on. I remembered thinking to myself, "This woman has had a mastectomy. She must have some sort of body image distortion. She must be suffering from terrible insecurity. Perhaps she feels like a freak, and in some manner is trying to normalize her wounded self-esteem." So, as professionally as I could, without being judgmental toward Joyce, I gently released my contact. After I let some time go by, I continued the massage. Everything returned to normal, I thought.

When I pulled back, I intended to give Joyce the message that what she was doing wasn't okay. I remember working on Joyce and thinking to myself of another therapist who had to "have a talk" with men who had an erection while being worked on while they were on the table. I think there is a certain naturalness to body functions, and I'm not one to be a prude when it comes to understanding my client's reflexes.

But after I finished the front of Joyce's body I had her turn over, and then as I started to work on her shoulder, she began to thrust her pelvis into the table. I said to Joyce, "You seem to be getting in touch with sexual feelings." Without missing a beat Joyce flipped back, "You are making me hot!" This was blowing my mind! There was nothing sexual about my work on this woman's shoulder. I couldn't figure out what was happening. A woman behaving inappropriately was something massage school didn't prepare me for!

I took my hands off of her again. She quit her pelvic thrusting. Then I finished the rest of the massage. There were no more incidents. But I remember thinking to myself that it was peculiar that on her way out, Joyce didn't make any comment, or apology, or explanation for what happened.

Later that day when I was alone, I began to reflect on my morning client, and I was becoming increasingly upset. What happened with this client was not sitting well with me at all. It was as if I couldn't digest the event. I kept dwelling on it. I felt uncomfortable with myself even though I tried to make sense of it. It was troubling all night long.

Talking this out with you on the phone has been helpful. As I am talking about the event, my feelings about it are becoming clear to me. Friend of a friend or not, Joyce's behavior was not acceptable to me. Next, this had never happened to me before, so I was taken off guard. I didn't know how to deal with it. It made me feel vulnerable.

Having talked about this now the situation is clear to me. If someone acts that way again, I won't put up with it. I'll tell 'er! Now I'm starting to feel a lot better. The only thing that is comforting about this situation is that I'll never hear from her again.

EPILOGUE

About four weeks later, Joyce called back. She wanted another appointment. I told her immediately, "What happened on the table last time was uncomfortable for me. I am not prepared to deal with your sexual stuff." Joyce then told me that she had had a three hour liquid lunch that day. Thinking back, I thought I smelled alcohol on her breath, but I never met her before; I wasn't sure.

Joyce apologized and told me, "It will never happen again." Joyce came in for another session. She left the cover on for the entire session.

DISCUSSION

LOCATION   An office at home may be more comfortable, convenient, and far less expensive than having to rent office space. It does have its drawbacks. A rented office provides a more professional image to clients. It communicates that the practitioner's work is not something done on the side as a lark, but is a major life endeavor. When working, one is a professional, and is to be treated as a professional. In addition, it implies that a formal decorum is expected from clients. This may reduce management problems.

There also is a safety component; one is not bringing business contacts into her or his home. This is especially important when one works with the public and also provides intimate contact with clients. Sandy assumed that "a friend of a friend" must be safe. She was mistaken, and sometimes you just cannot tell. Perhaps, if she had met with Joyce at her office location for the initial session, this experience would have been avoided.

CRISIS   Sandy was thrown into a crisis after her first contact with Joyce. The contents of psychological ingestion, just like the contents of food ingestion, can be unpalatable or unassimilable. Sandy reported, "I kept dwelling on it. I felt uncomfortable with myself even though I tried to make sense of it. It was troubling all night long." Somehow, her body had to cleanse itself of these experiential toxins. Sandy knew that she was under duress, and she did not know how to respond.

After a night of suffering a psychic bellyache from her "indigestible event," Sandy called a psychologist friend to discuss her experience. She was strong enough to admit her feelings. By the time Sandy made the call, she had realized that she had been in both shock and denial. Sandy was no prude. She could understand and tolerate a male's sexually reflexive erection. She could deal with an inappropriate male. But, there was a certain "unreal" quality to the series of deliberate homosexual events that unfolded during her session with Joyce. Sandy was agitated.

PSYCHOLOGICAL SHOCK   Sandy knew that she was uncomfortable with her client, however, it took a restless, difficult night before she decided to get help with her troubling feelings. Sandy had been thrown into a shock reaction by her contact with Joyce.

Psychological shock is an emotional state of being stunned or dazed following an accident, catastrophe, unexpected distress, or fright. In more severe cases, individuals may become stuporous, disorganized, or amnesic of the event. As a result of a shock reaction, victims are usually unaware of the extent of the damage caused to themselves. If these troubled feelings are not emotionally released, they may remain as unresolved psychological trauma and interfere with peace of mind, sleep, and general well-being. They may also create panic or phobic reactions. One does not have to be a victim of such a situation, but merely an observer of the event to have a shock reaction. Talking about the event and one's feelings as soon as possible with a patient, supportive listener is often an effective intervention for relieving the effects of psychological shock.

RATIONALIZATION Sandy recognized that Joyce's pulling off the sheet, placing Sandy's hands on her breasts, and then pelvic thrusting did not relate to unresolved feelings over her client's mastectomy. Joyce was simply "acting out" sexually. Joyce's sexual behavior accelerated as the massage went on. Joyce did not pick up on and respond to Sandy's non-verbal messages of discomfort. Joyce did not present and discuss her "hidden agenda" for her massage with Sandy. She just acted it out. Joyce was taking advantage of Sandy's earnestness and Sandy's boundaries were being violated.

Sandy felt overwhelmed by multiple issues. She did not want to lose a client. She did not want to appear out of control, nor did she want to further traumatize her surgically scarred client. She was afraid of how it would sound if she said what she was really thinking. Perhaps she was afraid of conflict or rejection. Even after Joyce told Sandy, "You are making me hot!" Sandy did not express herself. She was in shock and did not confront the issue with Joyce. Instead, Sandy tried to make sense out of her client's inappropriate behavior. She tried to rationalize the behavior by constructing an acceptable explanation for Joyce's unacceptable behavior, "This woman has had a mastectomy. She must have some sort of body image distortion. She must be suffering from terrible insecurity. Perhaps she feels like a freak and in some manner is trying to normalize her wounded self-esteem." Although Sandy provided herself with a logical-sounding explanation for what was going on with her client, she could not salve her distressed feelings.

Sandy was in shock because Joyce was making sexual advances to her. Sandy was unable to deal with what was happening in her session. At the time, the best she could do was to rationalize away her client's unacceptable actions. Sandy's rationalization was a futile attempt at ridding herself of Joyce's "mind blowing" homosexual behavior. It did not provide for resolution of the conflict or her own peace of mind. With time, distance, and discussion of this experience with a supportive friend, Sandy realized that her discomfort with the situation was the result of disregarding her own feelings. This recognition allowed her to begin calming her distraught feelings.

NORMALIZATION   After Sandy was removed from the immediacy of her situation, she realized how upset she was by the session with Joyce. The fact that Sandy was upset is not unusual, a sign of weakness, or lack of strength on her part. Quite to the contrary, if Sandy was not upset, that would be an issue for concern. If listened to, upsetting feelings, like the gas gauges in our cars, provide essential information about what is happening. Feelings tell us who we are, what is going on with us, and even what we need to do to take care of ourselves.

It was not until Sandy spoke to a friend and shared her truthful feelings that she started to feel relieved. Sandy shared how upsetting the event was to her, she shared how angry she was, and expressed her conviction that this type of behavior would not occur again in her practice. As Sandy gave voice to her feelings, her understanding of the situation became clearer, she felt better about herself, and she knew what she would do if a similar situation arose. Sandy defined for herself, "Friend of a friend or not, Joyce's behavior was not acceptable to me." "If someone acts that way again, I won't put up with it. I'll tell 'er!" The situation became normalized.

THE DECISION   Sandy decided that she was unwilling to continue to practice without protecting herself from such situations. Simultaneously, she no longer felt anxious about hearing from Joyce again. "I was not prepared to handle what happened. I was afraid of how I would sound if I confronted her, but I am not afraid of her anymore." Instead Sandy felt self-confident and prepared to establish her new limits with Joyce. "I am going to tell her what is going on for me."

ACTION   Sandy felt much better about herself after taking action. She received some support in sharing an uncomfortable situation. In spite of the risk of losing a client or upsetting the referring friend, she made a plan. When the opportunity arose, Sandy acted on her plan. The interaction not only established Sandy's professional limits with her client, but it demanded that Joyce be accountable for her behavior. This is the process of professional and personal growth.

DIRECT ACTION: A PROBLEM-SOLVING STRATEGY   Immobility often generates depression or anxiety. Positive action on the other hand, usually promotes a feeling of well-being. Sandy felt overwhelmed when she rationalized and did not confront Joyce. Just talking out her concern and generating a new policy helped Sandy to feel better about herself.

Sandy created a strategy to deal with her clients' improprieties should they arise again. After she talked out the issue with her friend, Sandy dropped the matter because she believed that Joyce would never contact her again. Though effective, this was an indirect strategy.

Taking immediate action would have been an alternative intervention. This would have set the record straight and bolstered Sandy's shaken sense of integrity. Sandy could have contacted Joyce directly rather than waiting for a similar situation to arise again. She could have shared her concerns and her limits. "What happened on the table with your sexual behavior was uncomfortable for me. That has never happened to me before; and I won't put up with it again!" Even more than to set the record straight with Joyce, the reason Sandy might want to take direct action would be to reinforce her own sense of integrity and reduce any remaining anxiety.

ALCOHOL ABUSE Drinking alcohol to the extent that it interferes in social functioning is a sign of alcohol abuse. Sandy did not identify her client's alcohol use as a problem she would have to deal with in her practice. If this issue recurs, Sandy may find herself forced to create a policy regarding her clients and alcohol consumption.

SUMMARY

Sandy found herself engulfed by a psychologically indigestible event when one of her clients confronted her with a situation her massage school had not prepared her for—a sexually inappropriate woman. At first, Sandy was thrown by this new situation. She maintained her personal and professional integrity by withdrawing her physical contact and thereby stopping the undesirable behavior. Her personal response to this situation was to rationalize away her client's inappropriate sexual behavior. Rather than comforting Sandy, this rationalization left her increasingly anxious.

Nothing like this had ever happened to Sandy. Understandably, she was taken off guard and consequently felt vulnerable. Certainly a client who would act out this way was unacceptable.

Sandy discovered that just being able to talk out the event with an objective listener helped her to put the situation in a more comfortable perspective. Once she had an opportunity to normalize the event, the answer to how she would handle this client or another client like her, became clear. Sandy's anxiety dissipated after sharing her traumatic event. She began to feel strong about herself after creating a coping strategy for the future.

6

BROUGHT UP TO BE NICE

Karen, in her late forties, speaks in a gentle, measured, calming, cadence.

What comes to mind immediately are some practical things that happened. The first thing that I think of is last year I was having trouble in my practice with people not paying for their treatment. They would cancel two hours before their appointment, and they wouldn't pay me for it even though when they first came in, I'd say I have a 24 hour policy. You have to cancel 24 hours before you are going to be here. Unless, you know, you have a car accident. I'm not that rigid.

That was the first thing that came to my mind. I struggled with it because I didn't have a policy paper. I'd just tell them my policy, "Please notify me..." when they started. Well, three years later, I still have the policy, but I haven't stated it for three years. And, all of a sudden I have these people calling in and saying, "Oh, my daughter has a soccer game. I can't come at 7:00, and it is 5:30. And, she didn't plan on paying me. And, I'm like, "I'm going to kill these people!" And, this kept happening to me.

Somebody else, they forgot. And, they figured, if they forgot, it didn't count. "Oh, I forgot. I was sleeping." It counts, ya know. I am still waiting here for you to come in. Right! And, you forgot. That counts! Or, ya know, they just decide they didn't want to come that day or something. Anyhow, this kept happening for a couple of months a lot with different people. And I was getting irritated.

I talked with my friend Anne who works upstairs...well she works next door now...and she suggested that I get in touch with my anger. Then she said, "It's probably time you put it in words and write a policy paper. And, make things really clear to people what you expect and what you don't expect. And, what is appropriate and what is not appropriate." Anne was the very first person I ever had a massage from in my life...here in this very building. Now, she has turned into a friend. She's not...I don't hold her up there so high she can't get down, ya know? But she, she can be really helpful. But, she was right. I needed to be clearer about my needs. And, it is okay to have a business. And it's okay to get paid. It's okay to take care of yourself while you are doing this job.

But it took me a lot of time for me to do that. I mean it took a long time of people canceling. And, trying to figure out how to be nice to them. And, call them and say, "Excuse me; but, you didn't show up last week. Do you think you want to pay for it? Or, not say anything about money...because, I hate money issues with clients. I hate that part of it. And, it was really different to write up a paper that said, "This is what I want you to do." Instead of, "Well, maybe, if you could do this, it would be nice." Ya know the difference?

It was hard to write this policy paper because I wanted to be nice. I was brought up to be nice. I was also brought up not to let people walk all over me. So it was kind of difficult to figure out how to write this thing up and be nice and sweet and get what I needed. So, I skipped the nice and sweet part; and I just made it very factual. "If you don't cancel, you pay." "If you can't give me twenty-four hours notice, then you owe me money." I didn't put anything in the letter about individual differences. That, I figured I could handle individually. If someone called and said, "My car broke down," or, "My daughter was in a car accident," I certainly wouldn't charge them. But, if they said they went to a soccer game, that doesn't count. And if their check bounces. And what my hours are...you know, I just put all of this into a very clear statement and gave one to everybody. And, I haven't had one problem since then.

Um, I still try to be really nice to my clients. But, like, I was nervous about the people who had just done all of these things. Getting the piece of paper. Because I knew they'd know, ya know—that they were part of the reason I had to do this. I mean the first person to come in was the soccer person. She comes in and goes, *(in a challenging tone)* "Did you write this *(chuckling)* because of me?" I said, "You were certainly a factor." And she paid me for it. But, she hadn't planned on it. I didn't lose her as a client. I didn't lose any of them.

I did lose one woman. I am not sure if it was over the policy paper or not. The interesting thing to me is that she is a psychotherapist herself. I know she has a policy—"You have to cancel." And, she didn't cancel for me. She just didn't show one time. So, when I saw her the next time, I asked her. I always find that out first. There was no reason. She just slipped or something…or, busy or something. She acted like it was fine. "Oh yeah, sure. No problem. I'll …, " ya know. She came back a couple of times, but then I haven't seen her since.

I let myself let go of it. But I didn't at first. There is a part of me that wants to be sure every need of every person is taken care of. Umm, I think, I don't want to be in control…that part of me wants to make sure that every need of every person is taken care of. I mean, I still hear that voice, but it is further away than it used to be. It is the voice of "The Great Caretaker" like my mother. But I don't do that. But I hear it.

I mean, I have to work on letting go of those things that people may bring in that isn't for me to take care of. But, you can't…you just can't do it all. You can't take care of everyone all the time and then, where are you? Where are you in all of this? Where is your self in all of this. And I saw that in my household. I saw my mother caretake every-one. Everyone, not just her kids. And that looked good to me. Because she looked extremely strong and capable, organized, orderly. She could do anything. I wanted to be like that. Wouldn't you want to be like that? You could do everything. And so that was the model I picked. As opposed to my dad…who was sick. He was physically sick a lot. He was one of the ones who needed caretaking. So I didn't pick my dad.

That was the model that I aspired to. Now, that is the model I am giving up. *(Gentle chuckle)* And it is much healthier not to be that way. I don't want to be like my mother now.

Therapy. Therapy. I wouldn't have gotten there, if it wasn't for therapy. I went to therapy before I got divorced. Because I thought we needed to go to therapy. I didn't think it would save the marriage. But I thought it was worth a try. *(Delightful but fatalistic laughter)* I thought we should go to therapy. We couldn't deal with our problems. I suggested it, of course. He didn't think we needed therapy, "Cause, men don't go to therapy." Those were his words. But we did go; and, we got divorced; and I continued with therapy. But I wanted more from therapy. That's when I switched to Rose. She did bodywork as well as brain work at the same time. Then my mother died.

My personal growth started when my mother died. I got to body-work because my first therapist said, "You need to relax. Go get some massage." So, I did. That's when I started to let go of taking care of everything. I gave it up—not for Lent, but for Life. I was able to separate from my mother. And, I began to see her and see me differ-ently…in therapy. I wouldn't have done that by myself. I don't think.

Now, I let go by talking to myself a lot. I use a…I have a visual image. Ya know those little hook and eyes that keep material together?

Well, I picture one of those and keep unhooking them and say, "That's not for me. That's not my issue. Unhook. O.K. Back up." I back up and let go.

That's not how I used to do it. I used to get in there and take care of it. Ya know. Because that's what you DO. That's what I learned to do. So, people came in and said, "Oh, I'm sorry. I forgot to come in." I'd say, "Oh, gee, I'm sorry too." But I couldn't ask them for money because they were sorry. That whole thing—they are sorry and they are nice people. So, I can't really ask them. The policy paper made it possible for me to do…to be stronger in the business part which is not mine, or anyone else's, favorite part to do.

I also think it is harder for women…I don't know this for sure, but it's hard for us to deal with the money stuff and ask for things. I think men and women do it differently. Men have more permission to get what they need…to ask for things and be more assertive. I don't think that women have as much permission for that. So, to be in the working world and have their own business and have money and have to…it's hard! People…ya know, my clients also expect, I think, that as a woman and as a caregiver I'll be easier on them if they don't pay me. That's the impression I get.

It is like they are very surprised…some people are genuinely surprised, I would write this paper or I would raise my fees. Some people are really surprised about it like, "But, you like this job…Don't you?" "Yeah," I'll reply. "Then why will you charge more?" It's confusing. Exactly what is it they are thinking?

Like one of my clients said, "I got your letter…I noticed you are raising your rates in September." I said, "Yes." "Well, I guess you are allowed. It's been two years," she said. *(Chuckling)* I think it is humorous because that is the way she is. It has to do with her and her personality. She is giving me permission to raise my rates. Yaaa! Then I got pissed at her. Like as soon as she said that it was okay. But she had to make sure to say that to me. It's odd, but that fits her…it just fits her pretty well that she has to be that way.

How can I describe her? She likes to be taken care of and expects more from this than I am going to be giving her. I can't take care of all her needs when she walks in the door. She says in a pouty way, or a kid way, or more manipulative ways than saying, "Damn it! I have had a bad day today." Not real straightforward; ya know, "My neck hurts," or something. It's more, *(In a whining voice)* "I've had a bad day; and I feel …" Ya, know. And she wants everything to be taken care of by the time she leaves. I'm supposed to minister to all her needs. And I think, "I can't do that."

When I first started in practice, I had several people like her…who wanted everything. They wanted their emotional state to be perfect when they left, their neck to be fixed, their back to be…ya know. They wanted to be fixed. And I knew that I couldn't. But, that's not how it is now. But it was a struggle.

I took it to Rose, my psychotherapist. I talked a lot to Rose about it. Getting permission not to take care of everything. I'd take it to her and say, "Okay, do something!" I struggled internally. Some days I'd actually tried to meet those clients' needs, but of course wouldn't, because you can't possibly do that for someone. Well, some people might leave here and feel that those needs are met. But not these particular people. These are people that you can never do enough for.

Rose said to me that this is not my job to fix. That I can be very clear with people that I am not going to be fixing them when they come in this room. I don't have to fix them and I could still be paid. And, I started saying that. These particular type…there are three of them…they all came in the same kind of way. I can't explain it, but they reminded me of each other the way they wanted everything. And, I am not willing to be a participant in it. They would not be helping themselves here. I was going to be doing it. Then they would come back in two weeks and I would be doing it again. They would live for those week periods, and in between it wasn't a possibility. I was not the one to be their fixer. They would have to learn how to work on themselves. I would not fix them every two weeks.

I told them this. They all kept coming to me except one. These appointments started to conflict with her weekly nail appointments. She had to figure out how to do this. She wasn't being fed in the way I hoped she would be. I would have liked to see her have gotten more from the visit than she got, or take it in a different way, or change. But, that wasn't where she was. So, I let that go too. And then I let her go. Then she didn't come back. I didn't feel bad. I believed my therapist. Well, I felt better work was easier when I didn't take responsibility for everybody's everything.

I'm a facilitator. I can facilitate a lot of things, but I'm not going to fix anybody. It's like if you had a broken bone. You can go in, and the doctor can set the bone. But the doctor can't fix it. He or she can set it, but they can't fix it. It is going to heal and take time. Well, it's the same thing…I think. I can't fix the broken things people come in with, but I can facilitate it.

I facilitate by helping people to know their bodies and to know themselves, and to figure out what it feels like to be alive, to be relaxed, to be tense, to be scared, to be numb. I talk them through their feelings. I start talking them through their feelings when they are here.

And saying, "Now how does this feel? What does this feel like? Where are you now? Are you here? Can you feel my hand on your leg? Does it feel numb?" And we usually start from, "I don't know," for a period of time until we get to, "I feel it! You are on my ankle." And, then they come in and start to tell me what they feel. "Well, I got up and my neck was like this today. And it is because of ..." Ya know.

DISCUSSION

TWO LEVELS   All of a sudden, after years of not having problems with "no shows," a number of clients suddenly failed to make their appointments and did not cancel. The fact that these people were making their appointments on time and suddenly changed their behavior is surprising. Furthermore, if it had happened with different people at different times that might be expected, but when a number of clients independently start to not show at the same time—that is puzzling. What's going on?

Karen has become a woman actively involved in her own personal and professional growth. Perhaps when she took another growth step, Karen assumed traits of strength and independence. These characteristics were very likely perceived by her clients. Some of these clients, with their own unresolved issues regarding their personal growth, may have felt threatened by the changes they were seeing in their bodyworker. Uncomfortable with the changes they were experiencing, they might have begun to "forget" and avoid their sessions.

SUPPORT SYSTEMS   Ultimately, Karen would have to confront her clients' limit testing on her own. That does not preclude her obtaining external support: a strong support system helps get the job done. Support may come in many forms: information, encouragement, skills, experience, sufficient sleep, additional physical help, relaxation, understanding, reward, financial backing, or timing. The support may be internal in nature, coming from one's own resources or external, coming from others and the environment.

When obstacles must be overcome, having several internal and external supports to rely upon becomes essential. This diversified portfolio of strategies becomes one's support system. Anne, Karen's first massage therapist, suite mate, and friend is an external support. She provides certain attitudes, ethics, and guidelines, "... put it in words and write a policy paper. Make things really clear to people what you expect and don't expect." These statements in the form of a policy paper are external supports. Massage therapists and psychotherapists are aspects of Karen's external support system.

Recognizing and having clarity about one's needs, accepting one's right "to have a business and get paid," and, "... taking care of yourself while you're doing this job," are internal supports. Karen's talking to herself, using visual images, and giving herself permission to feel her anger, which then provides her with the energy to act on her behalf are other examples of her internal support system.

TRANSCENDING THE NORM   Karen was brought up by her mother to be nice, and to take care of others. Karen wanted to be nice and to "look extremely strong, capable, organized, and orderly" ... to be able to "do anything." Karen did not want to "need caretaking." She wanted to be like her mother. For children to be like their same sex parent is the norm. For better or worse, children grow up to be like their parents. Children who rebel against their parents' role models also maintain the original role model as the norm.

Karen identified with her mother. She replicated the life-style pattern that she had observed and admired in her mother. However, Karen was becoming aware as an adult of what was indiscernible to her as a child. There was a package deal that came part and parcel with the role she emulated. She was becoming dominated by the role of the "Nice Daughter of the Great Caretaker," who takes care of "every need of every person." The desire to be nice and to caretake others conflicted with Karen's desire not to be walked all over. The role interfered with her true self.

Karen points out that she still "tries to be nice." What is interesting about this point is that Karen did not choose to totally and indiscriminately reject that part of her mother's role model. Indeed, if she had chosen to "be her own person" by opposing whatever "nice" might imply, and acted displeasing, uncooperative, insensitive, or irresponsible, she would continue to maintain her mother's model as the norm dedicating her life to rebel against that norm. Karen would have failed to create her own unique niche if she chose that path.

This bodyworker transcended both her mother's model and the social norm of automatically and unconsciously replicating parental patterns. She achieved her own identity by analyzing her problem. She recognized that what was unacceptable about her mother's behavior was the aspect of being nice at her own expense and trying to do for others what rightly they ought to do for themselves. Karen designed a program which allowed her to achieve her own goals.

Karen underestimated her genuine spirit as she continued to believe that she had to "try" to be nice. This implies her gentility is merely a role that she superimposes on an empty frame. This denies her responsiveness, attentiveness, and poise which convey her genuine, natural, wholesomeness as a person.

PACING Change is a process. When one goes about it in a healthy fashion, it takes place in steps. Realistically, genuine change takes time. Letting go of those deeply ingrained, internalized maternal role behaviors was exceedingly difficult for Karen in spite of the insults to her own integrity, schedule, and pocketbook at the hands of her self-involved clients. Karen's early professional motivation was dominated by the part of her that, in childhood, decided "to be sure every need of every person is taken care of."

Perhaps, the divorce was an early change step for Karen. Later on, she began to recognize stresses in her professional relationships that forced her to reassess who she was and how she wanted to be as a professional. Even with the internal support of her realization and discomfort, Karen still maintained the external support of a psychotherapist and friends to assist her in standing her ground as she built up momentum in her growth process.

IMAGERY Karen states that she talks to herself a lot. Whether she answers herself or not, this is an excellent internal support strategy because what she says to herself is positive. Furthermore, not only does she talk to herself—which is a left-brain activity, but she uses right brain imagery. This right brain imagery somatically sends the message of "unhooking" her old dysfunctional "nice," "helper" role behavior while she verbalizes, "That's not for me. That's not my issue. Unhook. Back up."

The right-brain imagery message triggers powerful neurotransmitters, encephalons, and endorphins which allow for profound relaxation and painkilling responses. These messages promote muscle relaxation, immune system strength, and sensations of well-being, comfort, and relaxation. The verbal message to "unhook" and let go of undesirable behavior patterns is reinforced on anatomical, physiological, and psychological levels.

ATTRIBUTION Karen attributes her new strength to the policy paper that she distributed to her clients despite a policy that had been working for three years. Yet, the relevant variable to achieving compliance with her policy may have been Karen's readiness to back up her words with courage and determination. This affective-behavioral change is the real break-through for Karen. Her new business policy works because she has developed the internal fortitude and strength to stand behind it. This core strength further increases her genuine self-esteem and self-respect.

IMPLICIT SELF-CONTRACT Complicating the issue of standing behind her intent may be an implicit contract that Karen made with herself. The contract is part and parcel with her nice-guy, helper role. It reads like this: "If I am a nice person, then you will be a nice person to me. If you are a nice person, I will be nice to you." But when a person does something that is not nice, Karen is blocked by her own implicit self-contract to be nice to them. She says to herself, "I couldn't ask them for money because they are sorry and they are nice people." This forces her to swallow her hurt feelings and her protective anger.

Sometimes even nice people can be short-sighted, unaware, or misinformed. Bringing an issue of concern to their attention should only make the relationship stronger if they are also people of good will. Incorporated into Karen's decision to be up-front with her clients about her policy must be a willingness to share her honesty with nice people. This, of course, would imply a new self-contract: Karen's being honest with herself.

HARDER FOR WOMEN In addition to her personal struggles to be personally assertive, Karen experiences a social resistance against herself as a woman in achieving financial stability and success. She believes that men are raised with an expectation that they are economically deserving and can comfortably ask for what they want or need in an economic market. "Men have more permission for that."

As evidence of this double standard, Karen speaks of her clients who are unable to understand why she would raise her rates if she enjoys her work. Can it be that these clients are unaware that enjoyment does not pay the rent, food, medical expenses, etc.? Would these same people advocate that baseball players, airline pilots, surgeons, or corporate executives not seek reasonable compensation if they are male, and enjoy their work? "To be a woman in the working world and have one's own business…is hard."

Interestingly, the opposition Karen encounters in taking care of herself responsibly comes from women. Karen tells of one female client who "gives her permission to raise her rates." Karen provides sufficient information to suggest that this woman is controlling by nature. Consequently, her comments to Karen are not regarded as personal. Nevertheless, this woman's grandiosity in allowing Karen to raise her rates rather than providing understanding, support, and reinforcement to her caregiver serves as a kick to Karen's psychological Achilles' heel.

This lack of female support confuses Karen, "Exactly what is it that they are thinking?" Perhaps, "they" think the same thing that Karen thinks—"they are undeserving."

MARITAL THERAPY   Karen spoke of marital therapy[1] with a snickering laugh. She went to marital therapy to give the relationship a last ditch effort, but Karen was pessimistic about the outcome. People often enter into marital therapy without an appreciation for what it is, what it can do, and when it can do it.

MEN DON'T GO TO THERAPY   Karen's husband declares, "Men don't go to therapy."[2] He cites his personal belief and perhaps the social norm that the average man does not consider undertaking a psychological quest for self-truth or liberation from the bonds of past trauma. While this may be normative truth, it is more a condemnation of men and their resistance than a justification or validation for the husband to maintain his denial system in the face of the death rattles of his marriage.

Karen's husband does more than abandon himself to suppressed ignorance and the marriage to a terminal state. He reinforces for himself, and men in general, the perpetuation of an underachieved identity status. He may retain his unwillingness or inability to confront, deal with, and overcome uncomfortable or embarrassing obstacles. To the degree that he actively, though perhaps unconsciously, embraces his obstacles and the energy necessary to maintain them, he will continue to limit his capacity, strength, and depth, as well as, the richness of future relationships.

The individual man shrinks his own stature when he allows himself to be dwarfed by his fear or unwillingness to self-confront or self-express. To the extent that Karen's husband is accurate about the normative behavior of men, society at large is also diminished and placed in a more precarious position because it is deprived of the full measure of all its members' talents, skills, abilities, and knowledge.

A FACILITATOR   Karen goes to her psychotherapist Rose and demands, what her clients demand of her. "Okay, do something." Rose is no more able to "do something" to change Karen's life than Karen is to change her clients! Rose can provide Karen with a safe environment in which to view and create alternative perspectives regarding her life. Rose can encourage Karen to explore these alternatives. She can reinforce Karen's growth by identifying the risks Karen takes and assisting her in her awareness. Rose can provide a cognitive structure from which Karen can make sense and meaning of her life and can integrate her growth into her sense of identity. Rose, by engaging in these tasks, helps Karen to appreciate and celebrate achievements that might otherwise go unrecognized.

There are people for whom no matter what you do, it is never enough. These people gain a sense of contact from conflict and stress.

When they ask for something and become dissatisfied, it is the stimulation of the dissatisfaction that they are seeking. Perhaps, earlier in their lives they learned from a dysfunctional parent that disapproval, dissatisfaction, and complaining were legitimate ways to obtain attention which they equated with love. With the meaningful people in their lives they try to replicate this "love." This is crazy-making for Karen who is motivated to please. The whole issue of pleasing, and in turn being accepted, liked, and loved by her clients, is eliminated if Karen's motivation is to do the best job possible rather than to fix her clients' ills. This is the perspective that Rose offers to Karen.

At first, Karen found changing roles difficult. Some days she "struggled internally." Some days she had setbacks and "actually tried to meet those clients' needs." Karen soon discovered, "...better work was easier when I didn't take responsibility for everybody's everything." Slowly, she began to do her job differently and to reconceptualize her role. Karen emerged from her psychological core into a "facilitator." She could facilitate her clients' awareness of themselves by the knowing of their bodies and the experiencing of a greater vitality.

PERSONAL GROWTH   After her divorce and the death of her mother Karen decided, "I want more from therapy." When she chose to change therapists she was making a decision to support the growth of herself as a person as opposed to being more adept at playing the role of being "nice" or being the "caretaker." Personal growth comes at personal expense.

One must pay the price of experiencing internal and painful feelings which were previously submerged in one's unconscious awareness. The physical pain is evidenced indirectly in terms of aches, pains, numbing, forgetting, and/or fatigue. At the point that one chooses to become more honest with her or himself in growth, the pain is experienced fully, directly, and consciously. This is neither fun nor comfortable, but necessary.

Often, when an individual grows and changes, people who were friends, relations, or lovers before the growth may no longer be interested in a relationship with a stronger, clearer, more self-articulating, honest person. Karen paid the price of a divorce and the struggles and feelings that went with that divorce. If she had had children, their turmoil or their possible resistance to her growth would have been an additional price she would have had to pay. Nevertheless, personal growth was Karen's choice as a life path.

Not everyone values personal growth. They may be unwilling or unprepared to endure the life changes through which Karen put herself. Not all of Karen's clients wanted to be "facilitated." They may not have understood the alternative, let alone been willing to pay the price of undertaking it. Some may have wanted the fantasy that someone could "fix" them or have wanted Karen to provide them with only a physical release from their muscular tension they built up between sessions.

Each client comes with her or his agenda and contract. These clients may not know or appreciate that Karen specializes in "facilitating" body awareness. If they understood this they may not have been interested in bringing their business to her.

Karen may need to communicate or advertise that she specializes in body awareness facilitation. She may offer two services, facilitation-oriented bodywork and management-oriented bodywork. Each can be supportive and each is legitimate. Furthermore, if her clients choose one type of support over another, it will no longer be a blow to Karen's ego because her identity will not be defined by playing the caretaker role. If they choose to accept facilitation, though, she will gain a special sense of meaning and satisfaction from her work. Karen's growth and achievement of a new level in her own identity development opens the possibility for a new kind of growth for her clients should they choose to pursue it.

SUMMARY

Karen discovered some of her clients were suddenly not showing up for their appointments and not calling to cancel. These clients did not respect and value her time and efforts. Karen realized that she had to respond to this infuriating circumstance. Karen spoke with a supportive colleague who told her that she needed to take care of herself. This was not easy. Karen was meeting resistance within herself from her life time role of "nice person." She was a caretaker of others at her own expense. In order for Karen to move forward in her business, she first had to confront the internalized model provided by her mother.

Karen needed psychotherapeutic support to be able to undo the powerful emotional learning that she had internalized as she grew up. Well-integrated, solid, internal strength would be required for Karen to confront clients who were as stuck in their roles of "being taken care of" as she had been in "taking care of" them.

Karen may not have appreciated the conviction and strength that psychotherapy required. It is not a choice made by many. Indeed, within her own clientele she recognized many who are in need of self-examination and change. Because of her awareness, Karen may clearly see a psychological level of reality that some of her clients are unable to perceive and to which they are unwilling to respond. Karen can bring these clients comfort, even though they are unwilling to transcend their psychologically related aches and pains. Karen's gentle presence and comforting hands can provide temporary somatic relief, and her facilitating spirit, at some point, may offer them encouragement to go yet further. In the process of clarifying her professional identity, Karen found the internal strength to take care of herself.

END NOTES

[1] **Marital Therapy** Marital counseling or therapy provides for an exploration of the marital relationship. It provides clarity by highlighting a couple's strengths and weaknesses; their expectations—both reasonable and unreasonable. In the process, past or present wounds may be revealed. These wounds may be the result of poor communication skills, naiveté, inexperience, or incompatible expectations of one another. Wounds may emerge from events or customs that existed in the couple's families of origin. They may be the result of indiscretions that occurred because one or the other felt her or his expectations were not being met within the relationship. In marital counseling, with the expression of mutual caring, understanding, and forgiveness the wounds may begin to heal. This healing is the result of a newly gained sense of mutual empathy and is reinforced by commitment to a new life style which is predicated upon fully addressing the needs of both spouses. The process also builds more cohesiveness and love as the couple participates in constructing a positive future.

Marital therapy is similar to tailoring a generic marriage contract to more closely fit the needs of both members of the particular relationship. Like any contract negotiation, the most optimistic outcomes can be anticipated when both parties appreciate that the good of the other ultimately will enhance herself or himself. Therefore, the best outcome will occur when both parties enter the process in this spirit and are truly willing to work with honesty and earnestness for the mutual good of the relationship. Each partner must feel able to be expressive without recrimination or reprisal.

In a relationship as close as marriage it is inevitable that one, the other, or both parties will hurt each other. Unlike what the popular media suggests, true love does mean that you need to say you are sorry. Not only do you have to say that you are sincerely sorry, but the words must come from a place of remorse in the heart. And there must be a behavioral commitment to make up for or not replicate the injury. With this heartfelt apology the pain of the initial injury can begin to heal and a deeper, richer, more intimate bond may be established. Without this reconciliation full forgiveness is not possible, an emotional barrier is created, and a limit is drawn as to the depth of emotional expression and support that can be reached.

The prospect of a positive outcome will be diminished if one or both of the parties is unwilling to come to the negotiating table in a spirit of good faith.

The outcome may not lend to the longevity of the relationship if it becomes clear that both parties are uninterested in empathetically listening to, understanding, and appreciating each other in the struggle. Each must be open to exploring alternative ways of approaching life situations, and to providing for the other's needs or desires. The resolution may not be favorable if the wounds created by past conflicts go so deep as to make trusting, opening, and giving to the other untenable.

Marital therapy can help a couple to communicate more effectively, understand one another better, allow old wounds to heal, clarify the couple's needs, both as a unit and as individuals, and create a new, more workable, explicit marriage contract. Marital therapy may help save a shaky relationship, as the partners recognize what they receive from one another and genuinely express their sentiments of gratitude and appreciation in a way that is meaningful to the other partner. Such expressions deepen the bonds of intimacy. As with any negotiations or arbitration process, successful outcomes are linked with positive intent, available energy, sustained effort, recognition of the other party's contributions, and patience. When treatment continues and these variables are not present, it may become apparent to one or both parties that there is no spiritual bond, no mutual commitment to honor, support, and cherish, consequently, a healthy union is impossible.

2 **Men Don't Go To Therapy** Psychotherapy is a quest for the discovery of psychosocial truths and actualization of potentials. Once these truths are known, problem-solving skills can maximize strengths and overcome weaknesses and limitations left by past trauma or present obstacles. The potentials that are actualized are deeper levels of awareness, understanding, and empathy. Additional benefits of this process are increases in energy, creativity, productivity, well-being, self-esteem, and the capacity to love oneself and others.

Yet, as Shakespeare suggested, there is a "rub." The "rub" is that one of the major obstacles in the psychotherapeutic process relates to the awareness that is liberated with self-confrontation. The content of one's awareness may be undesirable, inconsistent with one's self-perception, shameful, or painful. When a person is unwilling or unable to face that unpleasant material, resistance to conscious awareness is generated. The result of this resistance is to avoid and arrest the growth process.

7

CANCELLATION

Yvonne, in her early forties, has a pleasant tone. When she speaks, one has a sense of her intellectual depth.

There have been many changes in the last year and a half. I think the thing that I tend to struggle the most with is cancellations...what to do with that. Just this year I redid my office policy letter. They would be billed for the time they had scheduled if they did not cancel within twenty-four hours. I have had the opportunity twice now to handle that verbally, not just hand the paper to the client and say, "Be sure to read this office policy," having to come forward over the phone and say, "My policy is..." so that is probably my biggest breakthrough.

When I first started...first of all, I am a nurse. I've been in the helping profession for 17 years. I was ready to move on from that. I have not seen any improvement in the quality of time that I was allowed with a patient. We were always short-staffed and had to get this, this, and this done. And I couldn't deal with that. I could see other things that people needed, and I didn't have the time to give it to them under the structure that I was working in...so, I decided to get out of patient care. Massage has brought touching back for me.

So, when I went to massage school, my heart's goal was to market to health care professionals...to give them a chance, an opportunity to feel what that balance was like...between stress versus non-stress and to recognize that stress can be manageable. That was my heart's goal. It still is.

Working at the hospital, especially working with physicians, because I worked closely with physicians, some of them would open up and talk about their frustrations with their work. Some would go away to conferences. They would mix business and pleasure. However, within a week or two after returning, they were right back in the same stressful space as when they left. I said to myself, "Gee, ya know, there's a better way here. There is hope, and there is something that can be done to help manage it." That was my impetus for going to massage school.

Anyone in the health care field could benefit. But I am discovering that they are really hard nuts to crack. As I talked with one physician, he said, "They are in denial." And it was just like a brick that hit me. Here we are in the whole cycle of dependency-codependency. And it doesn't always relate to drugs and alcohol. You can apply it to anything. It helped me to refocus. I still wanted to market to that group; but I realized there may be some other way to do it. Or there may be other people out there who would benefit from my service. I realized it would help me to open up my perspective.

So, I'm doing that. When I first started, I was real eager to allow people to experience my perspective—to the point of giving my services away. When I started out, I gave umpteen free gift certificates, thinking that people would surely rush to use them. I found out that less than twenty percent would use them. I couldn't even give it away! As the months went by and I had paying clients canceling on me, I had anger...about that. But as I worked through that—I could see, it was the way I started out. I didn't put value on my work from the beginning. I wanted to just give it away and then expected people to value it when I wasn't. My goals were not directed enough to say, "This is valuable!" Not so much in a monetary sense but just in a sense of getting people to come to it. But then you have to go through certain changes to do that.

When I found myself getting angry because people canceled, then it made me take a look again at the ground work I had laid. It was a laid-back, social, non-structured time. I'd go over the hour or the half-hour—whatever they had scheduled and not charge for it. I'd say, *(in a sing-song voice)* "Now, you know, I needed the time to work slowly." But really, I needed to get the structure for myself. I needed to say, "This is business." I have an hour to do this and get it done within an hour, and stick to it!

Now that I think about it, a friend of mine that I knew from work was having some personal problems, but she had scheduled for that day. But whatever happened on that particular day, she just forgot. When I called her to say, "Did we get our times mixed up, I had you down for ten o'clock?" She just said, "Oh, I forgot!" Like it was no big deal! "We're friends; I just forgot." And I didn't say to her, which I should have at that time, "Well, my time is valuable. I wish you would have let me know. I have a new policy this year. The next time that happens, I'll have to charge you." But I didn't.

I was angry about it...because the way she said it was like, "So what? We're friends, so what?" But she did reschedule, finally, and then followed through with that session. And between the two times I was able to go to her...but at that moment I couldn't say that to her because I was so angry that I would come across as not caring...ya know, just looking at the money...which it wasn't the money, it was the time. But the anger wasn't with her; it was with me because I was not up front. I waited until it happened, and then I'd have to run back and say, "This is the way I am doing it now." The anger was with me because I didn't make it clear up front. I hadn't made it clear with myself. So I couldn't have made it clear with her or any of my other clients.

That's how I got to it. That is the situation that triggered it. And from that point on I started to work with it. I redid my letter. I wrote it out and then said to people as they called, "I have a new policy: If you don't call to cancel within twenty-four hours, you will be charged."

Prior to that I had cancellations. But it seemed okay because it was like, "Well, you are just getting started. You could do something else." I wasn't valuing that time as business time. I was mixing personal stuff with business. My time became something more valuable to me...and when people were canceling on me...and it was my time that I had scheduled for them...then I said, "I need to get this in a business perspective." That whole first year was about running it as a business.

It goes back to...well, I'm divorced. My ex-husband is chemically dependent. I worked on a chemical dependent unit. It was working on that unit that I realized my husband was chemically dependent. Because prior to that it was always, "Well if I could just do better. If I would just do this, then he wouldn't do that." So the whole codependent issue which I am still working on, I will continue to work on through readings and self-awareness. So I think it triggered some of that for me. The...my time is not important enough. Ya know, always wanting to fix it for someone else...when it's not okay. The trigger was there. And it all does fit together. It's all in the same circle; but I do need to get the clarity and the boundaries for business versus personal.

That's what I see. It is like an affirmation for me of the continued work I do with my codependency, to try to change those behaviors so that I don't repeat destructive and dysfunctional things again. I have been learning about the whole cycle of codependent behaviors. After I detached from my marital relationship, in other relationships I was still manifesting codependent behaviors. That's why I say the work with codependency is a life long process. There are different levels you get stuck with and sometimes you can find yourself repeating.

What I was going to originally talk about...*(Sheepishly)*...when I first started massaging, I would have...um...I would actually feel symptoms that the client would have. Usually, the person that would come, I wouldn't know ahead of time what...where...what space they would be in. But, I had one client that had chronic fatigue syndrome, or, what else is it called? Epstein-Barr. And I had gone to the bank that morning. She had an early afternoon appointment. And, when I left the bank, I felt like I couldn't drive home. I felt, "If I closed my eyes for a second, I'm gone! What is this?"

When I got home, I got ready for the massage. I interviewed her...did her medical history...and she described how she would feel when she was in these low periods. She explained to me exactly what I felt. It was exactly what I felt. *(repeating for emphasis)* It was exactly what I felt. And, I thought, "Wow!" I am not going to be able to do this kind of work if I get this reaction with every client I have. Ya, know? I may wind up in the grave, before I get going here! *(Laughter)*

I went to a workshop with the intention of asking the leader, "I want to do this work...but, I have this fear of not being in control of these feelings." He said to me, "Remember you are in control. And think of this as just passing through you. You do not have to take them on as your own." So, I said, "Okay."

But even before I graduated from school and opened my practice, I would sit in meetings at work *(laughter)*...um, when I'd ask people how they were doing...usually they'd say okay. I would feel these things like really you are not okay...and I'd look in their eyes or there would be something about them that would say they were not okay. And if you would have the time, I would say a little more and they would open up. Sitting across the room in a meeting and I would get these feelings of depression or sadness or, "Gee, I have all these problems." I would get this fear of not being in control of these feelings. It is like I am helpless.

I am back where I started. I guess that's where I am supposed to be. My feelings with helplessness tie in to low self-esteem and not being in control. Well, when I would pick up those vibrations, there was a fear within me of not being in control. Whether that equates to not feeling good enough to be in control, I am not sure. But they were like feelings I had in the past of not feeling good enough.

My mother is a recovering alcoholic. I didn't realize until I was well out of high school she was an alcoholic. I can't put my finger on it. During my growing years...I don't know how it came about. But, what I did see through my marriage was that my father was military and he was gone a lot. So, he wasn't home. The man that I married was physically in the house, but mentally and emotionally he was not with the family. He was not available. So, what I saw…well, as I was processing up to the divorce and even after the divorce…I had really recreated the same situation of wanting a father—that was there and present with this marriage. It was the same…the same stuff just a different manifestation. So, maybe it goes back to not having a father around a lot. Maybe, I'm not sure where those feelings of not being good enough…except with the marriage. I was…he always told me, "Well, if you would just do that." And, that is where I can relate to it the most. Maybe, if I just would, ya know, do whatever he expected…it would be okay, it would be better.

DISCUSSION

ASSERTIVENESS   One of the first issues to confront Yvonne in her business was the need to be assertive. She began her practice with clients who neither canceled their appointments nor showed up for sessions. Yvonne was unable to "come forward" when she first spoke with her clients and tell them her policy. She had a written policy. The policy stated that her clients would have to pay for Yvonne's time if they failed to cancel their appointments 24 hours in advance, but she was unable to back up her policy. Yvonne's bodywork was an expression of her personal caring, and she was unable to place a value on it. She was angry with herself over her inability to be verbally assertive.

Assertiveness is the ability to make a statement or take an action relating to one's needs or expectations. This statement or action is neither at someone else's expense nor the expense of the assertive individual. Assertiveness can be differentiated from passiveness and aggressiveness. Passiveness is an unwillingness or over anxiousness to state one's needs, feelings, or limits. Usually the passive individual does what others want her or him to do. This other-directedness is often at the expense of the passive individual's integrity and peace of mind. Aggressiveness is a self-centered stance, stating or taking care of one's own needs or interests with little or no consideration or concern as to how others are affected.

Passive and aggressive individuals often seek each other out. Passive individuals may seek out an aggressive partner to provide lifestyle structure or protective skills that the passive partner lacks. The flip side to this is the passive partner who as an amenable helper, supporter, and available companion will offer neither argument nor resistance to the aggressive partner's wishes. The passive partner becomes dependent upon the aggressive partner for structure. The aggressive partner becomes dependent upon the passive partner for support. Change in the balance of influence in this relationship can become extremely threatening to the dependency of both parties.

If a passive partner in such a relationship begins to get stronger, the balance of power is upset. The aggressive partner is unlikely to tolerate a loss of power, having her or his opinions questioned, or her or his resources directed to the partner's needs. If the passive partner in a relationship attempts to become stronger, the aggressive partner may retaliate by becoming angry, demeaning, threatening, or punitive. The aggressive partner may also withdraw by rejecting or abandoning the passive partner to find another, more compliant, passive partner. Growth with an aggressive partner requires strength, perseverance, and courage. Outside support is often essential.

Consequently, what appears to be a rather straightforward issue of just telling people one's business policy can be a far more complex personal issue. To "just" make a statement of one's policy is to make a declaration. On one level, the declaration indicates the value or worth of Yvonne's work. On another level the declaration makes a statement as to the value Yvonne places on herself.

To say that her time is valuable is for Yvonne to realize her own value. When she herself was uncertain, it was difficult for Yvonne to make a declaration of her worth. Furthermore, Yvonne would expose herself to public scrutiny in making her declaration. Her clients might say, "I'm not going to pay you for your time. You are not that good. You don't deserve it." This response would traumatically confirm her own nagging doubt.

Holding oneself out for public scrutiny and possible evaluation, judgment, and rejection can be disconcerting, even for those with high self-esteem. The prospect of self-exposure would be exceedingly intimidating for those with low self-esteem. One can appreciate how difficult the assertiveness task is for Yvonne when it is placed in the psychosocial context of her unsupportive, nonconfirming, early family background and her blaming, punitive, marital relationship.

In her bodywork practice Yvonne has to provide structure for herself. She realized in order to make changes she, herself, would have to "go through certain changes." Yvonne took the first steps in that direction by courageously confronting herself.

ANGER   Anger is an emotion that generates energy for self-protection. In and of itself, it is neither good nor bad, it is simply an alarm that says something is wrong. What becomes good or bad is how a person chooses to deal with her or his anger. Yvonne chose to use her anger to generate a new policy statement. More than that, she committed herself to backing up that policy during the first phone contact with a client. She also resolved to confront her friend. Yvonne realized that she expected her friends to value her time and she needed to let them know. That was a mature and constructive use of her anger.

BRING CARING TOUCH BACK Yvonne was a nurse struggling to find meaning in her chosen career in a medical establishment. She found that because of short-staffing and over-demands on her time, she was unable to provide the quality of personal contact that originally attracted her to the nursing profession. Her decision to become a bodyworker allowed her to deliver the quality care that first gave her a sense of personal-professional meaning. Incorporating massage into her life allowed Yvonne to bring caring touch back into her professional life.

TOUGH NUTS Yvonne went into the bodywork field with the "heart goal" of marketing her services to health care professionals. After all, she had the confidence of many of the physicians that she worked with and knew of the stress that they worked under and lived with constantly. This nurse believed that if these physicians availed themselves of her expertise, they would be more able to manage their daily stress.

Yvonne quickly learned the difference between people's complaints about stress and their willingness to take action to ameliorate those complaints. If Yvonne and her medical friend were correct, work for some of their colleagues represented "a codependent relationship." It is no wonder that this targeted, medical market was not lining up to give away its defenses. Rather than remaining rigidly fixated on her dream, Yvonne wisely broadened her scope of target markets, all the while, keeping in the back of her mind that she still wanted to cater to health care professionals.

GIVING IT AWAY Yvonne was extremely tough on herself. Having given "umpteen free gift certificates away," she had a twenty percent return rate which is a respectable return rate. Yvonne did not give herself credit for her early efforts and successes.

Beginning a practice from scratch is hard work. Building a successful business takes time. Often it takes years before a referral base is sufficiently large to generate and maintain a practice. This task may be harder and take longer for an introvert. Many people who choose to work with one person at a time behind a closed door are introverts. What may be psychologically helpful in the process of building a successful practice is to have realistic expectations, patience with oneself, support of others when possible, and recognition of one's efforts and appreciation of one's labors.

Sometimes giving freebies can provide certain invaluable, intangible benefits. While waiting to develop a viable practice, Yvonne was developing her skills and personal style. Good will was developed with those twenty percent who came to Yvonne. Knowledge of Yvonne's skill, ability, and presence began to spread in her community. Finally, a person can become anxious sitting around waiting for a practice to develop. Activity helps to allay anxiety even though it may be at the expense of freebies.

PROFESSIONAL TRANSITION   At some point Yvonne felt that she no longer wanted to give her time and sessions away as part of a marketing strategy. She believed that she was giving her labor away out of a lack of emotional strength to stand behind the value of her effort. This was the issue over which Yvonne became angry with herself. At this professional transition point Yvonne had to change her office procedures to live comfortably with herself. She could no longer, in good conscience, allow clients to miss sessions, not pay, or give extra time without charging for her service.

Anger is an outward sign of gathering strength for self-protection when a person has been hurt or threatened. This massage therapist was hurt by her own actions. Yvonne had sufficiently developed her skills to believe that giving them away for nothing was a violation of her integrity. She took a growth step. She marshaled her strength and created a new policy that she was prepared to stand behind. By recognizing and responding to her feelings, Yvonne achieved another step in her personal and professional development. This is the process of building self-esteem and integrity.

DUAL RELATIONSHIPS   Yvonne was caught in the bind of a dual relationship with her friend from work. The rules of friendship suggest one or the other friend can come or go as is needed. Perhaps in friendship, an apology is not required if a meeting does not occur. In business relationships, however, there is an implicit, if not explicit, contractual understanding. One party will provide her or his time, effort or supplies, and the other will provide compensation.

Both Yvonne and her friend were operating in a quasi friendship-business mode. This dual relationship left the door open for confusion, misunderstandings, and hurt feelings. Yvonne became angry when she felt her friend took her for granted. She then had to deal carefully with her feelings toward her friend-client lest she lose both a client and a friend. Some people decide not to work with friends and relatives in order to avoid precisely such conflicts. An alternative is to clearly discuss and differentiate the expectations of the business contract from those of the friendship before providing services.

CODEPENDENCE   Yvonne recognized that in her relationship with her husband she was a codependent[1]. In supporting him, she was supporting his dependence on alcohol and his avoidance of facing and assuming responsibilities. She further disempowered herself by accepting his projections of her inadequacy.

Yvonne's codependence may also have made it difficult to confront clients who, like her husband, may have taken her intrinsic value for granted. If Yvonne felt that she was of little value, then she could only expect to be compensated for what she did, not for her time. Fortunately, Yvonne realized that she needed "to get clarity" between personal and business boundaries.

One can psychologically understand and explain a phenomenon such as codependency, but in and of itself this is not enough to bring about change. A home environment can be identified where parents were unavailable to provide for recognition, acceptance, affection, protection from fear, feelings of worthiness, pride, encouragement of unique abilities, and unconditional love. Yvonne intellectually recognized that she had a father who was never home and a mother who was alcoholic. This left her childhood need for love and confirmation deeply compromised. The mechanism for transcending[2] the wounds of codependence is not merely a matter of intellectually recognizing or understanding the phenomenon, but a matter of affectively and behaviorally confronting the internal fears and taking independent behavioral action. As Yvonne stood behind her policy, not only did she improve the quality of her business, but she began to strengthen her psychological core and overcome her codependence. She took the steps necessary to be able to enter into a relationship and not get sucked in by another's avoidance mechanisms.

LOSING CONTROL   Yvonne held back on the first issue that she wanted to share. She finally voiced her initial concern which related to control. This somatic, intuitive nurse experienced the symptoms of her clients even before she met with them. This was a frightening phenomena to her. Yvonne had both the feelings of loss of familiar boundaries and loss of control. This particular combination of losses can be particularly disconcerting; it is like going crazy. No wonder Yvonne hesitated to share these stories.

CONTROL VS. COMMAND   Control is a holding-on process by definition. A controlling person may find that rather than having fleeting experiences, passing thoughts or feelings, these experiences become recurring or chronic which may be accompanied by anxiety over losing control. This quickens the breath, fills the blood with more carbon dioxide, tightens the muscles, and deepens the experience of anxiety, and loss of control. A full blown anxiety attack may be precipitated or chronic fatigue created if this becomes a common pattern.

Loss of mastery or perfection is a constant conscious or unconscious concern for those who are preoccupied with being in "control." Ironically, a person is out of control to the extent that she or he is unable to know her or his thoughts, feelings, and sensations and freely choose the best paths from which to confront them.

Even more powerful than control is "command." For those into control, there is only one way to deal with a task. These people can be seen to become anxious, constricted, and inflexible as a consequence of deviating from the familiar. The individual in command has the freedom to search for the many ways a problem can be confronted, demonstrating confidence, flexibility, and expansiveness when encountering the novel. This person is able to utilize her or his wisdom to choose from the alternatives the one which is most appropriate, inexpensive, expeditious, fun, challenging, exciting, popular, or unique.

It is not that surprising that Yvonne experiences the symptoms of her clients. If she were an intellectual intuitive, she might think of the theories that relate to a given client's ailment. If she were a visual intuitive, she might see the faces or experiences of patients at the hospital with similar ailments. But, Yvonne is an affective, somatic intuitive. She intuitively uses her medical knowledge and somatically tries on the symptoms of her clients. The experiential results frighten Yvonne. In her fear she tightens her muscles which then lock in both the symptoms and the emotion.

Yvonne need not hold onto this kind of experience. She can take slow easy breaths, relax, keep her musculature soft and allow it to pass. Her experiences are the result of her unique sensitivity, talent, and understanding of the medical model. She has a richer and more empathic life than most. Who she is provides her with the opportunity to be more aware and supportive to her clients and their needs. Though from time to time it can be a pain in the neck, she is blessed!

SUMMARY

As Yvonne spoke, she became increasingly comfortable sharing her professional experiences and their relationship to her personal life. Yvonne began by telling where her achievements had taken her. She concluded by telling where her growth journey began. After a year and a half of being in practice, Yvonne had struggled with three major issues. One related to abandoning her dream to provide services to a health care clientele. Another was dealing with "no shows." The final issue related to Yvonne's low-self confidence and the difficulty it created in trusting her intuition.

Pragmatics and a kindly conversation with a colleague helped to resolve the first issue. If the clientele she wanted to work with were unavailable, then Yvonne resolved herself to a clientele that was available. Yvonne overcame her second problem with "no shows" by confronting the issue of her low self-esteem. Yvonne did not believe that her time and her presence were of value. This was fostered by her former husband who did not value her efforts. He did not assume responsibility for himself. He simply blamed Yvonne for not living up to his expectations of being a perfect caretaker. Yvonne recognized that both in her home as she grew up and in her marriage she received the messages that she was not important. Transcending her past experiences, Yvonne chose to value herself and convey that value to her clients. She decided to personally make the statement of her policy to her clients.

Yvonne learned to value herself through her work in developing a massage practice. Furthermore, she learned to insist that those who worked with her value her too. Yvonne is overcoming the ill effects of feeling out of control. She is achieving a new mastery of life with regard to a romantic partner, meaningful vocation, policy for no-shows, and being in charge of her somatic experiences. Yvonne is developing a new and deeper sense of integrity, self-esteem, command, and professional competence.

END NOTES

1   **Codependence**   Codependence is a complex psychosocial phenomenon in which a codependent individual derives a sense of identity or meaning by playing the role of helper to someone who is engaged in the role of being needy or dependent. In addition to interpersonal relationships, dependency may be identified with alcohol, drugs, gambling, work, recreation, eating, sex, shopping, or any activity that one could engage in to receive feelings of pleasure in order to avoid discomfort or pain. The focus of dependencies may vary; however, they all have in common the engaging of the dependent individual in an activity which fosters the avoidance of some conflict. The area of conflict is usually one for which the dependent lacks knowledge, experience, support, or the psychological strength to confront.

There is a psychopathological nature to all dependent avoidance behaviors. The dependency defense, like all defense mechanisms, is protected by powerful unconscious denial mechanisms resulting in the dependent being defended against awareness of the defense mechanism itself. At least four issues of dysfunction emerge from the psychopathological nature of avoidance. First, as long as the defense is in place, the original problem cannot be addressed and resolved: second, the defense behaviors slowly and gradually demand more time, energy, and resources. Consequently, the avoidant individual's life style increasingly becomes refocused upon engaging in and maintaining the defensive behavior. As the avoidant behavior becomes figural, previous life goals diminish. Third, everyday logical dialogue has little effect on influencing the unconsciously-motivated, avoidant, dependent behavior. Four, this avoidant behavior ultimately hurts the dependent as well as others in that person's life.

In the case of alcohol, the alcohol dependent may first drink to avoid insecurity, inadequacy, or some other feeling brought about by life conflicts. The avoidance is achieved as the depressive central nervous system effect of the drug provides the drinker with a sense of well-being. As tolerance develops, more and more of the substance is needed to gain the same psychological effect. A physiological, as well as, psychological dependency on alcohol is created. With time and repetition, the drinker begins to drink for the sake of drinking. This preoccupation with the object of dependency creates secondary problems. Alcohol abusers suffer from problems of lost work, belligerency with others, traffic tickets, mood swings, domestic conflicts, health problems, and bodily injury from falls and accidents.

In spite of the secondary problems, the object of the dependency serves as a "solution" to the primary problem for the dependent. The dependent has low motivation and even resistance to change. The codependent, on the other hand, is usually preoccupied with supporting or covering up for the dependent. As the dependent is locked more tightly into her or his defenses, the codependent becomes increasingly enmeshed with the partner's dilemma.

By definition, the codependent derives a sense of fulfillment by attempting to help someone who is dependent. As a result, dependency unconsciously possesses a certain attractiveness for the codependent. If the dependent partner actually gets better, she or he will no longer fit the definition of dependent and will no longer be attractive. The codependent might be out of a relationship if the primary problem that spawned the relationship is resolved. However, should the dependent partner relapse, then once again she or he becomes unconsciously attractive. Should the relationship end because of the dependent partner's damaging behavior, the codependent partner is likely to seek out another, pathologically-dependent partner. The cycle then begins afresh.

Just as there is an awareness that is too emotionally painful for the dependent to confront, there is an awareness which is too painful for the codependent to confront. This might relate to not feeling accepted by a parent or parents. Having such a parental experience may result in feeling unworthy of being in a relationship with someone who likes the individual for her or himself. Another possibility is that the codependent learned in the primary family, that her or his value was in playing the role of caretaker.

As a result, the codependent seeks meaning from recognition for something that she or he does.

The codependent does not believe that she or he is essentially worthy. No matter how much she or he does, it will never be enough. Complicating matters, the dependent person, for whom this role is played, does not appreciate someone trying to take her or his defense mechanism away. There will be little or no gratitude expressed for the codependent playing her or his role. Quite to the contrary, the codependent is likely to be the subject of the dependent's defensive rage if the object of dependency is threatened. The codependent will then have to try harder to get acceptance from someone who is unwilling or incapable of being accepting. The relationship is likely to be most compatible when the codependent enables the dependent by supporting the abusive behavior. There is little likelihood of recovery for either if the codependent is serving the drinks.

Both the dependent and the codependent are wounded at the level of their affective cores. Each plays a role to deflect awareness and attention from her or his core wounds. Neither one is able to express feelings from or receive feelings into the core. Each performs and remains arrested in a role: one is the helpless, the other the helper. Without awareness of the role one is playing, the courage to change, and help in the process, a person can be trapped for a lifetime in self-destructive behavior.

2 **Transcendence** To achieve transcendence from her or his "stuckness" the dependent or codependent must be willing to turn her or his psychological eyes inward. They must identify their inner conflicts. They must be willing to accept, experience, and work through their unresolved issues. New more appropriate resolutions to the conflict will then emerge from the creative core. This will promote a stronger internal core and a stronger external relationship with a partner.

One should wisely be prepared for disappointments along the way. A dependent partner is unlikely to reinforce another's healthy growth or change. That would be tantamount to losing the object of her or his dependency. Ineffectual, helpless, dependent partners can muster shallow and emotionally impassioned pleas for their partners not to change. This can accelerate to paranoid anger and even violence in an attempt to protect their defense system of which the codependent has become an integral part. This defensive assault may be lodged against the codependent helper if the helper threatens to take her or his enabling support out of the relationship. Relationships that were cemented upon unhealthy foundations of "helping a lost other" may not survive when one member of the couple chooses to embrace a healthy alternative life path. Ascending from a codependent relationship is exceedingly difficult. To emerge from the dependency quagmire, one must not only develop a healthy psychological core, but healthy external supports.

8

INTUITIVE SELF

Flo is an attractive bodyworker in her early fifties. This body-worker spoke of a number of interrelated experiences that she confronted seven years earlier when she began her career. An intellectually bright woman, she often repeated herself. She struggled to achieve clarity over a crisis regarding her intuitive capacities.

I was not quite through with my licensing exam. I did not really have much experience connecting with people. And it would probably be valuable to preface this by saying that when I went to massage school in the first place, I went basically to lean about touch. I realized the one thing I never learned in my family was about touch. I didn't feel confident about touch. And, I was trying to do something different. I chose to do something different than I had ever done before. I had worked in musical groups as a musician and a music teacher. But I didn't have personal contact with others. So, originally I went to massage school to confront—just to confront my fear of touch.

In my career in music, I spent a lot of time on my own. It was between me and the notes. So working with people was not something I was used to, and this was entering an entirely new, different career. I didn't intend to pursue the profession, even as I went through massage school. I didn't dare do it as a career. I just did it to confront my own fear.

I thought it was pretty incredible what could happen with touch. I liked what could happen. I knew one way or another I wanted to do more work with it. But it pretty much freaked me out. I was a Trager® student at the time, when all of a sudden, I knew things I didn't know.

Perhaps, it was a different way of experiencing my intuitive self. I'd be working with somebody, and I'd have a sense that something was going on in their back. I would ask. And what my experience was would correspond with what they said was going on. They'd tell me, "I was about to say something to you that I had a problem." Or, "I was experiencing pain."

What confused me was the way I sensed these wasn't consistent. At one point, it just might be my idea, "I should ask this person about their leg," or I would wonder if something was going on...I don't even know why I had the idea. Another time, I might even feel my own back hurt, or, feel a sensation, thought, or feeling. It wasn't consistent. But it was as though I was accessing some kind of information or some kind of connection with this other person that really freaked me out.

It was like there was a voice inside me saying, "I don't understand why this is happening. It shouldn't be happening. It is not okay." And, I would get frightened. I contemplated quitting bodywork. But part of me loved it. It seemed very real and exciting and connected. It was nice. Because I would check it out with people. At least I had enough nerve to do that. I get shy about being asked questions. I also get shy asking questions. So, it took an act of will to actually ask questions to check it out.

But, it was one of those experiences where I didn't know how to fit...I didn't have a conceptual framework to know what was going on. I'd get worried about it. What I'd end up doing was withdrawing. That was my first reaction. But a part of me was very excited. Like, "Oh my gosh! This is what the world is like, and it is neat." And another part would somehow say, "I don't understand it. It can't be right." I don't know why I did that, but it was my reaction.

And so I went through a period where I withdrew from the intuitive awareness and Trager® work. And it felt like I put a curtain there. My bodywork would still get good results. People would still give me the same kind of reports about their experiences. But, I would not be aware of this direct connection. It was as though I put a veil on my own awareness of what was happening.

And my fear level went down. My anxiety went down. Things were no longer happening that I didn't understand. But it wasn't nearly as much fun anymore. The excitement was gone. And, I was a lot less clear about what was going on. Whether or not I understood it, when I had that direct connection I had more of a sense, "I know I am tracking on something, and I can trust it." Even with that fear there, there was a sense of trust. But once I put the screen up, it was like swimming in a pond on a dark night where I really didn't know, even though the reports kept coming out that I was on track, I always felt lost about it.

So, I did some work in psychotherapy and struggled with that. I decided what I needed to do was back off until I got more comfortable.

I talked about it with friends. I said, "Gosh this weird thing happened to me. Has anything happened to you like that?" I took it back to my training group. I was receiving advanced training in bodywork at the time. I said, "Gosh, I'm worried, have any of you had an experience like this? And, what the hell is going on anyway! What is this about? And, why didn't you warn me?" So, I started talking about the things that weren't part of my world view; trying to find people who could give me some understanding and a conceptual framework that would allow me to live with it more comfortably.

I read about meditation, auras, and the chakras. Just to read them was too far from my way of thinking. It would have been to dump my conceptual framework to just pick up another. And I was unwilling to do that. But I knew that they were there. Other people think the world is such a place where these things can happen. Somehow just having these thoughts around was comforting. But I wasn't really ready to sit down and absorb them.

It is funny to look back on that now. In a way that early thing began to open...no, I had already by that time had other experiences that gave me the same information. That raised some of the same troubling issues for me. But then I was better able to encapsulate them and stash them away to be a thing to look at in the future. But when I ran into this in my massage work, it became something that I was going to pursue. I couldn't leave it encapsulated. But I didn't know how to work with it.

Since then, I made the decision that it wasn't going to be something that I was going to let bother or stop me. But, I still did not know how to go forward. *(Smiling pensive in thought, then bursting out in laughter)* It is one of these events where it feels like I set something into motion by making that decision. So even though I didn't know how to pursue it...if I knew how, I would have pursued it more directly. But, I've chosen to shield myself from having to deal with my intuition. I am feeling much more comfortable about it now.

(Flinching) I studied bodywork with a man who was also my lover. Actually, I didn't want to have the sexual relationship with him. First, he was my instructor. He was very seductive. He logically explained how the sex could help me to work through my blocks and improve my work. He said that's how his instructor taught him. Then something happened. *(Shaking her head and grimacing)* I am not comfortable about this and I am still not through working it out. He did the same thing with other women. I know some of them who have not yet recovered. Anyhow, I told him of my sensory experiences with my

clients. He told me, "All of that was a bunch of bull shit! Those kinds of things don't happen. People who talk about it are basically fantasizing or living in an unreal world." However, by then I knew those experiences happen. I was not denying that. But I didn't know how to make sense of it. So, in a way he solidified or validated my own experiences. Because as soon as I would hear someone say that doesn't happen, I would hear an internal voice saying, "Come on, get real! Of course this happens." So the relationship let me hide because I didn't have to deal with my experience directly and also allowed it to grow thicker within me. His denial made it clearer within me. That is a curious phenomena!

I backed off from experiencing it with other people. I…it was during that same time period that I became involved in spiritual growth work. That was a way of accessing some of those intuitive capacities working with myself rather than working with someone else. And it was much less threatening. There is much less for me to sort out just dealing with myself, than having those experiences in the context of a social relationship. That made a big difference; it gave me a chance to play with it in an arena in which I felt safe.

I have a wall. My wall is like a way of turning up or down the sound level. It feels very much like a sensory protection…very much the technique of avoidance…an old style of mine. I would not allow myself to feel something. I am not sure how I do it, but I do it real well. I don't know exactly how to regulate it…only how to avoid or choose to confront it.

One of the things I have studied since is cranial work. Cranial work involves tuning into a level of connection. And I don't question that that connection is there. When I first started studying that work, it was pretty weird. It was hard to give myself permission to feel. Again my sense was, " I don't understand this. Why am I feeling this? I shouldn't be." When I think that way, it is like I am turning down the volume on my awareness. Much of the cranial work to me was the learning process of opening to my intuitive capacity. I was taught to relax and just hang out and see what came to me. It was a heartbeat.

Most people are not used to feeling throughout the body. But if you quiet yourself and are available to what is there and hang out, you can feel the heartbeat is there…you can tune into it … the cranial pulse, and many, many, other rhythms. It involves the process of just softening, to be open to what is there and to connect with it.

My experience and many other people's experience was to be suddenly hit by whole worlds of different "noises." Yes, the cranial pulse was there but it was there with a hundred, a thousand other things. Much of that work is learning what not to pay attention to. And to realize any of those other things might be more pertinent than the cranial pulse at any given moment.

Your ears are not very selective. Right now if I listen I can hear the dogs bark in the street and the birds. At the same time I can hear the creak of my chair. All of those sounds are not mutually exclusive. They are all coming in at the same time. None of them are particularly relevant to what I am saying. It is a matter of learning how to modulate the volume of how much I get affected by and interact with each. It is the way of learning the on-off switches or the volume level.

The key is learning what to pay attention to. It took me a long time because I would get overwhelmed by the "noise." After doing it long enough, I take for granted certain kinds of connections. I think that is one of the ways I have assured myself, not in terms of learning about it out there, but in terms of experiencing it within myself in a safe way, what this is about. The thing for me was, if I really numbed out or kept a very tight focus on what I'd allow in my reality, then things were simple. But if I open the door, I would suddenly be flooded with not just one thing to listen to, but a whole world of things. And I would get lost.

Now, I'm personally comfortable about this. But it is still difficult talking to some of my clients about my intuitions. I'd rather leave it at the level of, "If it is working, I'm, grateful," unless someone shows a lot of openness to talking about what is going on at different levels. But I don't like identifying myself in peoples' minds as somebody who is doing something that is weird. And I know that is where I am.

DISCUSSION

PERSONAL ACTUALIZATION VERSUS VOCATIONAL SUBLIMATION Flo began to learn bodywork disciplines because she wanted to overcome her fear of touch. This fear began in childhood. Her family was not a touching family. Making contact was not familiar. Later in life she chose a career which was mechanical and often isolating. When she worked with a group, the focus was on product development and the contact was impersonal. This left a void in her life. Flo attempted to overcome both her fear and the void by studying bodywork. Her decision to become involved in bodywork was motivated by a desire for personal actualization though she never considered entering the field as a professional. A career decision was made for Flo when she discovered "how powerful touch could be." Flo's experience provided her with an undeniable truth regarding the work she wanted to do.

Flo's vocational choice further provided her with a type of expression which was absent and unacceptable in her childhood—physical touch. Sometimes unacceptable needs can be unconsciously directed into socially acceptable behaviors. This serves a double function; it allows the original anxiety to be avoided and allows for legitimization of the needs.

Sublimation represents a socially acceptable means of gratifying one's needs, however, it is predicated on the person's original needs being unacceptable. In Flo's family, members did not make physical contact. This left her with a deficit regarding knowing how, when, and with whom to touch. Perhaps, it also left her with a conscious or an unconscious belief that there was something wrong with touch. Part of her "fear of touching" might be the fear of violating the authority of her parents' rules.

Flo's degree and license granted her permission to touch in a professional setting. Yet they lacked the power to help her overcome the personal prohibition she may have received from her family regarding touch and feelings. To overcome the inner prohibition that might have stopped Flo from feeling comfortable with touch, she would have to undo the verbal and non-verbal messages she received as she grew up. This is the type of work that goes on in psychotherapy.

Flo's bodywork may be socially and professionally gratifying, but if her underlying motivation for getting into bodywork was to meet unsatisfied personal needs for contact and confirmation, then her excitement over touching professionally may have steered her away from her personal needs. Flo may still feel there is some unidentified, unarticulated element missing in her life—being touched. Touching professionally is very different than receiving touch personally.

GENUINE THEME   Flo discussed the two-fold nature of her intuitive discovery: first, she would get "freaked out" and "worry about it," second, she felt "excited." Growth themes represent unresolved issues that must be overcome for an individual to move on in her or his psychological development. When they are recognized, tackled, and overcome, a person usually feels lighter, and has a sense of achievement and well-being. Genuine themes of growth usually present themselves with both a goal and a resistance or anxiety over attaining that goal. It is helpful to recognize this, rather than to be surprised or concerned about it, when anxiety occurs.

When the theme appears, one can either focus on the goal or on the resistance in order to promote one's growth. Early on, Flo began to read about her new perceptual phenomenon. What she read did not help her, but she was comforted by the realization that her experience had happened to others and was recognized. She was not the only one to have these experiences. This information-gathering addressed her resistance and reduced her anxiety.

In addition, Flo spoke to her instructors and fellow students and asked about their experiences. Getting more information is an excellent means of allaying anxiety. After coping with her anxiety, Flo was free to problem-solve how to handle the issue of her disquieting perceptual awareness.

CONCEPTUAL FRAMEWORK Initially, Flo lacked a name and acceptable definition for the distressing perceptual phenomenon that she experienced. Feeling the cranial pulse...at first was "pretty weird." When Flo was provided a scientific, theoretical explanation for this phenomenon from her craniosacral training, she stopped questioning the authenticity of her connection.

Clearly, with regard to craniosacral work, Flo had no problems with her experiences. Flo discussed how she had learned to "modulate the volume," to "cut down the outside noise," when she did this form of bodywork. However, Flo found trusting her sensations and intuition unacceptable when she did Trager® work. She could not modulate the incoming messages. Sometimes it was a thought impression, her own somatic sensation, or a feeling. Receiving these instantaneous messages had a frightening overtone for her. Flo attributed this to not having developed a conceptual understanding for these experiences.

What Flo might have suspected, but was unwilling to express, was that she was having a psychic experience—mental telepathy. Mental telepathy is a person to person communication without any visible means of transmission. Flo did not say so, but she may believe that psychic experiences and people who claim to have them are "weird." If others thought that Flo believed she was receiving telepathic communications, they too, might think she was weird. Consequently, she began to disassociate herself from her new, unusual experiences so she did not have to reject herself or be rejected by others.

PSI PHENOMENA In practice, psychic perception involves sensing someone or something else's experience and being able to interpret or express that experience. The more a person is able to open to her or his sensations and accurately label the resulting experience the more that person is said to have psychic abilities[1].

PERCEPTION AND INTUITION Extrasensory perception (ESP), as it suggests, implies having perceptions without the presence of sensory stimuli. In opposition to ESP, perception and intuition both involve contact with sensory stimulation. Perception involves observing, sensing, and discriminating in order to become aware of objects in the environment. Unlike perception which is a gathering and organizing of sensory data, intuition involves spontaneous insight. Intuition does not require reasoning or a reflective process. It involves some, though minimal, sensory data or conscious deliberation.

People who are either intuitive or psychic have a special sensitivity which is often directed into areas of familiarity. Some people are able to interpret the underlying messages in a glance. Some people "read" meaning in the innuendo of slight changes in the voice. Is it so surprising that Flo be able to interpret messages of pain from her physical contact with her clients' tissue? And, if she can perceive messages from this contact, is this really ESP? Was there really an absence of a tangible form of communication between Flo and her clients?

Flo clearly received sensory messages from her clients. These messages were not in the form of words or visual observations. Flo read these messages about her clients' states of being the way a physician might read heart pulses. This former musician's sensitive hands and fingers read the language of her clients' bodies. To the degree that she was able to zero in on specific conditions quickly, she was perceptive. To the degree she could identify certain themes with minimal data she may have an intuitive gift. In either case, while such perceptiveness and intuition were not usual or familiar for this shy, socially withdrawn bodyworker, they were not "weird."

Flo brought herself to massage school to learn about touch, but, there was more to learn about touch than merely making physical contact. Flo came from a family that was emotionally distant. She spoke of being socially distant from people in her previous career. Flo was unfamiliar with close contact. Her massage experience may have felt overwhelming to her since she was unaccustomed to feeling such intimate contact. Suddenly, she was touching people and feeling the somatic signs of their life stresses. From the information this bright woman received from touching, Flo began to perceive her clients with a new intensity. She became insecure over the "volume" or perhaps the intimacy of information that she perceived.

RESOLUTIONS Intuition can be a helpful tool in learning about a client's physical as well as psychological strengths and weaknesses. In can also be a guide to what kind of support or intervention a client may need. It can also be harmful. Intuitive information can be damaging when it is misinterpreted, inaccurate, or when a client is unprepared to deal with the information she or he is given. It can be retraumatizing for a person who has underlying wounds. Other issues may arise which can cause intuitive information to have adverse consequences. The person who perceives intuitive or psychic awareness may feel burdened by the information of which they have become aware. Being privileged to intimate information, one may detrimentally change one's thoughts or feelings toward the other person. The intuitive perception a person has of another may be an artifact or projection of the intuitive's own unresolved issues. One should be concerned about detrimentally influencing another person based upon unsubstantiated intuitive beliefs. It takes a wise and skilled practitioner to know if, how, and when to use intuitive knowledge.

One need not have ESP to feel uncomfortable being too familiar with another's personal life. Clearly, Flo felt distressed when, although her clients did not choose to share those details with her, the sensitivity in her hands was allowing her to eavesdrop on her client's private reality. Flo has a sense of propriety, humility, and integrity. Perhaps she had a realistic intuitive awareness that naively sharing such information can be harmful. For Flo to assume the potential for such influence would have been to take on too much responsibility. Most figuratively, her struggle had to do with accepting her gift and determining what she wanted to do with it. Her resolution was to choose to discontinue using Trager as a bodywork modality. She chose instead to use her abilities strictly for her own personal growth.

CRANIOSACRAL VS. TRAGER®   Why would one bodywork intervention foster Flo's intuitive awareness and not another? This is a hard question to answer. Flo herself was uncertain. A guess would be that in a more meditative state, Flo would be more open to her intuitive self.

Craniosacral therapy calls for palpation, sensing, and monitoring the craniosacral pulse. The procedure provides gentle manual support while recognizing an impasse in the craniosacral rhythm. This intervention requires the practitioner to have a gentle touch, patient presence, and an attentiveness to subtle movement. While physical movement is at a minimum the procedure calls for active awareness on the part of the practitioner to attend to bones and their movement, cranial rhythms, holding patterns, and still points. Changes in body temperature and pulse rates are noted. These are logical, linear, cognitive processes: a left-brain intervention. Flo could perform this type of bodywork without being subject to her distressing, intuitive awarenesses.

Milton Trager, the developer of the Trager® bodywork intervention, like John Upledger and Hugh Milne, major proponents of Craniosacral Therapy, asks his practitioners to use a gentle touch. In contrast to Upledger's or Milne's Craniosacral work, Trager does not ask his practitioners to direct their awareness in order to feel for pulses or to release chronic holding patterns. Trager asks his practitioners to be in "hook-up," a meditative state, maintaining an awareness of the questions, "What could be lighter? What could be freer? What would the experience feel like of being more flexible?"

This is ostensibly a right brain meditative state. When Flo was in this state, she was subject to her troublesome awarenesses.

It is hypothesized that when this former musician is in a right-brain meditative state, she is more open to her intuitive awareness. When she is in a more discriminating left-brain state, she is freer from these awarenesses. Flo believed that the left-brain Craniosacral interventions allowed her to be free from her troubling intuitions.

ALIENATION   When one's sense of self-definition is weak, needs for support and external confirmation can become more important than needs for one's own integrity and growth. At such a point, a person may choose to make life decisions by deferring to others' benevolence and wisdom. These people may have their own agendas and priorities. They may be unwilling or unable to give a dependent relative, lover, or friend the disinterested, empathic, and individualized support that is appropriate or desired. When receiving "others'" acceptance or support is more important than one's own growth, little by little a person begins to abandon a clear sense of her or his own perception, needs, and identity.

Flo had ambivalent feelings toward her newly discovered sensitivity. While she was exuberant over discovering her ability to identify somatic stress using her tactile skills, she was also anxious over her ability to know things that she was previously unable to know. As a result, Flo deferred to the authority of her teacher-lover. She allowed him to take responsibility for her decision. He obliged her by giving Flo permission to avoid pursuit of her own clarity. This teacher did not support his student in appreciating or understanding her ability. Under the guise of helping her to learn about touch, he taught her not to trust her own experience, her own intuition.

Flo's insecurity made her vulnerable to this man who appeared to possess structure, wisdom, and clarity. While Flo went along with this man's opinion, internally she knew he was wrong and abandoned what she knew to be her own truth, her own wisdom. As she chose to do this, she avoided developing her tactile abilities and talents. The loss and diffusion created in her own personality by believing one way and acting another was the cost of Flo's dependency on her relationship and her shying away from assuming her own responsibility.

PERSONALITY DIFFUSION   Flo became alienated from her intuitive abilities as she defensively embraced what she believed were others' intolerance to her unique capabilities. She chose to compromise her personal integrity and rejected herself in an attempt to avoid rejection from others.

Preoccupation with the opinion of others can be tyrannical but is not without some wisdom. To open and to expose oneself is to run the risk of either acceptance or rejection. Exposing oneself is not something to be done naively. If one does not risk at all, then the person both internally and externally restricts her or his growth. If the person risks with someone who is not trustworthy or someone who is incapable of appreciating the preciousness of what has been shared, she or he may feel invalidated and hurt.

There is an anxiety that many possess, "If you know who I really am, you won't like me." Indeed, to the extent that someone really knows who you are, they may discover some things about you that they do not like. If a person is sufficiently insecure she or he may downplay, hide, conceal, or lie about who she or he is in order to avoid potential rejection. The flip side of this is that if another does not know who you really are, then genuine acceptance is impossible. This self-denial can eventually lead to resentment of the one who never fully accepts, and a loathing of oneself for the lack of courage to be authentic. In order to be truly accepted, one has to run the risk of being truly rejected.

Fortunately, the anxiety of being rejected can be diminished. This anxiety is effected by one's inner self-acceptance, the strength of one's external support system, the intensity of another's rejection, and the closeness of the other person. These variables interact over time, contributing to a person's strength or weakness. However, they are variables, not constants. They can be changed by a person's personal growth. To the degree that she accepts and respects herself, including her intuitive capacity, Flo will be able to internally buffer or deflect the disapproval or rejection of others. Since Flo did not receive unconditional acceptance early in her life, she does not know that such acceptance can exist, what it feels like, or how different her life-perception would be if she had it.

Personality diffusion involves maintaining an unclear self-image. Flo maintained a diffused sense of her own personality by depending on others for acceptance and by avoiding the struggle and pain involved in accepting herself. To the degree that she was not appreciative and respectful of herself, Flo was vulnerable to the prejudices, projections, and insults of those who lacked the capacity to understand and appreciate her.

DUAL RELATIONSHIP   Flo spoke of seeking support from her teacher-lover. He reacted to her intuitive experiences with a verbal explosion, "… all of that was a bunch of bull shit…people who talked about that were basically fantasizing or living in an unreal world!" He told Flo that her experiences were invalid, that she was fantasizing and living in an unreal world. This is a hostile and callous way for a lover to address a partner struggling with her vulnerability and self-doubt. It is also an unprofessional and unconscionable approach for a teacher to take with a troubled student wanting to explore a personal issue. Flo's experience confronted this man and in the process of defending his own beliefs he lost sight of and emotionally abandoned his student and lover.

Maintaining a dual relationship, that of teacher and lover, is exceedingly difficult. As lovers, it is important that both parties have freedom to make decisions, to enhance their individuality, to withdraw, or to choose to be together. As a teacher it is essential to remain disinterestedly present in order to help a student to develop her or his own skills and abilities. It is both an honor and a challenge to nurture a student's growth toward her or his unique life path. A teacher remaining intellectually and emotionally objective and present is crucial to a student in her or his struggle to gain personal clarity.

A master teacher, in addition to knowing her or his content area, must appreciate the nature of role relationships and the vulnerability of a student to a person in a position of authority. The roles of teacher and lover readily become incompatible. Teachers have a powerful advantage in a relationship. A student in a dual relationship is vulnerable to being exploited by such an authority figure. Moreover, this kind of a dual relationship is dangerous because it can compromise the integrity of the teacher and the student. Both are susceptible to her or his role and personal needs becoming confused. Many vocational and professional fields deem dual relationship unprofessional and unethical.[2]

SOMETHING HAPPENED   Like Flo, many may find themselves vulnerable to the abuse and punishment of charming and insensitive, misguided, rigid, or narcissistic, authority figures. Why would students compromise themselves in such a situation? Why did a bright, educated woman like Flo find herself in a situation that she originally decided she did not want?

The emotionally needy and vulnerable child matures socially and vocationally. She or he possesses adult skills, tools, appetites, drives, and needs. Emotionally, though, she or he can remain stuck in feeling undeserving of genuine love. In the face of an unaffectionate, unnurturing adult or authority figure, the submerged needy child comes to the experiential foreground. The old pattern of trying to be accepted for some pleasing deed immediately comes into play. This regression to the childhood coping pattern is automatic and unconscious. Furthermore, it is protected by unconscious emotional defenses.

A person can be bright, intelligent, and rational. She or he can have a clear intellectual sense of her or his personal identity, needs, intentions, and limits. Yet in the presence of a person in authority who experientially replicates the unresolved childhood situation, even a bright, intelligent person like Flo can transform into an emotionally needy child ready to compromise her sexual integrity and boundaries in the hopes of attaining a long lost and never known love.

RATIONALIZATION Flo herself was puzzled by her behavior. She entered into her instructor's training program because she wanted to learn what he had to teach. She was clear with herself. She was not interested in a sexual relationship. The best she could make of this puzzling situation was to say, "Something happened."

This teacher provided his attractive, emotionally hungry, intuitive student many logical reasons to have a sexual relationship with him. "It would improve your professional work." This man was either intentionally manipulative, or he was rationalizing.

Rationalization is an unconscious mechanism used to defend and justify unacceptable behavior. People can make up all kinds of justifications, to free themselves from guilt, or provide themselves with a facade of appropriateness. Flo's teacher provided her and the many other students he had seduced with the message that it is okay, if you have a logical reason, to seduce an unwilling student. The truth of the matter is that this man, far from helping his student, so emotionally damaged Flo, that years after the incident, she had not yet fully recovered.

Flo reported that she knew other women who had been seduced by this man and had not yet recovered. Many people look at teachers as parental figures—parental en loci. If they were seeking any kind of emotional attention from him, maybe it was in the form of understanding and acceptance. When this foolish, self-indulgent man imagined their need to be one of sexual fulfillment, no doubt his own preoccupation, he violated their need for parental protection. This may be why so many of these women had such a hard time overcoming their experience with him. This man may have replicated a childhood trauma for these women by not accepting who they were. And, he compounded the old wound by confusing it with a sexual event which had nothing to do with their needs.

What is apparent and unfortunate about such a situation, is that this man, probably because of wounds that he received earlier in his childhood, is callous to the hurtful effects of his manipulative behavior. He acts out his own unresolved needs and justifies the use of his professional status to be sexually exploitative of his female students. This victim-victimizer further rationalizes his behavior by stating that he is only treating his students the way he himself was treated by his own instructor. This "teacher" may not be likely to respond to confrontation because of his own emotional defenses.

GROUP PHENOMENA   Any group environment, for example educational classes, training groups, work groups, church groups, political groups, can heighten the possibility of exploitative encounters such as Flo had with her teacher. The group phenomena recreates a family atmosphere which fosters transference reactions. Participants in such environments may regress to unresolved childhood roles in which they were needy of acceptance or approval from a parental figure. This may be particularly enhanced if the group leader assumes a matriarchal or patriarchal role.

Also, a training group environment provides participants with an arena in which they may transcend their familiar, daily roles and discover their core "feeling selves." Being truly seen, recognized, and appreciated can feel extremely confirming, nourishing, and flattering. However, if one's emotional core is diffused and open in an exploitive, unprotected environment, the participant will be vulnerable to misguided or malevolent intentions. Flo's experience may have incorporated both of these group phenomena.

The responsibility for self-protection falls upon the student. What is truly unfortunate is that the very students who must beware of such an exploitative person are most vulnerable to succumbing because of their unresolved emotional issues and desires for acceptance from an authority figure.

Hopefully, just being aware of the sexually exploitative possibility may provide an ounce of prevention for some and may provide others with information to make sense out of what has already happened to them. Finally, such information may provide a framework for others to gently protect and support their friends or colleagues who may be going through or have gone through a similar experience.

INTERVENTION: A PROBLEM-SOLVING STRATEGY   Intervention is usually easiest and most effective when it occurs as soon as possible. As harassment mounts and an individual's peace of mind and level of comfort begin to dissipate, intervention becomes increasingly difficult. However, bringing one's discomfort with the "unwelcomed" behavior to the harasser's attention earlier on, is relatively easier—though it might not be easy.

Sharing one's discomfort first with supportive friends, relatives, therapist, or doctor before attempting to bring one's discomfort to the harasser may also be of help. This outside sharing will allow a person to feel more supported and less alone when they actually confront the harasser. Others' awareness and understanding can be invaluable should the confrontation not go well.

A first confrontation need not be an angry one. It only needs to be brief, frank, and direct. One must communicate without laughter or joking, "I don't welcome your saying or doing these types of behavior. This kind of behavior is not comfortable for me and interferes with my ability to work effectively. I would appreciate your not doing it any more."

Whatever that individual might say at the moment is of passing significance. What becomes essential is the behavior that then follows. If the behavior does not change, the chances are that the harasser is not merely interested in sexual favors. This individual is using her or his position to exercise intimidative power over the worker. If the behavior does not change, a worker or student is then forced to go over that person's head in order to make a formal complaint.

Legal consultation is necessary if higher officials are informed of the harassment and fail to take significant corrective action. Employers are liable for the behaviors of their employees when they have been informed of the harassment and fail to act upon the information. In addition, when contacted, state licensing boards and professional organizations' ethics committees will take corrective actions regarding sexual violations. Whatever course an individual chooses; taking legal action, leaving the situation, or putting up with the abuse, following through is not easy.

SUMMARY

Flo came from a family which did not allow its members to touch. Flo originally undertook her bodywork training in order to overcome her discomfort with touch. In addition to her discomfort with touch, Flo also had little psychosocial contact. As a result of her training, this former musician decided to pursue a career in the bodywork field.

In the process of becoming a bodyworker, Flo discovered that she had intuitive insights regarding her clients in their sessions. She experienced this awareness as she touched her clients. This awareness came in the form of thoughts, somatic sensations, and feelings. For this bodyworker, who had a psychosocial history that was void of physical touch and had minimal personal contact, her intuitive insights alternately felt exciting and overwhelming. What appeared to be difficult for Flo to manage was the degree of immediate, intimate contact. What became further upsetting for her was the fact she lacked a cognitive framework from which she could understand what appeared to be an extrasensory phenomenon.

Flo actively sought out information. She asked friends if they had similar experiences. Flo explored the theme in psychotherapy. There she defined for herself that she had to back away from the frightening experience until she gained intellectual understanding which ultimately would provide her with comfort. Flo numbed her experiential awareness. This led to a lessening of her anxiety and a loss of her sense of excitement. She also shut down her intuitive wisdom.

Finally, Flo shared her experience with a man who was her body-work instructor and lover. This man was punitive, derogatory, and unprofessional toward her. His negation of her experience only served to highlight its truth.

The fact that this instructor attempted to intimidate Flo into invalidating her intuitive wisdom is not at all surprising. He had already successfully achieved the same goal by seducing Flo to enter into a dual, sexual, relationship with him. Years after the event Flo was still smarting from the unresolved emotional wounds of her encounter with him. The fact that Flo was aware of a number of women who also found themselves victimized by this charmer, points to this man's abuse of authority and power. He learned that it was okay to rationalize away his violation of his students' sexual boundaries. If he did not offer his same expertise to the less attractive female students and the men in his classes, his behavior constituted sexual harassment of others, too.

Flo originally went to massage school to learn about touch. In the process, she uncovered her powerful intuitive self. This intuitive self allowed her to get far closer to her clients than she was comfortable. In coming to grips with this aspect of herself, she resolved to keep this ability separated from her professional work. Flo discovered through spiritual growth work that she could access her intuitive ability with regard to her own self-awareness. In this private context she was comfortable exploring her intuitive self.

END NOTES

[1] **PSI Phenomena** PSI phenomena relates to Parapsychological Phenomena. Being psychic implies various kinds of extrasensory perceptions. These are sensitivities to non-physical forces. That is, the stimulus of a psychic perception, PSI phenomenon, is not the direct reaction of the ear to sound waves, the tongue to taste, the skin to pressure, or the nose to aromas. There are numerous explanations for PSI phenomena. Some offer mystical answers. They claim to channel entities from other dimensions or times. Some believe that they receive messages from extra-terrestrials. Some have no idea where the information originates.

The following is a less mysterious interpretation. We already know that we have more than five senses. There are proprioceptors which tell us our position in space. We have a sensitivity to our natural rhythms such as eye movements, heart beats, sleep cycles, and menstrual cycles. From all of these cycles many are able to tell or estimate time. We even have an ability to entrain or get into a synchronized rhythm with another's senses. Or it may elucidate how our five senses have provided for latitudes of survival that have been lost with a modern shift in emphasis to left-brain cognition. Perhaps under certain conditions we can reclaim these lost capabilities.

2 **Sexual Harassment**   The Equal Employment Opportunity Commission states that sexual harassment has occurred when a person is subjected to unwelcomed behavior of a sexual nature. "Unwelcomed behavior" implies unsolicited behavior. Harassment is recognized to occur in three separate types of situations. The first is called "quid pro quo." In this situation there is a promise or a threat regarding security or promotion. Flo's instructor clearly spelled out the conditions of his teaching her special techniques. His sharing his expertise was dependent upon her entering into a sexual relationship with him. This is "quid pro quo" harassment.

"Hostile work place" is the second form of harassment. It occurs when a victim is subject to verbal or physical behavior of a sexual nature making the work environment uncomfortable. Harassment in a hostile work place situation is defined as a behavior that would create discomfort for any reasonable person of the same sex. It is deemed harassment when it is of a repeated nature.

A third form of sexual harassment occurs when an outside party loses a work related opportunity because it was offered to another person in exchange for sexual favors. This third party or parties are then entitled to sue the harasser for harm done them as a result of lost opportunities.

Part III

SIGNIFICANT PSYCHOLOGICAL PROBLEMS

9

A BAD FEELING

Alice is a soft spoken, gentle woman in her early fifties.

Bob phoned the shop and I received the call. He asked, "Do you give gift certificates?" I told him, "Yes we do." He said, "Oh, great!" And then said, "It's my girlfriend's birthday, and I am planning out a day of surprises for Denise. Her sisters are massage therapists in California. I'm sure she will be thrilled to start out her day of surprises with a massage." I put down a morning time in the schedule book for Denise's birthday.

When Denise's birthday came around, I was sitting at the front desk. She was my first client on that Saturday morning. I could see her coming through the clear glass office door. Denise approached the door, stopped, then turned around to leave. Then she turned around again and came back. I had a bad feeling.

Denise was a twenty-five year old waitress who came through the door impatiently chewing gum. She then confronted me, "What's going on?" I told her that Bob was planning a day of surprises, and it was to begin with a massage. In an agitated fashion Denise demanded to know what else was going to happen during the day. I explained that I only knew that the massage was a birthday present Bob got to celebrate her birthday and did not know what else was planned. Denise intimated that the couple already had began to celebrate earlier that morning—perhaps with alcohol.

I showed Denise to my massage room and explained my philosophy toward massage. I told her I take a gentle approach to massage. Denise gruffly insisted, "I want it hard...especially my legs. I work on my legs all day and they get tired. Work on them hard!" Once Denise was on the table, I could smell alcohol on her breath. I said to myself, "The celebrating earlier this morning must have been a champagne breakfast."

Denise appeared to drift in and out of sleep as I worked on her. I took this as a compliment. I thought, "Obviously this woman is so relaxed by my work that she is going to sleep." I had Denise turn over after working the front side of her body. Then she told me again that she wanted her legs worked "hard." When I got to Denise's calves, I was aware of the muscular tension. Denise again seemed to be in a deep sleep. I responded to Denise's request and placed a considerable amount of pressure on the calf muscles. I remembered thinking to myself that my thumbs were fatiguing as a result of the pressure I was applying.

I am not a clock watcher when I work. But, I was aware that Denise had a particularly "tight" body. While the gift certificate was for an hour session, the massage actually took an hour and forty minutes. I was not concerned that I was giving away my time.

Bob was there and waiting when I left the massage room. I talked with him for a bit before Denise came from the massage room. She was in a huff. She opened with, "Well, that was totally unsatisfactory! I specifically told you that my feet and legs were tight; they needed to be worked on. You didn't even do my legs! Was that a whole hour?" I told her I worked on her for an hour and forty minutes, not an hour. She was not going to be talked out of being agitated. She then demanded, "Give me your supervisor's name!"

Bob was mute while Denise's scolding was going on. I was thinking to myself, "This woman wants me to give her this session for nothing. I'm not going to do it!" I explained to her how I work. I would have refunded her money immediately, or after the first ten minutes, or after the first twenty minutes. But I sure wasn't going to refund her money after the hour and forty minutes of my labor.

I wrote up this incident and put my notes in the office record book. I wanted my colleagues to be forewarned of Denise and Bob. I wanted to spare them the unpleasantness of such a situation. And I made a decision regarding gift certificates and surprises. I assumed Denise understood what massage was from what Bob had told me about her sisters being massage therapists. However, I decided to speak personally to the client before they showed up for an appointment. I want to brief them about what they can expect.

After I finished reporting this encounter, I thought, "My father was an alcoholic." When I met and was working on Denise, I thought of my father's irritable, agitated, fault-finding behavior. I think I am overly sensitive to alcohol use because of my father. My memories of alcoholic-related issues are painful for me. So, I pushed my intuition of Denise being alcoholic out of my awareness. I let these thoughts go no further. I certainly did not take the action I would have taken if I acknowledged my intuition.

The guidelines say that you shouldn't work on anyone who is on a drug or alcohol which might effect their awareness or decision-making. However, I work with patients who are taking anti-inflammatory medication. The massage helps to ease the pain in their joints. Besides, I wouldn't have denied Bob's wish to give Denise a massage for a birthday present just because she has one or two drinks several hours earlier with breakfast.

I don't know that I wouldn't work on someone who has had a drink. But I think if I had to deal with someone like this again, first, I would ask them if they had been drinking. Then I would let them know I am concerned for them. I'll explain that I would not want to do something to them that might hurt them. At that point, I would give them the choice of a refund or rescheduling. That's what I think. And, that's what I say. But, I do not know if I will have the courage to do it.

Massage without explicit permision is intrusive. What is called for is not even permission but welcoming and enthusiasm. I believe the receiver must be in total control and can choose to offer or withdraw their consent at anytime. Because of this it is important for the giver to be ever-present to the awareness of the status of their client's permission. One shouldn't enter into or give massage naively.

This must be acceptable to the practitioner. The client's choice not to go on further or deeper is not to be taken as rejection. I have to be able to distinguish between tolerance and enthusiasm. Sometimes clients are not sufficiently self-aware to know the difference for themselves. Or they want to be polite or strong. So, externally they accept, while internally they are shutting down.

EPILOGUE

Several months after telling her story, Alice received a phone call from a dentist. He told her that he was getting married and "wanted to celebrate" on the morning of his wedding. Alice inquired if he was a drinker and when he was going to have his bachelor party. She then explained her concerns of working on someone who is or had been drinking.

DISCUSSION

DEFENSE When Alice observed her new client struggling over whether or not to walk through the door, she intuitively knew there was a problem. She just could not figure out how this problem was going to manifest.

Denise came into her surprise birthday session looking more defensive than pleasantly surprised. Most people are eager to give up their tension. However, muscle tension or rigidity can be part of a psychological defense against what has been, is, or may be a hostile or threatening environment. To take someone's defenses away is to leave them exposed and vulnerable. This prospect can lead an insecure person to become more defensive. At that point they are not reasonable, logical, or flexible. Defenses are there to do exactly that—defend. Unless someone has a better alternative that they are able to put into effect, it is not a good idea to take a person's protection away from them. The one who is removing their protection may become the target of their defensive attack.

ALCOHOL Alcohol use may also serve as a defense. When someone drinks a lot, often, or even starts drinking early in the day, this is a clear sign that this person may be dependent upon alcohol for coping with or avoiding life stresses. Alcohol is a central nervous system depressant. It dulls the senses, the functions of reasoning, judgment, memory, and motor performance. It subjects the abuser to mood swings. There are some people who experience alcohol as energizing. It is impossible for a depressant to energize a person, but alcohol may have a paradoxical effect on some people. For a person who is chronically inhibited, the dulling property of alcohol has a disinhibiting effect. Because their usually inhibited tension is released, they feel an uncharacteristic freedom or energy.

The abuse of alcohol is sufficiently prevalent to suggest that the possibility of running into an abusive drinker in one's practice is likely. As a result, it makes good sense to have some sort of policy about alcohol and what to do with a problem drinker if one shows up. Prevention may be the easiest policy. Bells are certain to go off for Alice next time she gets a call from a boyfriend planning an all day celebration for his girlfriend. The initial phone contact would be an excellent opportunity to inform someone of one's concern over performing bodywork if they have been drinking. When Alice smelled alcohol on Denise's breath that would have been another appropriate time for an intervention.

BLACKOUTS Perhaps Denise was drifting in and out of sleep because she was tired. Maybe Alice was doing a good job and as a result, the tension was dissipating from Denise, drawing her into sleep. The alcohol that this client consumed earlier may also have placed her in a somnambulistic state, or all the above may have been true.

An additional possibility is a phenomena called a blackout, which can be experienced by alcohol abusers. During periods of blackouts, a person can walk, talk, dance, negotiate contracts, drive and park cars. However, a person in this state is unable to remember afterwards what happened. Denise had no memory of her legs being worked on, nor did she have a sense of tension being reduced in her legs. Relaxation of tension may not be a comforting experience for Denise. Indeed, it may be experienced as a threat to her maintenance of a sense of control. It may also suggest that this woman's drinking is sufficiently severe as to cause blackouts.

CONTRACT   The issue of alcohol abuse is one of the issues in Alice's scenario. The kind of service that Denise wanted performed was another. Denise wanted her legs worked on "hard." Alice shared her philosophy of gentle bodywork; at this point there was a contractual difference. Alice could have clarified her policy for Denise. The less intrusive approach may have more readily released Denise's muscular defense. If this client did not like Alice's orientation or simply did not want a massage, she could have said so. Alice chose to accommodate Denise at her own physical discomfort and emotional expense. She may decide to do otherwise if a similar situation presents itself in the future.

INTEGRITY   Alice did not try to explain away or talk Denise out of her anger, nor did Alice attack back. She maintained her professional stance. She also maintained her integrity by not refunding the client's money. To the degree that Alice recognized and appreciated her clarity and strength in both problem-solving and limit-setting, she has reinforced her psychological core and professional integrity.

PROFESSIONALISM   Alice also thought to alert her colleagues of Denise's behavior. Though Denise's return was doubtful, the communication may prevent this client from acting out her anger on anyone else in the group. Writing this little situation up in her notes was Alice's responsibility to her colleagues. And, it may have served an additional function. It can be a cathartic outlet if there was no one around with whom to share such an unsettling event. Writing, like bodywork, can be a psychophysical release.

ASSUMPTIONS   Bob assumed that because Denise's sisters were massage therapists in California, she would be thrilled to have a massage for her birthday. The life path one sibling chooses to take may not reflect on another's. Just because Denise's sisters were massage therapists in California, did not imply that she would be thrilled to receive a massage for her birthday.

SUPPRESSION The brief whiff of alcohol on Denise's breath painfully reminded Alice of her father. This noxious association led Alice to block out of her awareness the similarities in behavior: Denise's irritability, agitation, and fault-finding. These traits added up to alcohol abuse for Alice, but she was unwilling to be aware of her intuitive equation.

Suppression is a deliberate, conscious attempt to push from awareness or to forget something that is too troublesome or painful to contemplate. Alice suppressed the horrible reminder of her painful past which had been triggered by Denise's alcohol-scented breath. Alice knew that she was consciously pushing painful memories of her father out of her awareness. She likely responded in the same stereotypic pattern toward Denise, after all, that pattern had protected her from her father's belligerence and aggression. At the same time Alice masked her traumatic awareness of her father, the manner in which she chose to deal with Denise also became masked. Thus, Alice was unlikely to realize that her avoidance of conflict with Denise was part of a larger pattern of coping learned in childhood to avoid conflict with her father.

Suppression may have been an appropriate intervention for Alice to utilize as a dependent, helpless child against an irrational, aggressive parent. Using this same strategy as an adult in her bodywork practice left her vulnerable to the irrationality of an inebriated 25 year old. As Alice becomes aware of her feelings and what she does with them, she creates the potential for a new means of coping with this stressful situation. Alice, as an adult, has more appropriate and powerful coping alternatives available to her.

RECOGNITION OF NON-EVENTS Non-events are negative events that do not occur because a person has taken positive action to prevent them. Non-events are important to recognize. They are the DNA of prevention and the RNA of behavioral change. They are a sign of someone's process being healthy or becoming healthier. Recognizing non-events fortifies one's health and growth. People who have low self-esteem have a very hard time rewarding themselves. They have an especially hard time rewarding themselves for a non-event. Yet self-recognition and self-appreciation are essential for the growth process.

Alice was not judgmental of Denise even though she did not like her client's unsettling behavior. In spite of her discomfort, Alice did not call Denise names. She did not project or displace anger that she felt toward her father onto Denise. Alice remained firm on collecting her fee. She maintained her own integrity and demonstrated respect for her client's integrity. Though it left Alice shaken afterwards, this bodyworker allowed her belligerent client to air out her feelings. Maintaining a professional rapport and not blowing up at Denise were signs of Alice's strength and maturity.

Another issue was Alice's doubt about putting her newly developed policy toward drug and alcohol abusers into action. Alice's inner reality may have felt like self-doubt, weakness, or lack of conviction, however, Alice's failure to recognize her achievement was unfortunate. She had not taken the final action steps of self-growth.

The impetus to take the next step can come from the energy liberated by self-recognition and self-appreciation. What is essential for Alice to appreciate is that changing life patterns is extremely difficult. The change must be viewed as progress. Awareness and acknowledgment of her doubts about making a change, therefore, is an intervention. Alice had the honesty and strength to recognize and admit to having a problem. She then invested her time and energy to develop a solution. Alice's admission of reluctance to change helped her to deal more smoothly with change than if she had denied that reluctance. These are the steps of Alice's problem resolution leading to growth.

DRUGS AND ALCOHOL   Alice realized that the answer to the drug and alcohol issue would not be a simple one for her. She recognized that there were cases in which her clients may legitimately use drugs or alcohol, and this use would not inhibit her from working with them. What remains for Alice to clarify are those conditions in which her clients' use of alcohol or drugs would be contraindicated for her massage practice.

ALICE'S PHILOSOPHY   Alice is not judgmental, moralistic, or simplistic. While not yet fully integrated with regard to her thoughts, feelings, and actions, Alice has developed a sophisticated philosophy of bodywork. For Alice, bodywork is an on-going relationship. In this relationship, the practitioner is responsible for obtaining the client's explicit and implicit consent to enter the realm of their being, holdings or releasings. "Massage without explicit permission is intrusive. What is called for is not even permission but welcoming and enthusiasm." The meeting of bodyworker and client with the client's permission is intimate and healing. Without permission, the same act is an intrusive violation. For this reason it is essential that neither party's senses, reasoning, judgment, memory, emotions, or motor ability be dulled beyond intentional, conscious command.

Alice also notes that she must maintain a close watch on her client's pulse of permission. "Sometimes clients are not sufficiently self-aware to know the difference themselves. Or they want to be polite or strong." The practitioner needs to be alert for physiological signs in the body of "shutting down."

Finally, Alice recognized that a significant degree of personality integration is essential to working with clients. She warns, "One should not enter into or give massage naively." If a person is to be well grounded in her or his role as a provider of bodywork, he or she must be able to maintain a core integrity especially when the client has difficulty doing the same. "The client's choice not to go on further or deeper is not to be taken as rejection." This is a particularly wise professional stance.

SUMMARY

Alice was confronted by her first client on a Saturday morning. Watching through her glass front door, she could see the ambivalence of this gift certificate recipient about receiving a massage. This placed Alice on alert. And there were other non-verbal cues that pointed to trouble. The woman was impatient, agitated, confrontational, demanding, and her breath smelled of alcohol.

As Alice intuitively met her client, she perceived disturbing behavioral patterns that were similar to her father's alcohol dependent behaviors. She immediately pushed these thoughts from her mind and tailor-made a session to meet her client's demands. The session did not run the usual hour, but an hour and forty minutes. Her client emerged from the session dissatisfied, pressing to get her money back, and wanting to complain to Alice's supervisor.

Alice remained calm. She stood her ground. She made no refund. After telling her story, Alice deliberated over this event. She then created an action plan. She decided that before taking on new clients who might be inebriated, she would confront them with the issue of their sobriety. However, Alice had doubts as to whether or not she would be sufficiently strong to follow through on her plan. While Alice had been unable to confront her father in childhood, she professionally confronted the next client about whose sobriety she was concerned. By doing this Alice not only enhanced her professional skills, but she further allowed her childhood wounds to heal.

10

CERTAIN LIMITS

Nancy, a massage therapist in her mid-thirties, was earnest and straightforward in her presentation. At times when describing behavior that seemed peculiar to her, she would chuckle in a half-humorous, half-anxious manner.

There was one client in particular that was quite challenging on all levels. Not just the bodywork, but the personal levels, too. Shelly was a saleswoman in her early twenties when I began to work with her. She had just been in an automobile accident and sustained a neck injury. When her emotional life would get rough, her neck pain would increase.

I could tell that this was going on on all sorts of levels including psychologically. She has a lot of problems; a lot of them she didn't even know about until later on. I worked with her for a couple of years. Later she found out that she and her three sisters had been sexually abused by her father and her brother. Her sister, after a hospitalization for a suicide attempt, told of the sexual abuse that occurred in the family. Shelly didn't remember anything about the sexual abuse until then. When I first started working with her…it was very interesting to me, that even when I touched her very lightly, she would jump up…*(Chuckle)* whenever I would touch her *(Again Nancy chuckled nervously)*, that kind of thing. I always wondered, "What is going on here?"

There were a lot of questions that came up for me. "Oh, what am I doing?" "Why is this person jumping up off the table?" Plus, she was very demanding. She would call me up later on and ask me, "How come this isn't working the way it is supposed to?" Emotional incidents would trigger her neck pain. I'd go, "What?" *(Chuckling)* I'd have to figure out what to say. It made me think about the whole process and what was going on. I had to reconsider my whole concept of how people change...because it was so frustrating for me. It would seem like we were getting somewhere and all of a sudden *(with frustration)* CRRRRRRR! *(Chuckling)* Things would just erupt.

She was very highly verbal. So trying to do bodywork with her was a challenge. She would be talking all the time and sweating profusely throughout the whole time, because we didn't know about these abuses. *(Chuckle)* She just had lot of questions whether God would forgive her for doing this thing or that thing. *(Chuckling)* How am I supposed to know! She would ask me things that were beyond my realm. I'd say, "Well, I don't know."

So there was a lot of processing and figuring out how to deal with her questions. We wanted to find some answers because I was not completely satisfied, and she wasn't completely satisfied about it. I was starting to discover that there were certain limits as to what I wanted to do with my practice. I didn't want to be her psychotherapist. That's what I finally figured out. I felt really inept. *(Hearty chuckling)* This was totally out of my realm. So I told her that finally, "You are going to have to seek other help."

Part of the problem is that she has tried to seek other help, but the help she ran into was putting her on drugs and was not very helpful. Plus she was having issues with men. She was afraid of men, but getting involved with abusive men. She saw a counselor and a priest, but they both had sexual feelings toward her! In her main relationship she was pushed into the sack. I'd tell her, "You don't have to get into the sack if you don't want to, or you could just kiss and hug without having intercourse." She was amazed! *(Chuckle)* When I think back on it, she did find one man that she did like after I made the suggestion. I told her, "I'm not even going to work with you anymore until you get a therapist. Then you can deal with the mental part that is going on because I can't deal with—I can't be your All!"

She was real resistant. She really got mad. She started "damning" me. She'd call me up and cry on the phone. *(Chuckling)* She was trying to guilt trip me back into doing it. I had all these pangs of guilt myself. "Oh, no!" *(Chuckle)* Ya know, I really felt kind of inept about the whole thing, but I stuck to my guns. I tried to give her as many suggestions as I could about getting her to professional help, where to find it, and that kind of thing.

She had a whole slew of people she counseled with and talked with on the phone. Her mother got angry over the phone bill. She finally hooked up with a counselor who was fairly good for her. She went through a lot with that counselor, but what it opened up was this whole issue with her father. So I guess in a way it was okay.

(Chuckle) She got in it through the whole alcoholic syndrome. She started drinking after that. *(Chuckle)* I guess she wanted to belong to this alcoholic group. Her counselor would tell her she was getting better and then she would start to drink abusively. Then she would ask me, "Am I really an alcoholic or am I just doing this?" *(In astonishment)* I mean she even said that!

After that, after she got the therapist, I still saw her, but I refused to deal with the head stuff. That is not my role. I'll work with your body. But I won't work with that part. Really, that allowed me to make more definite assertions that I was not going to play that kind of role. Even though a part of me was wanting to help her.

She finally got into a treatment center where she had more ongoing treatment. She got more like twenty-four hour care. Things that would happen to her were too much for her. She would get panic attacks and all that. Finally, when she did get the therapist, our whole relationship changed and she could see what I was saying. Our bodywork sessions changed dramatically. She was still kind of verbal, but I could be in a still place with her more often. And, my focus shifted a little bit in there, too.

What this taught me at that time period was to respect emotional boundaries. I didn't want to throw her off in horrible stuff and then have her go home, and the whole thing. She had panic attacks on the way home. So I really learned about emotional responsibility. I really felt her emotional boundaries and mine. Because some of the things she would say would trigger memories from my adolescence, too. She'd talk about sexual sorts of things, and I'd remember back to being younger and not knowing what to do.

I had to separate all this out. I would feel where the edges were while I was working on her body. So that's when I really got into the sense of "the emotional body," that it is separate from "the physical body." But while you are working up here *(pointing to her head)*, you are also working down here *(pointing to her heart)*. And, I started to know it more and play with it and focus on it more. If I went too deep into it, her reaction would get real emotional. If I'd play on the edge of it she would calm down. It meant I had to learn those limits. Really, I wanted her to end up after the session on an even keel.

Once she started to work with her therapist she began to use me to process. She seemed to even out her thoughts and get a perspective. She recently left to go to a whole other therapy situation. This is quite amazing for her because she always lived around her home. She still had this real connection with her parents. It was really difficult to break that connection.

She is now in a facility where they are trying to rehabilitate her so that she is able to work. She was in sales until she had her accident. Unfortunately after the accident she was in constant pain, but they could not detect her pain on a physical level. She had real severe pain. She went to a specialty clinic. They couldn't find anything. She went through physical therapy, drugs, things like that to try to remediate it. Everything made it worse. Because they didn't recognize it. I think they should have recognized it was her personal pain rather than try to find out a physical cause for it.

At the time of the accident, she was out with a boyfriend that her father didn't approve of. This boyfriend was doing similar types of things to her that her father would do to her...abuse wise. He would scream at her, hit her, abuse her sexually, and stuff like that. The father did not want her engaged with this fellow. They had snuck out and gone driving when she had the accident. Then she had to expose herself to her parents. I could just see all of this emotional stuff. It is amazing to me how that whole context of how an incident like that can effect someone on multi-levels...and, how insensitive and inept so many people are...*(Chuckle)*...to it as well as myself.

It was a real growing process figuring out what role I could play in facilitating some degree of change. It was nice to see that all happen during the two or three years I was working with her. It was really great to finally figure out about this emotional stuff, too. That has always bothered me about bodywork in a way. It still kind of bothers me about trainings somewhat. That there is no real structure to deal with that kind of thing. Stuff comes up in training sessions that takes weeks or months to deal with. They kind of leave me up in the air. I don't think it helps to leave it up in the air. With this one it didn't help at all to leave it up in the air. *(Laughing)* Ya know, it just gave me more respect for that component of someone's life.

DISCUSSION

PAIN   Symptoms of physical pain from any source are often exacerbated by emotional stress. The physical area of injury may be aggravated as muscles tighten from stress. The behavioral skills of stress management are often a key to overcoming or managing pain. These are the skills of life style modification. Not only can pain be reduced, but the physical healing process itself can be hastened for those who are sufficiently motivated to take on a regimen of life style change. The converse is also true. Those unwilling or unable to take on life style changes to reduce stress often increase their pain and prolong the healing process.

Accidents, injuries, and illnesses often are accompanied by feelings of fear, anger, resentment, shame, or guilt. Consequently, accidents can cause emotional pain as well as physical pain. Physical injury can be treated and healed while the emotional pain remains.

PROFESSIONAL BOUNDARIES Nancy reported that Shelly saw a counselor and a priest both of whom had sexual feelings toward her. On face value, one might question the integrity of the counselor and priest. However, because of the sexual abuse from her father, Shelly may psychologically project similar sexual advances onto other men in positions of authority. This woman likely is confused about her boundaries; she may have confusion about men in general. She may also confuse feelings of love, lust, affection, appreciation, dependency, and sexuality. Shelly may appreciate her counselor's support and attention and unknowingly elicit or evoke sexual responses. For this reason it is essential that any helping professional who might work with such a client have crystal clear professional boundaries.

Without doubt, there are professionals in the health care field who are lacking in clinical skills, and who may behave inappropriately and unethically. These people not only harm their clients and patients, but they create a mistrust in the public for all members of the profession.

Nancy reported that Shelly's counselor and priest found her sexually attractive. If Shelly asked these men if they found her attractive she would have been placing them, as well as herself, in a double bind. Shelly might have felt rejected and in turn dropped out of treatment if they said, "No." On the other hand, they would have been perceived as unsafe, untrustworthy, like her father if they said, "Yes."

The fact that Shelly's priest and counselor might have found her sexually attractive in and of itself is not the critical issue. Being sexually attracted to someone is normal. What is critical is if these helping professionals, who were in a delicate position with regard to this wounded client's health and well being, were unable to maintain their professional boundaries. Their taking verbal, non-verbal, or physical action on their personal feelings would have violated Shelly's boundaries. They would also compromise her treatment if their thoughts were diverted from their professional task by a sexual preoccupation. Such violations would have compromised their status as healers and added to Shelly's incest wound. In addition, their actions would have made it more difficult for future helping professionals to establish a trusting rapport with this very troubled client.

APPROPRIATE REFERRAL Nancy spoke of a host of physicians who were unable to diagnose the psychological etiology of Shelly's pain.[1] It appears from Nancy's story as if all of the helping professionals who

Shelly met with were unprofessional, inadequate, and inept. Nancy was surprised that Shelly's physicians were unable to identify the underlying psychological factor contributing to Shelly's pain. It was obvious to Nancy.

The possibility exists that all of Shelly's physicians failed to identify the underlying psychological etiology of her pain problem, but it is unlikely. Shelly was treated on a number of specialty units. Specialty units are often hospital-based behavioral programs that are created for patients who have physical problems that are known to have significant psychological components. Admission must be ordered by a medical director, the patient evaluated by a social worker, and examined and tested by a psychologist. Furthermore, discharge from such a unit includes out-patient follow-up. It is unlikely that Shelly simply fell through the cracks in the health care system. From the psychosocial history presented and the symptoms of the patient, what is more likely, is that Shelly came from a highly troubled, dysfunctional family who were in denial regarding the status and their own involvement in the emotional disorders of their children.

MEDICATION Nancy was concerned that Shelly sought professional help and was only given medication. Psychotropic medication is often helpful in stabilizing a person who is having emotional distress. In and of itself, however, medication is not a magic answer. It is best used in conjunction with psychotherapy for someone who is experiencing severe emotional distress. While medication may be essential, it provides only relative relief for someone who has a long standing, chronic condition such as Shelly's personality disorder. Many counselors and psychotherapists refer their clients to physicians to prescribe medication while they are providing psychological intervention. The physicians who provided Shelly with prescriptions may have been aware that she was receiving psychological support from someone who had more time and expertise to address Shelly's problems.

PERSONALITY DISORDER From the start, it was clear to Nancy that there was something going on with Shelly that was more than the pain following an auto accident. There was something about her personality that defied Nancy's sense of the healing process. Shelly did not get progressively better with time; she seemed to create or thrive on conflict; even her accident appeared to be the result of an episode in which she was rebelling against or defying her father's authority. Shelly's pain seemed to serve as an attention-getting mechanism that she was clinging to despite how distressing it was for her.

On the one hand, Shelly's behavior was characterized by rebellious independence; on the other hand, Shelly was so dependent as to be unable to tolerate being alone. If not talking to Nancy on the phone, she had to be talking to somebody. She had little sense of her own personal boundaries and sought others who could define her identity for her. However, these partners were often self-serving and punitive toward Shelly.

Shelly's personality was characterized by black and white thinking. She suffered from constant mood swings. Nancy was either the most wonderful person in the world upon whom Shelly was helplessly dependent, or Nancy was the most hateful person in the world and subject to Shelly's wrathful "damning."

These characteristics are indicative of a psychological disorder which goes far beyond the complications of the emotional reaction to an auto accident. Indeed, the emotional overtones of Shelly's auto accident were superimposed upon long standing, pervasive personality traits that are characteristic of personality disorder. Personality disorder is the result of dysfunctional early life parenting which leaves a child with a weakened core personality structure. This in turn creates feelings of low self-esteem, on-going anxiety over autonomy, and exaggerated striving for perfection. Having a weak internal sense of strength, this individual is likely to be overly dependent upon external confirmation, acceptance, approval, and attention. Lack of such continuous confirmation is extremely anxiety provoking. Personality disorder is characterized by poor psychosocial boundaries.

BOUNDARIES   The skin provides for a physical boundary between a person and the rest of the world. The strength of a person's identity provides for a psychological boundary between a person and the rest of her or his social world. Physical abuse, sexual abuse, psychological neglect, dysfunctional, or emotionally inadequate parenting may leave a child with an insecure psychological core, poor self-esteem, and feelings of unworthiness of love.

These conditions also create poor psychosocial boundaries. Poor boundaries may result in chronic insecurity, emotional mood swings, identity diffusion, impulsive behavior, unstable intense relationships, and vulnerability to abusive relationships. Other common signs are substance abuse, body image distortion, and/or self-abusive behavior. Such behavior can be evidenced by recurring accidents, physical injuries, self mutilation, getting into fights, or suicidal gestures. A lifestyle of drama, trauma, and crisis can provide buffers against what otherwise feels like frightening emptiness, overwhelming boredom, identity distortion, struggles with intimacy, and the unacceptable awareness of self-confrontation.

Nancy stated that Shelly's boyfriends were abusive in ways similar to her father. This young woman very likely learned to equate abuse with love. Part of Shelly's difficulty establishing a healthy therapeutic relationship with a psychotherapist was probably related to her inability to tolerate the unfamiliarity of a stable, non-manipulative, supportive, and self-revealing relationship. Insecure individuals usually attempt to maintain a facade of perfection. In opposition to this, psychotherapy explores those areas in the core of the personality which may have been damaged or need support. To admit internal insecurity or scarring is to admit that one is not perfect. However, to grow to a stronger position a person must start from where she or he is. It takes a strong person to admit to imperfection. So establishing and maintaining a healthy therapeutic relationship with a young woman as troubled as Shelly requires, time, patience, and hard work.

Other signs of Shelly's boundary struggles can be seen in her difficulty leaving home. In spite of Shelly's abusive, dysfunctional home life, she was so insecure and dependently enmeshed that she was unable to separate from her parents. Professional support and internal psychological growth were needed to emancipate Shelly from her crippling dependency.

Lack of healthy, loving, parental support effects children to different degrees later in their lives. Some are sufficiently strong to maintain a job and personal relationships. They can function well in structured work environments. After five o'clock, though, they lack the core support to deal with planning, decision making, and conflict resolution. As in Shelly's case, many seek an over-controlling, and under-supportive mate replicating the behavioral pattern they had with their parent.

Older acquaintances, people in positions of authority, or institutional settings may be sought out as parental surrogates. Nancy may have represented a parental figure or surrogate for Shelly. Consequently, Shelly had difficulty separating herself from Nancy. When in a panic, she immediately called Nancy. These frequent and lengthy phone calls became both a frustrating and a troubling imposition for Nancy. Furthermore, Nancy had her own boundary struggles with Shelly. Nancy was caught between her unwillingness to abandon her needy, insecure client and her unwillingness to play rescuer for this young woman's insatiable demands for attention, reassurance, and companionship.

The frequency and duration of health care support required for the recovery of a young woman like Shelly is variable. Recovery is related to the degree of personal injury incurred, alternative environmental support available, the individual's innate strength to deal with familial trauma, current support, and motivation to recover. Sometimes periodic, time-limited, out-patient psychotherapy is sufficient to help a person turn a troubling life situation around. Often, long-term weekly treatment is necessary. Programmed hospitalization or specialty units with on-going aftercare and/or psychotherapy may be necessary in severe cases. Such cases may involve intensive abuse, self-destructive behavior, substance abuse, or eating disorders. In these cases it takes considerable time and support in a healthy, controlled environment to nurture the core of the personality that was damaged and malnourished in childhood.

The boundary problem Nancy encountered with Shelly interfered with Nancy's bodywork. Most people who come for bodywork are likely to feel relaxed as their muscles release and soften. Shelly maintained her boundaries, experiential reality, and self-protection by holding onto muscular tension. If too much of that tension was released too fast, she may have felt a terrifying crumbling of the tenuous structure of both her personal boundaries and her sense of reality. The unfamiliar experiences of muscular relaxation might have been experienced by Shelly as alien, out of control, and threatening. Shelly may have felt as if she were losing her "self," or even going crazy.

SYMPTOMS OF DISTRESS Nancy was quick to pick up symptoms of Shelly's emotional distress. Shelly's "jumping up" even when touched "very lightly" was a symptom of a behavioral trauma which had not healed. Profuse sweating is a symptom of anxiety as is incessant talking and fidgeting. Unlike the feeling of fear when there is a clear and present danger, anxiety is experienced in anticipation of a threat. Without specific training, Nancy was unaware of exactly what she was encountering beyond the symptoms of psychological injury due to Shelly's auto accident. These symptoms do not indicate etiology in and of themselves. Just because someone has the symptoms of anxiety, one should not jump to specific conclusions as to the origins of that anxiety.

It is important to recognize that Nancy's demeanor was not the cause of this anxiety, for that would be relatively easy to remedy if it were. A bodyworker need not psychologically probe to find out whether she is doing something that is creating anxiety. Nancy could simply ask, "Is there something that I am doing that is uncomfortable for you?" In this case, after Nancy's years of caring efforts with Shelly, it is doubtful that Nancy's demeanor or interventions were the cause of Shelly's anxiety.

Clinical concern develops once the bodyworker's behaviors are ruled out as a cause of the client's anxiety and the symptoms persist. Shelly's anxiety reactions continually interfered with Nancy's work. If Shelly behaved this way with Nancy, it is fair to assume that she acted similarly in other relationships. One might believe that this young woman's anxiety resulted from post traumatic stress following her auto accident, or one might suspect from Shelly's symptoms and the psychosocial historical information she shared, that she was sexually abused. In either case Shelly's behavior was sufficiently interruptive to justify referral for psychotherapeutic care.

SAYING NOTHING: A PROBLEM-SOLVING STRATEGY It is important to note that even if Nancy suspected that Shelly was sexually molested, she did not blurt out or confront her fragile client with that suspicion. Shelly, who was already overwhelmed with anxiety, could have been retraumatized by a confrontation with information that she was not ready or strong enough to hear. A wise bodyworker knows when not to share clinical hunches.

COMPLAINING Sometimes having a person to whom one can complain can be a relief. It can allow a person to continue carrying her or his life's burdens more easily. Sharing "beefs" can be particularly comforting when the person they are complaining to has a warm, understanding ear. It may even have therapeutic value if they are simultaneously receiving bodywork.

Complaining is constructive if it allows for affective release, problem solving, or both. Shelly used complaining as a means to maintain intense contact and perhaps in an attempt to fill her own emotional void. Out of genuine concern, Nancy listened. Nancy eventually became emotionally frustrated and drained when hearing the same complaints, and Shelly neither experienced emotional release nor availed herself of helpful suggestions. Nancy's setting limits as to how much she would listen to was both reasonable and healthy.

LIMIT SETTING Shelly's anxiety level was intense enough to interfere with Nancy's performance of her job. In addition, Shelly's demanding behavior was disrupting Nancy's peace of mind. Nancy's setting of her limits and insisting she was unwilling to continue to work with Shelly unless her client sought professional psychological support, was essential for her personal and professional well being. As already discussed it was also the appropriate action to take for a client with Shelly's instability. Shelly was in need of a responsible, caring adult, setting appropriate limits.

MANIPULATION Nancy confronted Shelly's problematic behavior with a reasonable referral. At that point, Shelly became manipulative. She pleaded, called names, and ran guilt trips on Nancy. This manipulative behavior is also common for those suffering from personality disorder. It may be helpful to note that Shelly's intention or motivation may not have been to manipulate, but may have been an expression of her fright over entering a new situation, running the risk of being shamed or rejected by an unknown person, or fearing that her psychological defenses might be stripped away and she would be left exposed and helpless. Nevertheless, Shelly's resistant behavior had the effect of thwarting her bodyworker in taking realistic measures to manage her practice, her life, and her troubled client. Nancy was already struggling with her own sense of guilt because her work was not having its usual beneficial effect. It confused her that the change process was not taking its usual straightforward course. Nevertheless, Nancy did an excellent job of maintaining her boundaries and the integrity of her stance. If she had succumbed to Shelly's manipulation, she would have only added to her own discomfort and Shelly's unacceptable behavior.

DENIAL Shelly came to Nancy with a history of being difficult to treat. She had received medical treatment from some of the best physicians available. Nancy indicates that "Everything made it worse." This history, in and of itself, is an indication that Shelly was a troubled client. One may suspect that if Shelly went to a specialty clinic, such as a pain unit, her psychological condition would be identified. However, the hospital-based health care team encountered the same resistance from Shelly to receiving psychological support as did Nancy when she first insisted Shelly get help. Both the patient and/or her family may have been in denial with regard to accepting responsibility for the psychological aspects of the accident and the family conflict that preceded it. Whether or not Shelly and her family could have accepted at least partial responsibility for the accident, the auto accident was just the tip of this family's psychological problems. This denial was one more reason for Nancy to set limits to support herself in working with this disturbed woman.

THE EMOTIONAL BODY Nancy discovered early in her work with Shelly that Shelly melted into anxiety and panic when her client's muscles indicated that she should have been relaxed and comfortable. Nancy recognized that she was working with a "physical body" and an "emotional body." In some complex fashion the "physical body" interacted with the "emotional body." They had to be considered simultaneously.

Shelly's behavior flew in the face of Nancy's beliefs about wellness. One might expect the deeper the muscular release, the deeper the experiential relaxation, but that is not what happened with Shelly. Deeper releases brought about more anxiety and tension. Nancy learned to regulate the depth of her physical intervention. Deeper into the "physical body" was not necessarily better for the "emotional body." Nancy learned to limit her work because of Shelly's inability to establish and maintain psychological limits as she physically relaxed.

If Shelly were insecure about the strength and integrity of her emotional core, she may have believed that by releasing her holding patterns she could literally lose control of her body: her limbs, head, and body would actually fly apart. Physical release, rather than being looked forward to with pleasure, may have been anticipated with apprehension or dread. This condition of Shelly's "emotional body" reversed Nancy's understanding of the healing process.

SELF   Nancy recognized that she felt inept in her relationship with Shelly. There was something about Shelly's personality that was different. But Nancy was less clear about her own frustrations. She was unable to articulate her experience as Shelly lost her personal boundaries. Often a client may push a therapist's psychological buttons. Learning about these buttons can provide clearer boundaries for the bodyworker as well as personal and professional growth.

As Nancy discovered her limits regarding what she wanted to do with her practice, she was discovering her "self." Nancy's limits were a statement of her truth and the boundaries of her personality. By recognizing her limits, Nancy realized she did not want to be Shelly's psychotherapist. She did not want to be ever-available to receive Shelly's phone calls. Nor did she want her client calling her names and trying to manipulate services she was unwilling to render. Nancy learned to respect her client's emotional edges or limits in order to feel comfortable with herself and her work. She also defined her "self" as she recognized that she derived pleasure from working with a long term client like Shelly and seeing growthful change.

CARE FOR THE CARE GIVER: A PROBLEM-SOLVING STRATEGY   Nancy's insistence on Shelly's seeking professional help was definitely an appropriate intervention. And, Nancy also needed support for herself. Discussing one's work with a knowledgeable colleague can often be emotionally enlightening and intellectually informative. Psychological consultation would have helped Nancy to work more appropriately with her client. While specific content or information regarding a client cannot be discussed, many psychotherapists, with their client's consent, will discuss intervention guidelines with another caregiver.

SUMMARY

Nancy recognized Shelly to be personally and professionally challenging. Shelly defied Nancy's concept of how people change. She behaved, on and off the table, as no other client of Nancy's ever had. Shelly was demanding of Nancy's time, attention, and advice in ways that outstripped Nancy's ability to respond. She confronted Nancy with issues that forced this bodyworker to examine her own psychosocial past. Shelly, almost a decade and a half younger than her bodyworker, verbally attacked Nancy when she did not get her own way.

Nancy liked, was concerned for, and wanted to help Shelly. But, her own peace of mind was being eroded by this demanding client. Finally, Nancy was forced to take a firm stand. Nancy determined that her young client needed someone who was skilled in psychotherapy, and it was not she. Furthermore, until her client was receiving psychotherapeutic support, she refused to work with her.

Nancy regretted that there was no preparation in her training to properly deal with such a client. Sometimes psychosocial issues would arise in training sessions that would take weeks or months for her to put into perspective. In regard to the issues that arose with Shelly, Shelly essentially became Nancy's teacher. Nancy learned to recognize her limits, identify her boundaries, their violation, and how to respect and protect them.

Nancy also learned about the mindbody unity. While Nancy originally believed she was just working on the physical plane, she quickly recognized that she was simultaneously working on an emotional plane. If she failed to attend to both her client's "emotional body" as well as her "physical body," Shelly would leave her office emotionally exposed and subject to panic on her way home. Nancy learned how to modify her sessions so she did not go too deep or overwork her client.

Nancy struggled to determine the limits of her role in the healing process. She recognized that when she worked with a client as troubled as Shelly, she was most comfortable being a member of a team of health care professionals. Nancy could feel the difference in the quality of her work and Sherry's behavior after this client was successfully in psychotherapeutic treatment. From the school of hard knocks, Nancy learned to recognize, appreciate, and value the relationship between mind, body, and the social environment. Hopefully, Nancy will also derive a sense of appreciation for the integrity, wisdom, and courage she brought to bear in working with this client for whom she demonstrated great concern, compassion, and caring.

END NOTES

[1] **Appropriate Consultation**   Many physicians believe in and are trained in biochemical or mechanical solutions to health problems. They search for the kinds of etiology and intervention that are congruent with their training and belief system. Psychological etiology may be overlooked, disregarded, or discounted. Some physicians may suspect solutions that are outside of their realm of practice. They may believe that their caution will protect their patients from being abused by charlatans. While this medical self-protectionist stand is understandable and often helpful, this belief system is also limiting.

One would be remiss to ignore psychological consultation when disturbing emotional symptoms persist, religious consultation if spiritual problems present themselves, or chiropractic intervention if structural issues are present. Many physicians accurately identify psychological conditions. They also recognize that treating their patients for these conditions is beyond the scope of their practice. Consequently, they provide appropriate referrals for thier patients.

11

MAJOR DEMAND ON MY RESOURCES

Jeanne is a calm, measured, soft-spoken, woman in her mid-forties. She has a mature, calming presence.

I have a client, Millie, a 70 year old widow of ten years. She is in robust health. I was offering a community demonstration six years ago and another bodyworker brought Millie so she could see my work. Millie was very eager to be worked on. Millie started out as a client. Now, she is a personal friend.

I don't do diagnosis. However, Millie could be classified as having a "spiritual emergency," or a breakdown in boundaries. That's how Millie described herself. She read *Spiritual Emergency*, and said, "That's me!" I was told by a spiritual counselor who also worked with Millie that her ethereal body was torn, and even with assistance probably would not heal in her lifetime. Millie can't keep things out and she can't keep things in. She is just unstable. This leaves her susceptible to outside forces. She has weak ego boundaries. In addition, she seems to be susceptible to her own psychic, emotional energy. She has extremes of emotional states and can change on a dime.

In the past Millie has had visions. At one point, a vision gave her instructions to kill herself. It was after this that her husband had her committed for psychiatric care. If she still has this now, she won't talk about it. There are things she won't even tell me. That is part of her being susceptible to outside forces.

Millie has periods of being in touch with a "great light," contentment, peacefulness, and clarity. At times when she projects

this...enormous radiant energy...she beams and glows and is efferves-
cent. She doesn't feel her aches and pains. Part of Millie's frustration
is with her radiance escaping. She's just about got it, but she doesn't
get it. And actually, her physical body doesn't change that much in
appearance...in terms of her posture or any more freedom in her body.
But within her, she feels a shift. Millie explained to me that when my
interventions work, her energy is released, and moves up her neck out
the top of her head. She said, "It was like having all these mushrooms
sprout on the top of my head and blossom." Millie could feel a release
and clarity.

I knew that Millie would present challenges for me when she
first got on the table. Millie was out of sync with the movements that
I was doing. She was turning, rolling, and wiggling on the table by
herself. She explained to me, "I am trying to raise energy up through
my body, up my neck, and out of my head." But for some unknown
reason Millie's neck would tighten and the energy often would remain
bottled up.

Millie had been involved in spiritual studies for many years. She
had worked with many spiritual teachers and masters. The spiritual
teachers were men and women on the Earth. The masters were
ascended spirits from the other side.

She is erratic. She probably has been this way all of her life—but
it's getting worse. She has tried hypnosis, acupuncture, and chiropractic. After being hospitalized at a local state institution and receiving
electroconvulsive shock therapy, she will not seek out a traditional
health care provider. She does not believe that a psychotherapist
would understand her spiritual journey.

She clung to me. She thought I had the skills to permanently get
her through this blocked condition. I don't try to fix her. I saw right
away that I couldn't. I was sure, whatever she needed, I didn't have it.
Though, she said I did. Early on in the relationship I made it quite clear
to Millie, I was not there to save her. She wanted someone to save her.
She latched onto me as a vehicle for that.

Millie can be very demanding about what she wants to accomplish. She knows the work I do and makes specific requests. She is
desperate when blocked. She wants to be open and free of pain.
Sometimes, she whines with a sad depressive sound, "I feel heavy!" "I
feel so stuck!" If the energy does not move, her eyes become dark and
she looks morose. When Millie is blocked she has physical discomfort,
particularly neck pain, and mental disorientation. Some of Millie's pain
may be due to numerous auto accidents that she has had in the past.
These accidents may have been the result of speeding because she
sure does speed now! *(Jeanne added with a delighted chuckle.)* She

never gets a ticket. She goes 85 miles per hour in a 45 mile an hour zone. The police always think, "This is a delightful little old lady on her way to church!" And she is on her way to church!

Sometimes Millie can be a space cadet. She can't remember the author of the book she just read. Or she cannot find the words to describe what she wants to say.

Through our work, sometimes the pressure is released, and Millie is ecstatic. When her energy is open she becomes joyful, assertive, lucid, and present. During these times, she speaks very fast, very forcefully. However, the symptoms would return within days.

Now, Millie does not always pay for sessions. Millie got some money in the sale of a house, but squandered it away. She pays sometimes. She often does exchanges. Millie studied reflexology. Sometimes she will bring me a book. In addition to squandering the money she received from her house, Millie has other financial activities that she engages in without regard for the consequences. She'll have a four hundred dollar telephone bill trying to get help for her pain; and she may get eight hundred dollars a month in income. The expense is secondary to talking to someone and getting assistance.

In the past, I worked with Millie two or three times a week. Now we have a weekly bodywork session which is usually followed up by two phone calls. In these calls Millie gives me feedback regarding her session. In the past, sessions were scheduled. Now the work has become less formal. Appointments are sometimes scheduled, but often emerge at times of social visits.

Millie used to call at four in the morning. I told her, "Millie, don't call before eight. I have to work tomorrow." Millie then stopped making early morning calls unless she was in a lot of pain. I've stayed there a couple of nights, and it is bizarre. Music plays all night. The lights are on. She wanders. She'll clean at night. She is compulsive about physical activity. She feels she has to be active every day or her pain increases or she becomes more disoriented because she has so much energy. She interprets that as being at a fairly high spiritual vibration.

Millie presented a major demand on my resources. She demanded I be clear about my boundaries because she has difficulty maintaining her own. I maintain a fair sense of detachment. I become reserved. I listen very carefully. I understand that this is one of the extremes of her experience. I cannot be responsible for pulling her out of it. Although, I certainly wish she could be out of her pain. I often have to step away from my work when I feel manipulated or used. I feel that Millie tries to manipulate me to rush in and attempt to rescue her from her pain. She is so much into her own dysfunction, she is not open to the work that I do to assist her. The challenge to me is to remain spontaneous, receptive—but clear about my role.

Millie's challenge to me is to be in the moment. There is no day dreaming, no...altered states. I cannot dissociate and go off into a daydream. There is no drifting away to think about, "What's for dinner?" I enjoy the challenge to be absolutely present. With other clients, I allow myself the luxury of a softer experience in a very quiet meditative state, and the session will flow. This one is more like being alert every second.

I still follow a flow, but it can shift so quickly with her emotional state. I follow her lead. It is not what she tells me. It is her blockages that I follow with an intuitive sense...where to put my hands, what to say to assist her in the movement of her energy. The same movements do not always produce the same release from session to session. So I began to work intuitively with Millie rather than working from a routine form.

I have never asked Millie for advice or consulted, or shared a personal issue as if I were seeking counsel from her. But Millie has offered me real insight in discussion or spontaneously in our social exchange. She has said things that were really quite insightful and on the mark. And I would affirm her insights when they felt right to me. I recognized that, whether I was working with Millie in a more physical hands on manner or just an exchange of friendly conversation, a central part of my motivation was to affirm Millie's clarity.

Millie has an intense focus on her complete spiritual transformation. She maintains an intense spiritual focus because of her age. She feels an immense pressure to get it done. Millie feels that there is no time to lose. Millie fears she will not have the strength to do it. It is the work of being completely open to the will of her God and having the strength to complete what she is told to do here on Earth.

EPILOGUE

(Two years later Jeanne reports.) I have begun to distance myself from Millie by seeing her less. She began to call more frequently. She would ask me to tell her what to do. She kept grasping and clinging to me to save her. I felt like, "I didn't even want to have her imagine giving me that responsibility."

Millie still calls several times a week. However, when she informed me that she had another telephone bill of $290, I realized that she is calling a lot of people. She is probably doing the same thing with all of them...asking advice about her health and asking about this doctor or that doctor or this procedure or test.

It is like a hysterical need. I don't think she listens to what I say. I don't even think she listens to what she says. I feel impatient with her.

In spite of all this, I respect Millie and feel affection for her and enjoy her. But I don't feel the equal friendship there anymore. But I'd do it all again. I learned a lot from Millie because she challenged me to develop my intuition.

DISCUSSION

SPIRITUAL EMERGENCY   Identity transformations regarding vocation, marriage, sex, and even self-definition are frequently referred to and legitimized in popular literature and media. Spiritual identity often goes unrecognized and unsupported outside of traditional religious confines. Stanislav and Christina Grof describe in their book, *Spiritual Emergency*, a certain state of emotional crisis that may emerge as a result of the turmoil of spiritual transformation. These authors view the stress that emerges from these crises as a natural part of the spiritual change process. Consequently, they do not identify the symptoms of stress and those experiencing the symptoms as pathological. The Grofs, in addition to depathologizing the spiritual growth process, call for a legitimization of support for individuals who are going through a terrifying, spiritual identity transformation process.

In any form of identity achievement, one must let go of the known as she or he reaches out for a potential, as yet unformed and unactualized alternative. It is reasonable to expect and accept that the experiential space between the known and the unknown would be fraught with doubt, uncertainty, apprehension, and even terror. Attention to or alarm at the specific signs may be of less significance than appreciation and support for the process that is underway.

One must be careful to account for all relevant data before diagnosing either psychopathology or spiritual emergency. A misdiagnosis will lead to failure to provide the appropriate and necessary interventions. Furthermore, a diagnosis in one realm of identity need not preclude a diagnosis in another.

Dual diagnosis may be appropriate as well as essential. Unfortunately for Millie, she was unable to find a mental health professional who was able to communicate with her in both the language of spiritual growth as well as psychopathology.

BIPOLAR DISORDER   The Bipolar Disorder commonly referred to as a manic-depressive disorder, is characterized by mood swings in which a person either feels expansive and high *(manic)* or constricted in deep despair *(depressive)*, with periods of normal mood in between. Unlike reactive forms of depression which result from emotional responses to life situations, Bipolar Disorders are the result of physiological changes. These physiological changes are genetic in origin.

Mood states may cycle rapidly as in Jeanne's description of Millie's moods, "changing on a dime." The expansive periods may be accompanied by restlessness or increased activity. People may become uncharacteristically talkative, have grandiose or inflated ideas about who they are, how others should treat them, and what they can accomplish. They may become irritable or belligerent. Their energy seems to go on and on. Some people who suffer from Bipolar Disorder attempt to self-medicate their manic episodes by drinking alcohol. Use of alcohol is not a cure for the manic episodes, indeed, it often creates an additional problem of alcohol dependence or abuse.

In the manic phase people who suffer from Bipolar Disorder may require little sleep. Jeanne characterized her nights spent at Millie's house as bizarre: the lights were on all night, the music was playing, and Millie was compulsively cleaning. Other symptoms involve self-destructive behaviors such as spending money in an unaffordable manner, gambling, getting involved in sexually indiscreet relationships, driving dangerously, or making poor business investments. Millie, without the stability provided by her husband, squandered the money she earned when her house was sold. She spent half of her meager pension check on phone calls seeking spiritual enlightenment. Millie also had pain problems which Jeanne believed were probably the result of her many auto accidents.

At the other extreme, the depressive episodes become so intense that functioning in normal family or work situations becomes impossible. Lethargy and long periods of sleeping are not uncommon. Millie's depression was sufficiently severe as to be accompanied by psychotic features. What Jeanne referred to as "visions" are clinically recognized as hallucinations. Millie had visual and auditory hallucinations telling her to kill herself. Millie's husband was forced to hospitalize her when her depressions involving "the great light" and "masters from the other side" drew her to suicide.

In the case of Bipolar Disorder, professional evaluation is essential in making an appropriate diagnosis. Psychopharmacological treatment is called for if an individual has several episodes of mania, depression or both in the course of a year. In addition, psychotherapy can help alter behavioral patterns which serve to trigger manic or depressive episodes. It can also help normalize the troubling feelings which result from these episodes. As with patients with any disorder, some bipolar patients are in denial with regard to their condition. Psychotherapy can assist a person to understand and accept the disorder.

Shock therapy is not a usual or customary intervention for Bipolar Disorder. Shock therapy is currently used when nothing else will work to arrest the helplessness and hopelessness that feeds suicidal thoughts and intent. The fact that Millie had shock therapy when she was hospitalized may have had to do with the depth of her depression and the lethality of her suicidal threats.

Medication is usually the treatment of choice for Bipolar Disorder. Some manic patients do not want to take medication because of the physical and psychological side effects they experience from medication. These must be carefully weighed against the benefits of the medication and the liabilities of the disorder. Others are reluctant to take medication because they enjoy the emotionally high feelings they have when they are in the manic stage. However, actions taken while in a manic state are often costly emotionally, economically, and physically to the individual, family members, and concerned others who are involved with the patient.

SECONDARY SYMPTOMS Accidents create immediate pain as a result of physical injury. Residual pain may continue long after the physical damage heals. This pain may be the result of psychological variables such as unresolved feelings of fear, anger, or guilt.

Sometimes accidents just happen. Sometimes accidents are caused by negligence. In the latter case, accidents may provide diagnostic information. Sometimes an individual's personality and behavioral style may have a causal relationship with regard to an accident. In these cases, the pains that people have as a result of their accidents are secondary symptoms to some primary personality issue.

Millie, an elderly woman whose vision, reaction time, and judgment are becoming less and less reliable, is still driving 85 miles per hour in a 45 mile per hour zone. Millie very likely drives fast during manic episodes. This psychobiological imbalance has either not been diagnosed, or if it has, is being denied by Millie. As a result, she does not take medication which might stabilize her extreme mood swings. By failing to address her manic episodes, she further endangers her health and well-being and that of others.

PAIN Pain is a message sent by the body in its wisdom to inform us that we have been injured. If we listen to the wisdom then we can minister to our wound. Perhaps we need to be protected from further insult: cleansed, closed, bandaged, or rested. Whatever the appropriate intervention, something needs to be done to tend to the injury.

Those who are familiar with hypnosis know that experiencing pain is unnecessary even for those who are physically wounded. However, this is only true if one is listening to the body's wisdom and taking appropriate action to care for the wound or the situation that caused the injury. Otherwise, the pain returns or even intensifies.

Even when pain is due to somatitization, the body is sending a message that something is awry and needs attention. In the case of somatitization, the physical pain is secondary to the holding-in or denying of some primary psychological issue. This makes understandable a client who shops for health care professionals, "whines" and complains, but is not psychologically available or willing to "listen to what" is said to them. This pattern is observed as Millie moves out of "sync" with her bodyworker in an attempt to free herself of tension. These movements only thwart her bodyworker's efforts and tighten Millie's muscles. This is a client, who for psychological reasons, cannot and should not be pushed to let go of her muscular holding patterns. Jeanne was wise to recognize, "I don't try to fix her. I saw right away that I couldn't."

Some people may choose to ignore their body's wisdom. These are usually people with forceful personalities, perfectionists *(those who drive themselves to perfection)*, those in denial, or those who lack sufficient self-esteem. These people may fail to listen to their body's wisdom and ignore the message of the pain in order to achieve some hidden goal. Major life-style changes are often called for from these people in order to ameliorate their pain. Such changes, however, may be beyond what they are willing or able to contemplate or undertake. Consequently, they may opt unconsciously to maintain their pain. They often seek simple medical or mechanical solutions to complex psychophysical situations. They may seek the aid of a bodyworker to do something to fix the pain. Through this external focus they deny their own responsibility in the etiology and the resolution of their pain problem.

Millie has not learned from her many auto accidents that she drives at dangerous speeds. She is willing to spend hundreds of dollars that she does not have searching for spiritual answers to her pain problems. She is denying and avoiding the truth: there is something in addition to spiritual uncertainty that she must confront. If she had appropriate medication she might drive slower and feel calmer. Millie might be able to relax her muscles more with her mania under control. She might also release some of her pain, as well as preventing further injury to her body. Millie could get on with achieving her life mission if she were not so preoccupied with and deflected by her secondary symptoms, her pain.

To achieve more comfort in her life, Millie must travel a course that may be wounding to her ego, pride or sense of feeling exhilarated. She may have to admit that there is something wrong with her that neither meditation nor bodywork alone will heal. Millie may have to acknowledge that she suffers from a disorder or disorders which can interfere with her judgment and reasoning. As a result of her disorder and her denial of that disorder, common sense, logic or volitional control of her actions, at times, may not be available to her.

In the past Millie felt hurt by the medical establishment as it attempted to minister to her problem. Then as now, Millie may not have been prepared to deal with what she was told or advised. She may not be sufficiently strong or skilled to accept the truth of her condition and to follow through with its implications. Until she is, she will remain locked into a life style that precipitates and perpetuates her pain. In the meantime, while she continues on her spiritual quest, Millie has the support of a gentle, caring, patient bodyworker who realizes that she must actively work to maintain her own limits.

ALZHEIMER'S DISEASE   Sometimes emotional disorders go into remission or dissipate. This is particularly true when there is a change in life circumstances that may have contributed to or caused the distress. A person can transcend emotional distress if she or he receives additional support in the form of meaningful activity, financial gain, emotional recognition, understanding, resolution of conflicts, or psychopharmacology. If there is no change in the source of distress, and if appropriate support is not forthcoming, emotional conditions tend to worsen with time and life circumstances rather than remaining the same or getting better. In addition, if there is a degenerating neurological problem, then symptoms are exacerbated. Jeanne recognized that Millie has been getting worse.

We know nothing of Millie's husband, however, Millie's emotional stability was already compromised while he was alive. His death may likely have been a blow to her stability. If she responded to that loss the way she responded to her Bipolar Disorder, she probably had functional or reactive depression as a result of internalized, unresolved grief. She may also have had other unresolved issues confront her such as dependency, loneliness, or fears of aging and having to manage alone. And, the physiological issues of aging may have compromised her condition. Jeanne comments on the physical status of her 70 year old client, saying that she is in "robust health." While her physical health was "robust," Millie's mental health was already in the process of progressive decline. Jeanne notes that Millie had word finding problems as she tried to describe a book she had just read. Word finding problems may be indicative of mental degeneration.

In addition, to her Bipolar Disorder, this aging senior may be suffering from Alzheimer's disease.[1] Alzheimer's disease is a degenerative cognitive disorder. This disorder would make Millie's ability to perform cognitive reasoning or thinking and speaking more and more difficult. In Alzheimer's disease, judgments become impaired as the intellectually declining individual begins to lose a sense of control or begins to overcompensate for a loss of independence by becoming overly controlling.

More than to obtain opinions or information, Millie's constant telephone calling may have been her attempt to assuage her anxiety about being alone and losing a familiar sense of her own body and its functioning. Millie's calls may have been a desperate attempt to hold on to a sense of reality that was slowly slipping away.

Millie's wakefulness so early in the morning and her inability to reason that such an early call is disconcerting as well as disrupting for a working person, might have been a function of her mania; it might also have been a function of Alzheimer's disease.

OUT OF SYNC Jeanne recognized from the very start that Millie would be a demanding challenge. Millie's movements were out of sync with her stated intentions. She was attempting "to raise her energy" by turning, rolling, and wiggling. Her independent movements were actually achieving the opposite of what she wanted. Millie was tightening her muscles and bottling up her energy by thwarting Jean's interventions.

Millie was a difficult client with whom to work. She was demanding and oppositional. Ultimately, Millie's behavior served to gain attention and to develop and maintain dependency. Jeanne patiently accepted this trait in Millie. She also recognized that Millie was a health care shopper. She went from one type of health care provider to another looking for a cure. Jeanne became the last of a chain of health care providers at the time Millie was introduced to her.

The issues of old age and death are sufficiently anxiety-provoking that many of us suppress or deny them. This lends to a lack of management or crisis management in responding to these issues. Preparation for old age must begin when an individual is sufficiently flexible and motivated, certainly long before senility begins or the ravages of Alzheimer's take over. Once the disease begins to incapacitate a person, others must provide assistance in order that appropriate care is provided.

When working with a client as emotionally, physically, and socially draining as Millie, it is essential to establish internal and external support as early on as possible. Internal support would be represented by limits and expectations that Jeanne had for herself in working with this client. External supports would come in the form of consultation with other health professionals that might be involved such as a physician, psychologist, and/or community social worker.

This support might have reduced the amount of strain Jeanne experienced with her client. External supports would have eased Jeanne's discomfort of not wanting her client "to imagine giving me the responsibility" for Millie's life decisions. It might have allowed Jeanne to take a broader perspective in treating a long term client with a degenerative condition. At some point it would have allowed Millie to make a gradual transition rather than suffering the abrupt loss of a long term dependent relationship with her bodyworker and friend. When the demands became too great, there would have been others already in place to whom responsibility could have been transferred. If Jeanne had been more knowledgeable of Millie's psychological and physical condition early on, she might have made different decisions about how to manage her client. Jeanne might have set different limits on the relationship so that it was not such a great "drain on her resources."

SUMMARY

From the very beginning, Jeanne experienced and was aware that Millie had begun to cling to her. Millie either believed, wanted to believe, or merely expressed her confidence, that Jeanne "had the skills to permanently get her through this blocked condition." Jeanne was honest with herself as well as with Millie regarding this issue. She knew that she did not have whatever Millie wanted for a permanent cure. Nevertheless, it was a constant tug on Jeanne's energy resources to maintain her truth and clarity with her demanding elderly client. Millie may have been unwilling or unable to hear or accept Jeanne's position. Jeanne could not save Millie; she was willing to provide her skills and concern to help support her. In doing so, she maintained her own clarity.

Taking Millie on as a client was never an issue of economics for Jeanne. Jeanne genuinely liked Millie, learned from her, and developed a keener sense of perceptiveness and intuition from their interaction. Both women shared of themselves and their skills and provided support for each other. Jeanne derived a sense of achievement and satisfaction from the relationship. Even as the relationship became more distant, Jeanne reported, "I respect Millie and feel affection for her and enjoy her."

Ultimately, Jeanne chose to distance herself from Millie because she could not maintain herself in a relationship with her client's unrelenting, unrealistic expectations. Millie's deterioration slowly eroded the basic mutual respect that was essential to the integrity of her relationship with her friend and bodyworker. Her manipulative, demanding calls sounded the death knell to the quality of her contact with Jeanne. Though it may have been unintentional or even unconscious, after ten years, Millie's abrogation of responsibility for her own life and transference of the expectation of that responsibility onto her bodyworker, simply became too much for Jeanne to manage. Jeanne admitted that she eventually became "impatient" with her client. Still, Jeanne's ability to maintain herself as a support for Millie as long as she did was admirable. On-going support for a woman as troubled and demanding as Millie may be best achieved by a mutually, supportive, interdisciplinary team of which a bodyworker and friend like Jeanne would be a special member.

END NOTES

[1] **Alzheimer's Disease** Alzheimer's disease is a disease of progressive degeneration. One in twelve over the age sixty-five are stricken and suffer from the debilitating effects of degenerating brain cells. It leaves some of its ravaged victims mute, wheelchair-bound or bed-ridden, and totally dependent on others for custodial care. The slow degenerative process of cerebral destruction makes it impossible for the victims to recognize or understand what is happening to them.

When working with someone who suffers from Alzheimer's disease, it is helpful to understand what that person is experiencing. Neural degeneration renders them unable to have volitional control of their behavior. If one can recognize and appreciate this fact about these elderly people, the reactive frustration and impatience that may be elicited by some of their symptomatic behavior can be reduced.

With Alzheimer's disease decreased reasoning contributes to poor judgments. Confusion intensifies if perceptions from memories become indistinguishable from direct sensation or from dreams. Furthermore, with Alzheimer's disease there are increasing problems with adaptability, isolations, and dependency. There are problems which make old relationships more fragile and new ones difficult if not impossible to form. Memory problems encompass issues such as losing pension checks, the way home, recognition of friends, and family members, recollection of how familiar items work such as keys in locks or bath tub plumbing, and language. Another loss that occurs with Alzheimer's disease may the ability to tell time or to recognize the time of day. As a result, such a mentally declining senior suffering from "sun downers" may be unable to distinguish 7 A.M. from 7 P.M.

12

EXTRA BUCKS

Linda is in her mid-thirties. She is a soft-spoken massage therapist and nurse.

It was during the summertime about midday. I had just finished a client. And I was just getting ready to walk out...'cause I didn't have any more clients. I was working in an office in a condominium. I was sharing the office with two other people. There were several rooms and about eight or nine of us working in the building. But at the time, no one else was there. I was the only one in the building when this mid-fortyish man showed up.

I asked him if he needed help. I wanted to know how he ended up at the building. His thoughts didn't seem to flow well. I couldn't figure out what he was trying to say. Then I didn't want to pursue it. He was real ambivalent and indecisive. He said he wanted a massage. Then he said he didn't want a massage. His thoughts were jerky. He wasn't totally coherent. He was preoccupied...kind of depressed. It was hard to follow his thoughts.

He asked how much I charged. Then asked, "Are you available?" I said, "Yes." But actually, I was thinking, "I want to go home. I am done with my clients. I'll just go home." But, it was fifty-fifty. I want to go home, or I'll go ahead and give him a massage. I had him fill out a medical release sheet...it has name, address, phone number, and physical history questions. But there was something odd about him. I don't know if he was missing teeth, but there was something about his mouth that looked like it needed some attention. He was very...almost skinny...very...almost unkempt looking. Something not real...he didn't look dirty, but there was a messy look to him. His speech was quick and abrupt.

I thought, "Well, it's another massage. I can certainly use the extra bucks. I'll go ahead and do it." But my intuition said, "Why don't you just go home?" But anyway, I went ahead and massaged him. He talked about Hitler the whole time. He seemed to be well read on Hitler. His information was fascinating.

Then it came time for him to go. He got off the table and got dressed. He had to pay me. He kept shuffling all of his money. All these bills were all crumpled. They were crumpled in his pocket. He kept shuffling them. Finally, he handed me a wad of bills. I didn't look, and said, "Fine." After he left, I opened my hand and...I forget...I think there were several ones...there was like five dollars or something.

Number one, I didn't check the money that he gave me when he was standing in front of me. In the past my clients were real up front and I just, made that assumption...I made the assumption that he was going to pay me the appropriate amount. But I also know my regular clients real well.

Then, my intuition...I need to trust it more. 'Cause my intuition was, "Na, this doesn't feel right." When he was filling out the form, he was having trouble with it. There just was something not right about this man. I was wondering if he couldn't write or read or something. That was my first thought. 'Cause he was being real funny about it. But I think in the long run he was putting phony addresses and things like that. There were just a lot of little tiny cues I saw and needed to be listening to it. He was real nervous.

I got the medical history form that I had him fill out and attempted to call him up. But according to the operator there was no such number. So I took the medical sheet and put it on the bulletin board. I wrote on it, "This man came in and did not pay." I posted it for every therapist to see.

I just...I think if I don't know 'em, I'll have them pay up front. If I don't know the client, if they just show up, I'll say, "Well, up front." It really makes me skeptical.

I really like to get referrals...people that are referrals would be great. And it works the other way, too. The client is more comfortable with the referral of a therapist, too.

I probably will advertise in the future. I'm thinking about it. My office mate would never advertise because she said she was too chicken shit to do that. She has a real extreme fear of who will show up. I am probably the other way. I probably need more of a fear.

(Then with a sense of urgency) But I want to tell you how I got into massage. I was trying to pass a state exam to get into nursing.

I took the test several times, but I kept failing it. That was exceedingly frustrating. I'm a college graduate!

Well, I then got this thought in my head that I would do massage. Where the thought came from, I don't know. But it kept coming to me. But I was too embarrassed to tell anyone because people would not think massage was an up and up profession. I told a friend and she said, "Why don't you just explore it. That is not going to hurt anything. Just explore it!" And I said, "She's right."

So, I got into massage school. And I got home one day, and I was jumping on one of those little trampolines, and my ankle folded under me and I slammed down to the ground. I had this huge...my ankle swelled up really, really, large. I went to bed that night. When I woke up in the morning tears just started streaming down my face. And I had a severe whiplash. I couldn't even get out of bed, it was so bad.

So things just went by and I didn't see anyone about this. It just kind of went by. And I was in massage school at the time. I was going to massage school and trying to get my nursing career going, and I asked the instructor if he could work on my neck.

At this point, with the nursing thing, I decided, "Forget it! It's not working, Linda." But I had already signed up for the test. So, I said, "I signed up for the test. I am not going to study. I am going to go in cold. I'm going to take the test. If I fail, that's it. The door is closed. So I signed up and I was just waiting for that day to roll around.

So, I went to massage school and said to my instructor, "Please, if there is anything that you can do about my neck, I'd be grateful. So, he worked on me. His touch was soft, slow, thoughtful, and deliberate. I respected his work and trusted him.

(Linda breaks with her train of thought.) I go back in the reels of my memory. There was no love in my house as a child. I can't remember my father touching me except to hit me. My dad would hit me and lock me in my room. I was constantly afraid of death. I really wanted to be with him and connect with him. But it was an impossible task. I can't remember my mother touching either—except violently.

(Then Linda continued with her story.) I started crying in the middle of this work. I mean a very, deep, deep, soul cry. And the feeling that came out was that I'm a failure. I failed again! Logically I said, "Well, the door is closed. Just choose something else." But the feeling was I'm a failure. I cannot pass the nursing exam. It was a deep, deep wound. As soon as he was finished working on me my neck was fine.

And, to make a long story short. I ended up taking the nursing exam, and I passed it. When I gave up on it, I passed it! I had a justified injury. But when I dealt with some feelings, the injury disappeared. Upon experiencing this I said, "This is something I need to commit myself to on a personal level. The healing that happened within myself was aided by his physical touch. If my touch could help in that same way then I want to provide it to others." So that's how I got into massage.

DISCUSSION

THE ONLY ONE   That summer day Linda was "the only one" in the office when a "strange" man showed up and asked for a massage. There is always a possibility of danger working with unknown people. However, a person can make her or his work environment safer by having a policy of working with other associates present. It is particularly important when working with a new client, and this would have been a prudent policy for Linda to have had in effect when a man that "just wasn't right" presented himself.

SCHIZOPHRENIA   Linda made a number of astute and distressing observations about her unexpected walk-in.[1] There was something wrong with the man's mouth that needed attention. He was unkempt and messy looking. His speech was peculiar. He had difficulty filling out the medical form. Linda recognized this man suffered from anxiety, "He was real nervous." Linda knew, "There just wasn't something right about this man."

Linda noted many times that her client had problems with his concentration and the articulation of his thoughts. "It was hard to follow his thoughts." His thought process was "jerky." "They didn't flow well." This man seemed to have difficulty in coordinating his thoughts and his speech. Linda, without knowing what it was, recognized that her client was suffering from a thought disorder. His disjointed speech jerked from one uncompleted idea to another unrelated idea. This type of miscoordination of thought and speech is indicative of schizophrenia.

Linda's client, for all of the difficulty he may have been having with his thoughts, personal hygiene, functional organization, may not have been in the active phase of his disorder. He was, in all probability, suffering from a later residual phase. In this phase symptoms are less severe and less disabling. Though, they still contribute to significant impairment in functioning.

PARANOIA   Throughout his massage, Linda's client talked about Hitler. This peculiar man was preoccupied by and obsessed with the disenfranchised painter turned dictator and mass murderer. Linda was impressed by his being "well read." She was not alarmed by this man's morbid preoccupation nor did she report anything that was physically dangerous or threatening about him. Nevertheless, the more contact she had with him, the more she knew that there was something abnormal about him.

Linda's description of her client's ambivalence over whether or not to receive a massage and his preoccupation with Hitler suggests that in addition to the schizophrenic disorder, he may have also suffered from a paranoid condition. Paranoia[2] results from intense insecurity or lack of trust and is also characterized by holding irrational beliefs.

INTUITION   Linda has an inner wisdom. But, she does not give due value and respect for her intuitive wisdom. She felt finished after a morning's work and was ready to quit for the day. Linda's personal value was to go home after her last client. She would have been taking care of herself. But, Linda talked herself out of her self-nurturing intuition.

Linda also talked herself out of her self-protective wisdom. She recognized on an intuitive level that there was something very peculiar and wrong with her prospective client. Her intuition had an intrinsically self-protective element to it. Again, she talked herself out of this wisdom and into doing another massage on a potentially problematic client for a couple of extra bucks. Linda's choices were puzzling.

BLIND-SIDED   Perhaps Linda does not listen to her wisdom because during her family life she learned to numb her fear and pain. Linda suffered from trauma in her earlier life at the hands of abusive parents. This trauma left her preoccupied with death anxiety. Perhaps, in order to survive her overpowering anxiety, Linda learned to numb all of her feelings. As she became more and more psychologically defended and unaware of her feelings, the messages of fright, alarm, and danger were not perceived.

Unfortunately, the psychological protection Linda created in her childhood and adolescence to cope with her abusive parents left her psychologically blind to a potentially dangerous situation in her adulthood. Fortunately this vestige of growing up in an abusive home is reversible. Reversal occurs as part of the process of working through the psychological scars of childhood abuse.

QUESTIONS INTO STATEMENTS: A PROBLEM-SOLVING STRATEGY   To undo her psychological blind-sidedness, a problem solving strategy that Linda may find helpful in the future is to turn her questions into statements. These statements may point to clear paths that she could then choose. If Linda were to simply make a statement out of her question, "Why don't you just go home?" her intuitive statement would have told her, "Just go home!" If she had listened to her intuition, she would have done what she needed to do to take care of herself. Her intuition had a number of other messages that would help her achieve a successful practice. Linda explains that the kind of practice she and her clients would feel most comfortable with is one which builds up by word of mouth. She wisely tells herself to attend to and give credence to the little cues she picks up, but is unaware of the contradiction when she toys with the idea of advertising.

BUSINESS DIALOGUE: A PROBLEM-SOLVING STRATEGY Business decisions are based not merely upon making a buck, but also out of a sense of vision. "What does one want her or his practice to look like?" "What kind of client do I want to attract to provide myself with a sense of meaning and fulfillment?"

If Linda had dialogued with an internal "business manager," she might have said: "I have an opportunity to work with an extra client this summer's day. This will be an opportunity to make some extra bucks. But this man looks like a vagrant. He is odd, messy, unkempt, shifty, and nervous. He may be dishonest and he may leave me feeling skeptical about the world. Should I take him on?" What would her internal business manager reply?

FIRM, HONEST, AND GENTLE: A PROBLEM-SOLVING STRATEGY If Linda had told this man what she charged for a session and then had informed him that he would have to schedule an appointment in advance when other colleagues would have been present to provide her with protection, he probably would not have followed through. If she asked him to call to confirm that appointment time, the chances of his following through would be nil. Under these circumstances, if he arrived for the appointment, he would have probably brought the agreed-upon fee and Linda would have been safer working with him.

It is always important when working with people who have bruised or damaged ego structures to be honest and firm. Such a person may have no idea, or at best be confused, about policies and limits if they are not clearly and firmly stated. This man, who kept crumpled-up dollar bills in his pocket, already had problems maintaining a clear sense of organization.

Just because a person is clear and firm, however, does not mean that she or he has to threaten or intimidate another's integrity. When working with a person who has a fragile ego structure, it is particularly important not to add to the damage that has already been done. Firmness and honesty can be tempered with gentleness and understanding.

"UP AND UP" PROFESSION   Linda looks to others to provide her with confirmation for her vocational interests. This woman, who came from a home where touch took the form of violent physical contact, might have mistrusted any understanding, support, or confirmation from family members. This mistrust would likely be generalized to others. Fortunately, Linda shared her vocational interest with a trusted and supportive friend.

There may be a dark side to every profession. Some business people defraud clients. Some surgeons perform unnecessary procedures. Some accountants embezzle money. Some lawyers exacerbate conflicts for their own power or financial gain. These are insufficient reasons to not enter these professions if one desires to do so. The dark side of any profession is the dark side of humankind. Professional integrity is derived from maintaining both professional standards and personal integrity. There is no reason for Linda to believe that she is not in an "up and up" profession when her labors ease clients' stress, add to their sense of well being, improve blood circulation, aid resolution of trauma and injury, improve posture, and promote health.

TEST ANXIETY   Linda was bright enough to pass her state nursing exam. She had already graduated from her college nursing program. She was capable of achieving complex intellectual tasks. Her anxiety, or fear of failure, was so intense that she was unable to perform in a manner that was consistent with her abilities. Test anxiety often causes students to be unable to retrieve the information stored in their memories.

As with any kind of anxiety, there are two strategies for reducing test anxiety. The first is to reduce the level of stress one is experiencing. The second is to increase the amount of support one has. Linda reduced her stress when she took the pressure off herself to pass the nursing exam by simply deciding to take her exam "cold" and close that door if she failed. She further reduced her stress by asking her massage teacher to work on her neck. By mechanically reducing the physical tension of her shoulder and neck muscles, Linda simultaneously reduced her psychological tension. Receiving the support of the "trustworthy, gentle, and thoughtful" hands of her instructor, Linda was able to have an emotional catharsis. She released the emotional pressure of self-doubt about being a failure.

Linda no longer had a sense of anxiety about passing the nursing exam because she had the back up of an alternate career in bodywork. In addition, Linda increased her amount of internal support by getting involved in massage and feeling good about herself, her new skills and abilities. And she passed her exam!

SUMMARY

A disheveled, preoccupied, depressed man showed up at Linda's office at a time when she was alone. She was about to leave, but decided that she would stay and work on one more client for some extra bucks. Linda's intuition told her there was something wrong with this man, but she chose not to listen to her inner wisdom. This bright woman left herself vulnerable to a possibly dangerous encounter with an emotionally disturbed man. While Linda may have been troubled by her encounter with this client who cheated her out of her fee, she did not struggle over her decision-making or policy-setting as a result of it.

Linda is the product of an abusive home. She was both physically abused and psychologically under-supported by her parents. Children cannot experience the basic feelings of being okay, lovable, and worthy of protection if they do not receive these messages from their parents. Instead, these children are likely to treat themselves the way they were treated by their parental role models. Once one appreciates this, it is understandable why Linda did not trust her intuition and consequently placed herself in a vulnerable situation with a peculiar new client.

This first troubling story that Linda told was not ultimately the story that she wanted to tell. Linda felt compelled to share the story about how she decided to get into bodywork. It is a story of ambivalence, frustration, physical pain, and a sense of a failure. In spite of Linda's basic self-doubt, she created a lifestyle for herself that was based upon discovery, acceptance, actualization, and desire to help others.

This second story is the account of an important discovery Linda made after a mini-trampoline accident and the bodywork that she received from her massage instructor. Linda recognized the relationship between physical injury, bodywork, and emotional liberation. She related how she went to her massage instructor with a sore neck. She related her experience of his soft, slow, thoughtful, deliberate, healing touch. This touch provided the safety to trigger Linda's affective discharge. She cried "a very deep, deep, soul cry" expressing and airing internalized feelings of being a failure. Much to her surprise, these released feelings accompanied a release in her neck pain. The combination of Linda's instructor's healing touch, her catharsis of troubling feelings, and her experience of a release of neck pain led her to a life-altering recognition. This recognition had such an impact that Linda decided to continue to pursue a bodywork career in spite of the fact that she passed her nursing exam. Linda made a personal commitment to contribute to the same "healing" process in others that she experienced herself.

END NOTES

1 **Schizophrenia** The Longman Dictionary of Psychology and Psychiatry briefly describes "Schizophrenic Disorder" as "a group of mental disturbances essentially characterized by: a) one or more psychotic features during the active phase, including bizarre or absurd delusions..., b) somatic, grandiose, religious, or nihilistic delusions, c) delusions of persecution or jealousy with hallucinations, d) incoherence with marked loosening of association, illogical thought, or poverty of speech together with either blunted, flat, or inappropriate affect, e) delusions or hallucinations, or g) gross disorganized behavior... Other common characteristics are deterioration from a previous level of job, social, or self-care-functioning, and onset before 45, with duration of at least six months."

The cause or causes of Schizophrenia have not been definitively identified to date. In addition, there are no known cures for it. To treat this disorder, major tranquilizers are prescribed by psychiatrists to help buffer the symptoms of schizophrenia. Psychopharmacology and supportive psychotherapy may assist individuals and family members to both understand and manage this condition, as well as to deal with the feelings that they have as a result of it.

2 **Paranoia** Illogical beliefs are maintained in spite of evidence to the contrary. This belief system may also provide a person with secondary gain. It may offer emotional support or comfort explaining away failure or absolving guilt. A result of these delusions is an increase in a person's feelings of inferiority. People who are not trustworthy may project their own dishonesty onto others, creating their own insecurity or paranoia.

In intense forms of paranoia, an individual may feel so insecure that neutral statements or actions may be misinterpreted as attacks on her or his integrity or even her or his very life. In order to protect herself or himself from such a perceived assault some paranoid individuals can become explosively enraged and violent.

Part **IV**

HELPING

13

SIGNING UP TO GET FIRED

Vickie has been a licensed massage therapist for eight years. She speaks forcefully and rapidly.

My dad was really sick and I was around medical care a lot...and, I wanted to be involved in the medical field, but I didn't want to wait until people were sick. I went to school at 18 and hated it, and I quit. So, I worked in nursing homes for a couple of years just to get that experience. And, then, I did house cleaning to put myself through massage school. There are more reasons than that. I also didn't know what else to do, and because when I would massage people they would say, "God you are really good at this. You should get into school for this." And it was a way that I could do something to make money at and be independent, and I was good at it.

I grapple with who I am professionally all the time on all levels. I grapple with it intellectually, emotionally, and physically. Physically there is always a push in the massage therapy field professionally within organizations. People within organizations want more power. They want to do things that we are not allowed to do by law. They are constantly trying to push the boundaries. I don't think we are suited to do that. Some people want to do ultra sound. They want to do...one of the big things that I don't want to have anything to do with is internal work—vaginally, rectally, or orally. I just think that we are not trained enough to do that. Even if you are trained to do the technique and do it correctly, I still think that emotionally, we are not prepared to deal with what could come up for the person, or what could come up for ourselves. So, there are physical limits that I tend to be very conservative about, and don't want to push the limits of massage beyond certain physical limits of what we are capable of doing.

But, there is a real conflict because I feel I am not being supportive of my colleagues who feel that they can do that and want to have that power to do it. And it is a really strong conflict within me to not...I don't want to push to have legislation that allows us to do that. And, personally I feel that I just won't do it. And I also wonder about whether they should be doing it. But I also trust them...and I think that they should be able to make decisions on their own about that. And it is a very big conflict. About where to put myself politically? What should I say when they write me letters and want me to write to my congressmen. It is a very big problem. How can I support them and support the profession and maintain my own integrity as to what the limits should be? So, that physical boundary is a very big issue.

Another boundary deals with emotional boundaries. Because what I am hearing a lot from the professional massage therapists and their associations, is that I am not supposed to be able to facilitate people's emotional releases. In an article from one of the associations I think they said something like, "Don't ask probing questions." I don't remember how they put it. But I think they put it something like that. "The practitioner does not probe for emotional or sexual information from the client, and the practitioner does not diagnose the client's emotional health or abuse status." Well it makes sense for us not to diagnose. But, as far as "...not probing," what do they mean by that? It's very unclear.

It makes sense to me, if someone is so tense that they can hardly lie there and have me touch them...it makes sense for me to start asking questions and ask what is going on...It's not that I am trying to do therapy. I am not trying to be a therapist. But, in order for me to make contact with this person and be real with them, I feel like I need to be able to talk to them. And I can't have my intuitive ability or my ability to be with people cut off because I am not licensed to do therapy. It is very confusing.

The conflict comes up with working with people on the table...always. Because I grew up talking with people, and people would tell me everything. I just developed this counselor-like ability. Out of my natural ability to do it. It is not something that I am trained to do. But the reality is when I ask people questions, I usually target at the right point and they often have things come up. And I often get confused. It's like, *(clearing her throat and again speaking quickly and forcefully)* I know that I am not licensed to be a therapist, and I am not trying to be a therapist. But my natural self would just say, "Ya know, what's going on here?" Or, "Do you want to talk about that more?"

I have a policy of telling people that I am not a therapist, and that I am absolutely not trying to do therapy. And you know, that is not what I am trying to do. And also, if people do not want to talk about things, I am not going to push it. But as to what I am going to do day by day, massage by massage, uh, uh, I don't have a specific policy because I haven't found anything that made sense to me to say rationally. "This is the policy." Except to give the client the ability to say, "Yes" or "No." I am always wrestling with this because every time I come up against it, I wonder if I am like doing something illegal. Am I trying to…I feel like morally I am doing the right thing.

This whole profession is not clear cut. People are struggling all over the place with the boundaries. And, ya know, I mean you'll run into it. You'll find massage therapists and bodywork practitioners who do psychotherapy while they work with people and some of them are trained and some of them are not trained.

As a client, what I find sometimes when I am getting a massage, the massage therapist has no ability to facilitate my process. And that is very frustrating to me as a client, because I can't get worked on without needing to do that stuff unless I just zone out. And that is not productive for me as a client. Mixing therapy with massage is not different for me basically than just therapy.

I'm not a therapist, but what I am trained to do very well is to do a certain kind of peer counseling. What is confusing for me is how…if, if, I should use that when I practice massage. Because what often comes up, is that I'll be massaging somebody, and they'll just start telling me about an issue and I know how to facilitate…not facilitate, that word is confusing because I don't think I am using it properly…what I know how to do, is talk to the person so they really get to the nitty-gritty of the subject, rather than, just skating on the surface of the subject. And so the dilemma I come up with is, "Is now the right time to invite them to really deal with it and not just skate on the surface of it?" Because they have probably been skating on the surface of it with people for years and years, and they are just waiting for someone to say, "It's O.K. for you to deal with that." "I'm not going to cringe." "I won't stop loving you." "It is O.K. for you to talk about that and tell me just how you feel about it."

Referral is easy when it is physical. I mean, I am real conservative about physical stuff. If I see something in a person that I am not comfortable with I say, "Go to a doctor." Psychotherapy, I refer when I sense that the person isn't going to trust me to the point where they can deal with it and they don't look like…they don't look like they have a lot of skills for dealing with it anyway. *(Chuckle)* And, I think that they really need one-on-one. "That's all we are going to do now," kind of work—and give them names and numbers. I guess, I do it based upon how much skill they have. And if they can take charge of dealing with it with me, ya know, then I don't think it is necessary, but if...it's not necessary for me to decide for them at that point. But if I really sense that they are not getting anywhere with me, and it doesn't look like they are dealing with it anyplace else, then I do some adjusting.

Let me tell you about the other limits. Spiritually, I have a real problem sometimes wondering whether or not I should encourage people to...ya know...whether I should talk about spirit stuff at all, and maybe, just letting go and trusting and stuff like that. But, I do, if I know that someone has this real strong, spiritual background and they are involved in organized religion, I'll use anything I know about that to encourage them to rely on that to relax. I don't remember an exact...I remember doing that. But, I don't know who it was or what I did. I mean just...I don't have a specific memory of who it was, but I specifically remember saying, "Just give it up to God. Just pray to God." Ya know, it was just like, I don't know what they were telling me about or what I was doing, but it just felt like, "Just give it up." *(Laughter)* I don't know. I don't remember...I just remember having made the decision that I would just say it. Ya know, that I would just say it. I think I made mistakes with that before.

I've said things to people that kind of blew them away. *(Subdued laugh)* Like, I think I said something to a feminist woman. She was talking to me about...I mean, I talk with people when I massage them. I am real verbal. It's part of who I am. She was saying something about religion or God or something about her background. And, I just told her what I thought about Jesus and Christianity. Which was, I was brought up Christian and I realized one day that...even though I am a woman and I am supposed to believe in a Goddess and all that...that inside of me the image of God is this man on a throne with a white beard. And, I just decided when I pray, I'm just going to pray to Jesus and that's okay. But, she didn't come back *(laughter)* and I think that was because I wasn't feminist enough. So there is that stuff. But that's really verbal. That really isn't about massage. But it is. It is about my practice.

I've been more cautious. *(Full laughter)* Ya! It always effects me when people have really strong reactions and don't...I mean, I can tell. It's like when the wall goes up. I can feel it. Ya know, sure, I don't think it makes sense to turn people off.

Sometimes, ya know, I am not bound to have just a client relationship with somebody. Like, psychotherapists are not supposed to socialize with their clients. Well, there aren't any ethics in my profession that tell me that I can't be friends with my clients. There are sexual ethics. I can't be having sex with my clients. But nobody is saying that I can't be their friend. So, a lot of times because of how open people feel with me…and they feel very close to me…they want to hang out with me. And that's okay with me. I'll hang out with people and even do emotional work on each other on a peer basis. And that hasn't worked in a couple of instances. Because, what happens generally is that people see me as this kind of perfect person because I am so…present when they are in my massage room. Then, when we try to have a normal relationship, they can freak out because I am not a perfect person.

I got dumped a couple of times, because…they don't come back for massages. They are not my friend any more. And I felt really abandoned. So that definitely changed the way I deal with that stuff. If I enter into any kind of relationship with somebody other than massage and they started as a client, I tell them right off the bat, "We'll have to work on this. If you want to be my friend and we want to have lunch together and we want to do stuff…we'll have to talk about this stuff. Up front I…what I say to people is, "This could be a problem," and I just put it out there. And what I also say to them is, "We will trade time as friends." I mean, I really specifically say that. "When you come into my room and pay me to give you a massage, I'm here for you. And, I will massage you and pay attention to you. But, if we are going to have a relationship outside of here, and we are going to be friends, I will have time to deal with my stuff too."

In the past I trusted this person more than their capacity to work with my stuff. Ya know…it was just…I changed my policy. It's an unwritten one. I've been taking it very slowly. So far, it has been working. But I haven't jumped into anything as deep as I jumped in with that client who just decided that I was a bad person.

She just cut the relationship off because I became the bad person who hurt her in the past. I am assuming that's true. This is a woman who is older than myself. It is because of this relationship…because of the relationship in here *(nodding toward her massage room)* where I was the authority. It had nothing to do with me. *(Laugher)* It was definitely the role. But it happened big time. And I think the biggest frustration I have with that is that *(clearing throat)* she just backed out and gave me nothing. Ya know, she just cut out of the relationship. She just left. And that seems totally unfair to me. I didn't sign up to get fired as a therapist! Because, I wasn't trying to be her therapist.

I guess I can see how that happens in therapy where the therapist basically agrees on some level to be that surrogate authority figure…so that the client can deal with that stuff. But, I didn't sign up for that. Ya know? From day one, I didn't say I was signing up for that. So that essentially...when she fired me, I wasn't in a role to be fired! She did to me what people do to therapists. And I know. I know because I did it to my shrink. I understand it. But, I didn't sign up for the role. So, that was really frustrating. I mean, not that I even think that that should happen to therapists.

I think, partly the reason that does happen, is because people who get into positions of leadership take all of the hurts from the people from our past and our parental figures into our profession, and we, on some level act like more of an authority than we are. And it invites people to dump that stuff on us because we don't come across as just being a peer.

Somehow anyone who gets into any kind of position of leadership, whether it is being a mother, or being a boss, or being at the checkout counter, anyone who is in charge, takes on some of the patterns of abuse that they have been abused by authority figures in their past. So on that level they are playing the part of getting all of that junk dumped on them. I'm totally convinced of this. So, for me, for my part, the more I clean up my stuff of leadership and how I am with the stuff of leadership in my life , I think the less I will be vulnerable to having people transfer that stuff onto me. I just think I will play less of a part in that. One way to not get so hooked into that whole system is to get the hooks out of yourself about leadership.

And, the other thing is, I know, I've been trying to be the perfect person in here. I tell people my stuff. I mean, I don't try to be a hundred percent there any more. It's made a dilemma where I am like the wonderful person who is there for them all the time, but they can't be there for me, and that doesn't make sense. So, I don't try to be perfect.

One more, I am told that I like thinking about things: emotionally, spiritually, physically, and intellectually. An intellectual thing is, "What I can say to people?" There are real limits in massage. I can't tell people how to eat. I can't tell them how to exercise. I am not allowed to diagnose their stuff. So basically it just totally limits it *(out of frustration stamping down her foot for emphasis)* to what I can do with my hands specifically with massage. Which is okay with me, because I don't want to be a doctor. I don't want to be a therapist. I don't want to be their pastor. But there is also something about having knowledge that they may not have. I know books that they could read. I know ideas that could help them. And that is a conflict. When do I tell somebody?

Somebody said, "My friend's relative had their teeth taken out and their doctor told them to take like 10,000 grams of Vitamin C. It was this incredible amount of Vitamin C. And, I thought, "That is too much!" Even from my knowledge of nutrition, I thought, "That is too much!" So, I said it, I said, "I think that is too much! I think you should have your friend look it up in a book." But, see, I could get into trouble for saying something like that, for doubting the doctor's word. So there is a conflict there. And I do. Every time I say something I think, "Did I say the wrong thing? Am I stepping over my boundaries?"

DISCUSSION

A REAL CONFLICT   In her story, Vickie identified a number of issues related to identity boundaries that she had encountered in her practice. In addition, she highlighted some of the struggles that can arise when one has not clearly defined nor developed the strength to maintain her or his boundaries. Bodyworkers encounter medical issues though they are not physicians. They encounter emotional issues though they are not psychotherapists. They are confronted with spiritual issues though they are not ministers. They make familiar contact but are not friends. The bodyworker routinely encounters these boundary issues. If clarity of these issues is difficult, and perhaps frightening for the bodyworker, how must it be for the client who may have less familiarity with the phenomenon of professional boundaries? Clarity on the part of the bodywork practitioner is essential for the client to feel safe within the boundaries of the professional relationship.

One boundary issue for Vickie lies in the realm of professionalism and her relationship with some of her colleagues. She states that she is in real conflict over the issue of physical limits to the practice of massage therapy. She is clear that she does not want to have anything to do with internal work. In addition, Vickie does not believe that other practitioners in her field possess sufficient expertise to be able to deal with clients' or their own emotional reactions to such invasive interventions. Furthermore, whether or not her colleagues have the skills to perform these procedures, she questions whether they even should be performing these interventions.

ENDING THE DEADLOCK: A PROBLEM-SOLVING STRATEGY   A cognitive way for Vickie to solve her dilemma might be to prioritize her beliefs. She could have one list of pros and another list of cons. For example, a "pro" for doing intrusive procedures might be: These procedures allow for release of musculature in areas that external manipulation cannot reach. A "con" for this procedure might be: rightly or wrongly, a bodyworker might be unduly vulnerable to a charge of sexual assault by a client. Whichever list is longer points to the direction of her decision. This simple technique may allow her to emerge from her dilemma.

A more intuitive, alternative response to this dilemma is for Vickie to simply trust her feelings. What she knows about herself, is that, usually she is able to "target at the heart of an issue." What she knows about this issue, is that the people who believe they have sufficient technical skill to perform invasive procedures, neither have sufficient psychobehavioral understanding of their clients nor do they have sufficient self-understanding. That sounds like sufficient intuitive data on which to make a decision. That's what is right for Vickie.

In many situations in which Vickie is doubtful, we have seen her take action. What is somewhat puzzling, is that in this situation in which Vickie has a clear sense of her beliefs and feelings, she is unwilling to take a stand. What is figural for Vickie is that she believes in playing a supportive role for her friends. The conflict arises for her because these few colleagues "want to push the boundaries" in a domain that she believes is inappropriate. Vickie has two mutually exclusive beliefs which render her unable to solve her conflict. The struggle continues, and Vickie remains in a state of deadlock with regard to this issue.

Vickie's conflict might be resolved if she were willing share her dilemma with her friends. If Vickie's friends are healthy individuals, they will be able to both appreciate Vickie's supportive feelings toward them, and honor her belief system. If, however, they are solely self-interested, they may feel hurt and act out their feelings of rejection. Presenting one's honesty and truth in a relationship is always a risk.

PROBING   Probing is a psychological technique that allows a psychotherapist to ask questions, or follow-up questions, that will elicit additional information or allow a person to gain deeper awareness, insight, or understanding: "What's going on here?" "Do you want to talk about that more?"

At times, Vickie recognizes that some of her clients on the table are "so tense that they can hardly lie there." At such a point, touch might be extremely difficult for the client to receive. Vickie might want to make a statement or ask a question or two. These statements and questions, rather than pressing the client to greater emotional depths as a probe might do, would be aimed at assessing what could be done to ease the discomfort.

A non-probing approach to this situation would avoid inquiry into the underlying reason for the client's discomforts. One might gently state, "You seem to be uncomfortable." "Is there something that I can do to make this more comfortable for you?" To lessen the distress, one could employ any number of strategies including: returning to an area that was successfully treated, stopping the session for awhile, skipping the problematic area of the body, or ending the session altogether.

A client may spontaneously choose to discuss troubling psychological issues. The bodyworker's inner comfort with such expression will lend for the client's continued expression. External encouragement of deepening the expression is not necessary. If the expression is uncomfortable for either the bodyworker or the client, the bodyworker could say, "This work seems to be troubling for you. I am concerned for you, and I am not able to give you the kind of support you need to process this material. Some of my clients find talking with a counselor or with a therapist to be helpful. Have you ever considered this?"

Vickie is concerned with being "real" with her clients. One need not ask probing questions with a client to be real. Indeed, to ask probing questions is to assume a role rather than to be authentic. To be real with one's client means expressing one's honest concern. Furthermore, to be truly concerned for another does not require solving that person's problems.

Vickie wants to more fully help her clients with their struggles. This bodyworker would like to practice beyond her licensure. Vickie does not fully recognize or legitimize that part of herself. From her feelings, beliefs, and actions, it appears that Vickie does want to pursue psychotherapy with her clients. Vickie wants to be able to use her intuitive abilities with people. She becomes exasperated with the "real limits" that her massage license places upon her.

Vickie's major qualm is "when" to ask the probing question, not "whether" to ask the probing question. She indicates her desire to practice psychotherapy when she grapples with her desire to engage in depth analysis. Vickie becomes impatient with her clients' unresolved psychological conflicts when she wants them to "really deal with it and not just skate on the surface of it. Because they have probably been skating on the surface of it with people for years and years." At this point, the issue of delving appears to be Vickie's, not the clients'. Vickie decides for her clients, "They are just waiting for someone to say, 'It's okay for you to deal with that'." Vickie wants to be the person to play the investigative and information providing roles.

Vickie may be right. Her clients may never have had a person give them permission to go beyond skating on their psychological surface. She may also be wrong. They may not have explored their psychological depths because they were unwilling, unable, or unprepared to go beyond what was familiar, safe, or comfortable. Another possibility is that her clients may or may not know their issues. What they are ready and able to deal with is the physical intervention and release that accompanies Vickie's intuitively guided bodywork. Ultimately, the decisions of whether or not to delve into the "nitty gritty" psychological depths, when to delve, and with whom to delve, belongs to the client, not the bodyworker.

If a bodyworker repeatedly struggles with the issue of probing, the issue may have more to do with the bodyworker's unresolved issues than it does with those of her or his clients. The therapist may be doing for clients what she or he needs to do for her or himself.

Vickie suspects that what she tells her clients goes beyond the scope of her license. She has a chronic anxiety over practicing illegally. She justifies her actions as moral because her clients are in need of the support she offers. But, if there are qualified professional counselors or therapists in Vickie's community, is it moral to deprive her clients of their expertise? If Vickie has any doubt as to what to do about asking "the question," her professional newsletter told her, "The practitioner does not probe for emotional/sexual information."

NOT TRYING TO DO THERAPY Numerous times, Vickie protests that she is "not trying to do psychotherapy," which she refers to as therapy. Yet she reports confusion regarding the limits and boundaries of her role as a massage therapist. Exactly what is psychotherapy? And what is the difference between practicing psychotherapy and being psychotherapeutic?

Psychotherapy is the treatment of psychological issues, using psychological methods. Psychological issues relate to emotional well-being, personality development, and social conflict resolution. Psychotherapy is an intentional relationship in which a trained professional establishes a relationship with a patient in order to effect healing, growth, development and/or resolution. Psychological methods include hundreds of techniques guided by dozens of theoretical orientations.

Vickie verbalizes that she does not want to sign up to be anyone's psychotherapist. Her actions say the opposite. What Vickie does by asking questions is what psychotherapy is all about. If the issue is a matter of being real, there are many ways of being "real," healing, and even psychotherapeutic with a client without practicing psychotherapy. Possession of certain personality traits produces a psychotherapeutic, healing effect. One does not have to be a psychotherapist or licensed to possess these therapeutic traits which include an ability to be warm, empathic, understanding, and to maintain a positive regard for one's client. When a person possesses and actualizes these traits, she or he need not "do" anything to be therapeutic. Merely being in the presence of such a person has a healing effect. These traits can be even more powerful for a person like Vickie who understands, all too well, the tragic and painful events in life. Combining these traits with an understanding for the preciousness of life, compassion for each individual's struggle, a love of humanity, and Vickie's unique ability to apply touch is an exceedingly powerful healing force. These are traits which no institution of higher learning or professional training can confer.

OPENNESS TO CLARITY   Vickie looked to her field for clarity of role definition. Indeed, professional literature in her field provided her with that clarity. Vickie remained confused. On the surface, this confusion is puzzling. What may have been problematic for Vickie was not that her field did not provide clarity, but that she was not open to the clarity she received. As a result, she lived with chronic anxiety. She was anxious and uncertain "… if I am, like, doing something illegal."

A professional is a person who recognizes and respects the boundaries of her or his practice. Referral to, or consultation with, a specialist is the appropriate intervention when issues emerge that call for interventions that go beyond one's formal training and the limitations of one's credentials.

If nothing else, Vickie would do well to listen to the wisdom of her inner voice. If there is some major part of Vickie's personality that is frustrated by the limits of her massage license, it may be appropriate for this bright, verbal, young woman to consider returning to school to prepare for a counseling, social work, psychology, or psychiatry program that would allow her to engage in a kind of work that would be more gratifying. This preparation might allow her to utilize her intuitive interests and abilities to their fullest.

DIAGNOSIS   Psychological assessment and diagnosis is performed by a licensed or certified professional. This professional has training in learning theories, personality development, assessment and testing, and psychopathology. This person also has had advanced supervision in these areas. As a result, she or he may develop a treatment plan that may provide for referral to a supervised peer counselor. For a peer counselor to begin treatment before an assessment and a diagnosis has been made is to put both the client and the peer counselor in danger of being severely traumatized.

TRANSFERENCE   Vickie spoke of one client with whom she developed a friendship outside of her practice, and then the woman suddenly, "cut off the relationship." Vickie assumed this woman ended the relationship because Vickie became for this woman, "the bad person who hurt her in the past."[1] This is an example of transference. Transference is an unconscious process on the part of the client. To say that it is unconscious, is not only to say that the client is unaware of what she or he is doing, but that this person is unconsciously defending against being aware of the process. To actively confront the person with the behavior might result in a defensive reaction. This defense might come in the form of denial, belligerence, or withdrawal. In the transference process the client identifies some aspect of the therapist with some unresolved, emotionally unacceptable, or painful past event in her or his own life. The past and the present become confused in the process. Unlike the originator of the event in the past, the therapist is a safe target for the client's unresolved feelings. The client then feels, believes, acts as if, and treats the therapist as if the therapist was actually the originator of the unacceptable or painful experience.

Vickie provides two different and opposing explanations of transference. She suggests that transference occurs because of the nature of the therapeutic relationship. In this relationship, in which one person is in a position of authority, certain feelings may be projected onto that person because of the authority figure's role. *(Actually, projection is a defense mechanism used when a person is unable or unwilling to accept responsibility for her or his own feelings or motives. So, she or he places these thoughts and feelings onto another and believes the origin of the reaction is from them.)* In this first of Vickie's explanations, the projection is related to the role and has nothing personally to do with the therapist. In particular, transference has nothing to do with mistakes the therapist may be making.

Vickie's second explanation suggests that transference occurs because people in positions of leadership have internalized inappropriate, hurtful, or authoritarian leadership qualities from their past role models. When an authority figure acts in an inappropriate manner, clients may express their anger because the therapist is not being a coequal peer.

Vickie does not like being on the receiving end of a transference reaction. As she does not like delivering contradictory news to her colleagues, she does not like being perceived as a "bad parent" to be rebelled against or rejected by clients.

COUNTERTRANSFERENCE One sign of countertransference might be talkativeness on the part of a bodyworker during a massage session.[2] Talkativeness may be indicative of anxiety or avoidance of feelings related to unresolved issues on the part of the bodyworker. Vickie recognizes about herself, "I talk with people when I massage them. I am real verbal. It's part of who I am." Vickie admits that sometimes a thought comes to her mind. She internally struggles with the appropriateness of saying it. However, once the thought is there, she will just say it. In retrospect she believes, "I think I made mistakes with that before." The results of these mistakes were, "I've said things to people that kind of blew them away." While Vickie recognizes that there is something problematic with her being "verbal," the underlying nature of this problem remains unidentified.

When a client comes to a massage therapist and the massage therapist is doing a lot of talking, it becomes questionable as to which one is the client. If the client feels a need to talk, that's one thing. If the therapist is markedly verbal in the session, it may be the therapist's needs which have become the focus of the session rather than the client's. Furthermore, if the therapist is doing the talking, her or his attention may be compromised with regard to attending to the body and the person on which she or he is working.

RESPONSIBILITY   Vickie believes that her clients are free to say "No" with regard to answering her questions or taking her advice.[3] It is true; most people have the capacity to make existential choices. And, sophistication is needed in order to exercise that choice wisely. It requires awareness of having a choice, understanding the available alternatives, possessing the skills to act on one of those alternatives, and having both the strength and courage to make a choice which may involve painful consequences. This sophistication requires a type of education that most people never receive. The assumption that people are simply free to say "Yes" or "No" places an unrealistic and unfair burden on a client.

When people go to a therapist, they are trusting that the professional will be able to assist them to make the best possible decisions. It is helpful to remember how difficult it is for people in general to say, "No!" to any person that they perceive as an authority figure. And a person in the role of therapist, including a massage therapist, is a person in a role of authority. It would be particularly hard to say "No" to a therapist's probing while lying flat on her or his table clad in nothing but a sheet.

Clients may fear opposing a therapist lest they receive inferior quality work. Or a therapist's disapproval might be more than a client can tolerate if she or he is dependent upon the therapist's emotional acceptance. A client may lack the assertiveness to say, "No." Vickie promises, "It's okay for you to deal with that." "I'm not going to get blown away by that." "I'm not going to cringe." "I won't stop loving you." "It is okay for you to talk about that and tell me just how you feel about it." Yet Vickie recognized that, from time to time, she said things that blew away some of her clients. She "blew away" her feminist client over the issue of the nature of God.

Psychotherapists usually do not perceive themselves as advice givers to their clients. They tend to be reluctant or unwilling to rush in to make decisions for their clients. They want their clients to take responsibility for their own decisions and make them at their own pace. In the process, psychotherapists educate their clients in understanding what is involved in decision making and prepare them to accept the challenges, as well as the consequences, of their decisions and actions. When those clients finally take action, they are prepared to assume responsibility whatever the outcome might be.

PEER COUNSELING Vickie's experience of verbally processing with her clients and her own desire to have a massage therapist who can facilitate her emotional releases are understandable. It is intuitively logical. Nevertheless, peer counseling was designed to take place within the context of professional supervision for clients whose initial motivation was to obtain psychotherapy. Peer counseling provides for one possible course of treatment. This treatment is provided after a comprehensive evaluation has been performed in which the most significant features of a psychosocial history have been established, a tentative explanation of the origin and development of the disorder has been postulated, a classification has been made, and a therapeutic plan has been determined.

In the peer counseling model, a professional psychotherapist is readily available to explore problems that might arise. Vickie experienced her client's powerful self-protective energy when she talked about "the wall comes up," "being dumped," or, "the relationship cut off." These actions protect the client from the therapist as much as Vickie protected herself from her therapist by "firing" the person. It would be appropriate for a peer counselor to explore with a supervisor what is going awry in the helping relationship when the client becomes self-protective.

As Vickie discovered from several encounters, it was difficult for her to make the determination in advance who would be able to "take on" their own "stuff," let alone hers. It makes sense, if one wants to take a client as a friend, that she or he provide that client with a referral for another bodyworker as well as psychotherapist, pastoral counselor, or whatever is called for by the situation before entering the friendship. This lessens the chances of the emerging relationship being encumbered by transference, countertransference, or any of the many problems that may arise from a dual relationship.

IDENTITY ACHIEVEMENT Vickie's professional identity is evolving. She is assuming a more cautious professional role as a result of some very hard-learned, personally painful, and professionally costly lessons. This change will not only serve to protect her in the future, it will also serve to protect her clients.

Vickie is gaining a clearer sense of her professionalism with regard to assuming dual roles. She recognizes that she made mistakes by taking some clients as friends. She has decided not to repeat those mistakes. She is moving more slowly. She is being explicit about who she is as a professional and who she is as a friend. Vickie is also beginning to recognize that when she enters a dual relationship that began with her being a therapist, she runs the risk of having transference reactions projected onto her.

EXISTENTIAL CHOICE   Vickie was initially unaware of the consequences of developing friendships with her clients. Some of Vickie's confusion regarding the boundaries of her bodywork and psychotherapy may have been the result of unconsciously bringing her personal agendas to her massage practice. She took the massage relationship to a psychotherapeutic level. Then, she took her professional relationships to friendships. Finally, she took her friendships into a relationship in which she would receive consultation from the friend. At the point in a massage that anyone decides not to continue with "friction and kneading," and to take the action to "just ask the question," she or he signs up for the risk of being fired.

SUMMARY

Vickie's speech was fast and intense. She began by saying that as a child she was exposed to health care professionals because of her father's ill health. This made a lasting impression on her. She wanted to be able to help people. She did not want them to have to suffer as did her father. At the age of eighteen, Vickie "hated" higher education. The challenge of college education required developing a broad understanding of a diversity of subject matter. It involved memorization of theoretical and specific, non-readily applicable information. Vickie was intuitive and action oriented. She quickly identified problem areas, and based upon available knowledge, wanted to take immediate action. But, her good intentions and youthful zeal could not take the place of self-awareness, perspective, a specific well-integrated knowledge base, and deliberate, methodical pacing. As a result, Vickie found herself fearing that she overstepped her boundaries.

The growth arenas that Vickie encountered involved providing education and engaging in relationship issues that extended beyond her license to practice massage. When anyone intentionally, or unintentionally, pursues another's deeper levels, they are simultaneously opening the possibility for interaction with their own as well as the other's unconscious psychological motivation and defense systems. Vickie, after almost a decade of experience, was beginning to modify how she maintained the boundaries between practice and friendships.

END NOTES

[1] **Transference** Rather than being a "bad" thing, processing transference as it occurs in psychotherapy with a motivated client can be exceedingly helpful. Skilled, healthy psychotherapists are able to distinguish their personal selves, from the professional roles that they play. These therapists are not dependent upon their clients' emotional or social acceptance. They recognize their clients' unconscious projected material and do not become ego-involved or personally affronted by their clients' feelings. They differentiate this unconscious projected material from personal statements. The psychotherapist, from an objective, supportive stance, perceives the significance of these feelings which can be processed and placed in an appropriate context. The client can then understand and transcend the unresolved unconscious phenomenon. Clearly, transference does not occur because there is something wrong or unresolved within the therapist. Yet, should the client's transference not be identified and resolved, this defensive phenomenon of unconscious mistaken identity may interfere with and even cripple the client not only in psychotherapy but in other psychosocial situations.

Sometimes a client may not be emotionally strong enough to face the issue underlying a transference. Though the client may become emotionally arrested in her or his growth at that point, in general, her or his resistance must be respected. In cases where the client becomes overly threatened by the underlying issues, she or he may avoid therapy. Growth will continue if and when the client develops greater strength and chooses to face her or his inner self.

[2] **Countertransference** Countertransference, like transference, is an unconscious process. Countertransference unlike transference occurs on the part of the therapist. Unlike transference which can be a growthful phenomenon, countertransference, if not arrested, becomes a destructive therapeutic force. In countertransference, the therapist identifies with some aspect of the client and transfers unresolved feelings onto her or him. The therapist is unaware of what she or he is doing because this is an unconscious process.

Countertransference reactions will happen time and again when the role of being a helper is an attempt, though unconscious, to help others in order to recapture something that was lost earlier in the therapist's life. In such a case, the overt role of "helping" masks a hidden personal agenda. That agenda may be to gain recognition, appreciation, love, or a sense of completion. It is in these circumstances that the therapist may personalize a client's transferred anger or rejection. The result is that the therapist is unable to maintain an unconditional warm, supportive, understanding stance. Instead, she or he becomes deeply hurt and either defensively withdraws, or protectively, becomes angry.

Another sign of countertransference is evident when the therapist is more involved in working on and resolving the client's problem than is the client. A therapist may want to rescue a client who is having an emotional struggle. When the therapist has a greater interest in resolving an issue than does the client, this pursuit may be referred to as a rescue fantasy. Rescue fantasies are indicative of an unresolved issue or countertransference within the psychodynamic of the therapist.

3 **Responsibility** It might be helpful to keep in mind that when clients seek treatment, they may be unaware of the limits of a bodyworker's or a massage therapist's practice. The client has a certain willingness to trust the authority and knowledge of that therapist. Clients intrinsically trust that professionals know the scope and limits of their practice and will intervene to apply those limits when appropriate.

14

ADVICE

Kathy is a bodyworker in her mid-thirties. As she culled her thoughts from her memory, she spoke in pensive, tentative, halting, phrases.

I had a client...was divorcing...a man. I knew him through a friend...at one time. He asked to come to me for bodywork. And,...he had professional psychological training...and...after we had a few sessions together, it became apparent to me that he...kind of...had a crush on me.

His crush became apparent to me because of the nature and content of his dialogue. The kinds of things that he shared with me were really quite intimate. And...ah...I don't know if he said it directly...that he was having sexual frustrations, but it was implied.

And he admitted that he...sort of had a crush on me. And we arrived...we decided for both of us that was okay. And neither of us had to do anything about it. And,...but, I often felt like he and I both knew that just the contact stuff was important for him...that he was not having enough contact.

That made me feel good that I was able to recognize that and deal with it directly with him. It felt really freeing for us both to admit, "Yes, that is there. And I am real flattered. Thank you." I chose not to do anything about that. And he said also that...ya know, he...he respected where I was at...already being married and all of that, ya know. And he didn't want to do anything about that either.

But I remember before we arrived at the talking about it place...that, there were a couple of times that I was uncomfortable. Because I felt that that was going on, but neither of us said so. And, ah,

I remember thinking...I sort of wanted to feed that back to him. Say, "Gee, you know, part of me feels like...you might be interested in me as a romantic kind of thing." But, I didn't want to say that to be encouraging of that. I didn't want that to be like a lead-in to something else. I just wanted it to be like...feedback. I wanted to know if it was true. I wanted to ask, "Is that true?

There was a struggle...that I recognized this and I didn't know...whether to say anything about it or not. Or how to handle it. At this point, I don't remember if he...was the one who brought it up...or if I finally decided to discuss it...if, I finally decided that is what I needed to do for me. Ya know, later...I don't really know.

I am not always so hesitant to talk to my clients. Sometimes I even give them advice...Robert for example. I saw him for three sessions. He was married but he had just had an affair with a woman he worked with...and...he had...said, "No!" to the woman that he was having the affair with...and stopped it. He was going back to his wife. But he didn't like it. He felt very pulled between the two of them. He felt that his wife was beating him down somehow. And he told me all about that during the session. And I said something to him at that time about being attracted to...oh,...like it was okay to be attracted to women and it was okay not to do anything about it. He felt sucked in by the woman he had an affair with. He didn't want it to happen. He didn't know how it did happen. It was just there.

I remember telling him...I don't remember exactly what I told him. But I told him something like..."You should or shouldn't do something"...rather than, "What about this as a possibility?" I felt that I was being prescriptive...like, I was the one who knew all about what he should be doing. I don't really. But I suddenly went into that kind of thinking. I had something tied up in running him...to get this worked out. Somehow, I wanted him to get better...or something. I told him something like, "Shit or get off the pot. If you want her...have her! Divorce your wife. If you want to be with your wife, stop seeing her any more." And I don't think he wanted to hear that either...or he wasn't ready to hear that.

Lots of things that come out of my mouth are things that I need to hear. I remember having trouble with my own marriage at the time. But I was not taking action to deal with it. About a year or so later, I would be divorced myself.

He never came back. Looking back at the end of the session he said..., *(Kathy grimaced to demonstrate his statement.)* That look is a summary of...I could feel him drawing back from this woman, myself, telling him what to do or what not to do. He was there for body-work and that is not what he got, ya know? He got more than that.

There were other times that I shared my advice and then lost clients. There are other examples.

Now that I had the experience with Keith, I can be a lot more non-directive, or even say, "You want to have an affair with someone? Fine, go ahead! If you want to talk about it later—fine."

After losing enough clients, I hold back my thoughts. That's why the business with Keith was a big deal. I felt better about myself. Afterwards, I think I got more confident in feeding back to people gently what I was noticing. I have done that more frequently since then. Rather than just...not saying anything during a session. I remember several other instances recently. I've given information back to a person about what I noticed in general about their session, or what was going on with them. I was really accurate...just as feedback to them...not that they had to do something about it.

DISCUSSION

FANTASY   Kathy was having a fantasy about Keith's attraction to her. In order for Kathy to be grounded in her contact with her clients, it is important that she appreciates the influences fantasy can have on her practice. Fantasy can be an enjoyable way to pass time. Fantasies allow for exploration of new possibilities and creation of novel options. So long as Kathy clearly distinguishes the difference between fantasy and reality and does not get lost in her fantasies, no harm is done.

If a bodyworker finds her or himself spending a lot of time in fantasy, this may signal that something is going wrong in her or his life. Pleasing thoughts of a client can be used as an escape from confronting another more immediate and troubling reality. In the process of fantasizing about the client, the bodyworker makes the client the object of her or his fantasies. If this distortion goes unrecognized, the client then becomes an object of fantasy rather than a person and the subject of the session. Furthermore, the objectified client of the fantasy may not reflect the client's true personality. Any intentionality the bodyworker focuses into her or his work is inappropriately directed to that fantasy. While the bodyworker is entertaining the fantasy, she or he is not paying attention to the specifics of the person on the table. In these cases fantasy becomes destructive.

Similarly, clients may project onto professional caregivers, the fantasy of their ideal romantic partner. Keith was having difficulty in his marriage. Relatively speaking, his relationship with Kathy was simplistic. He saw her for a circumscribed amount of time. During this time, she listened to him. She touched and massaged his stressed muscles. She appeared to find him attractive. She appreciated his psychological sophistication. This seemed like an idyllic relationship. She was the ideal partner! This is a fantasy. It is unrealistic!

Fantasy begs or ignores the complex issues of the many realities of a relationship. Keith can fantasize having a perfect relationship with a person about whom he knows nothing. Keith does not listen to Kathy's problems; he does not have to share his income with her. He does not know what decision-making would be like with her. Nor does he know what it would be like either to respond to her psychosocial needs, or to have her respond to his needs. Perhaps Keith's fantasy is that life with Kathy will be her actively massaging him all the time and being selfless and satisfied in the process.

Keith may believe that he knows who Kathy is as a result of his experience with her in her role, being on the receiving side of her skilled professional hands for an hour once a week or once a month. In reality, he has little information about who Kathy actually is as a person. He does not know what her needs are. He does not know how she responds when her needs are and are not met.

What Kathy did not appreciate about either herself or Keith is that neither was ready for a new romance. Each was ripe and vulnerable to another needy person. A fine fantasy can seem like an excellent alternative when one is hurting in a dissolving marriage. If one chooses to act on her or his fantasy, the hard core reality eventually returns: having to respond to a relationship, a real person, and one's psychological core, shortcomings, unfinished past traumas, and needing for improved interpersonal skills. This is reality.

This reality existed equally for Kathy. She did not know Keith. She knew what Keith looked like. She knew what Keith told her of his frustrations, his wounds, the unfairness in his life. She did not know how he contributed to the conflict. She did not know the realistic or unrealistic expectations he brought to his relationship. Kathy did not know the family history that Keith brought to his selection of a marital partner. Whatever Kathy and Keith believed they knew about the other person, it is in facing life's obstacles together that they would truly begin to discover each other. They would begin to learn who the other person actually is. They would then be in a position to determine whether or not they want to continue the relationship. This is the relationship-building process. It can be fun, nurturing, confirming, filled with adventure and excitement. It can also be painful as these two already know from their own marriages. A healthy, successful, romantic partnership is a major commitment and hard work.

"JUST" LISTENING: A PROBLEM SOLVING STRATEGY   Robert, Kathy's other client, also lacked an appreciation for the hard work required to begin, maintain, or end a successful relationship. However sweet or nurturing the contact with the woman at the office might have been for Robert, he felt "sucked" into it. Intuitively, it felt wrong to him. He felt beaten down in the relationship with his wife. He knew that he had to complete the unfinished business with his wife before he could move on in his romantic life. He was at a loss as to what needed to be done or how to do it.

Whatever direction Robert might have taken, if he followed Kathy's advice, he would end up losing. Robert had already made a decision about his extramarital affair. His problem concerned his confused, ambivalent feelings. He needed to air them with someone who could appreciate his conflict. He needed to gain clarity about what he had to do to live comfortably, emotionally within himself. Robert was not looking for support in the form of advice. To overcome his confusion, Robert needed support in the form of patience, understanding, acceptance, and clarification.

Robert may have needed his bodyworker to have "just" listened. "Just" listening is no small feat. It is a powerful skill possessed by few. It entails being emotionally as well as cognitively present and understanding. It does not require saying anything in response. Kathy could have allowed her client to get a clearer sense of his own needs and direction. She could have allowed him the opportunity to express the thoughts and feelings that her bodywork was unlocking and given him the time and space he needed to make sense of it. Robert also needed help sorting out and understanding his feelings. This job would best be left to an impartial professional.

INTIMACY Responding therapeutically to another's feelings is a sophisticated skill. It is much different than giving advice. When someone gives advice, she or he assumes a one-up role. This is the position of one who knows more and is in control. From the safety of that controlling role, she or he addresses the other person's vulnerability. This position of authority may even shut off Kathy's intimacy and vulnerability to her own marital distress. As an advice giver she foreclosed awareness of the complexity of her own feelings and struggles.

If Kathy talked about her own feelings, she would have been a coequal with Robert. She would have been baring her intimate self, sharing her vulnerability, and not assuming a protective distance. If Robert were capable of meeting Kathy's personal honesty with his earnest spirit, contact would have occurred and both might have grown from the event. However, if Robert were unwilling or unable to receive Kathy's sentiments on a sharing level or Robert perceived Kathy to be overwhelming or attacking him, he would become defensive. In this case, Kathy might have felt hurt by her attempt to share honestly. Sharing feelings is intimate, potent, and risky. When one is already embroiled in the emotional struggle of one relationship, trying to make sense out of what is going on in another only complicates the matter. Soon there are two relationships in which to struggle.

RISK   Kathy did run a risk in sharing with Keith. Whether Kathy was successful or not with Keith, sharing her feelings with him demanded courage. In this instance discussing her feelings with her client helped make the relationship more comfortable. Being open and honest with another mature, open, and honest person is usually helpful. Since not everyone is mature, open, and honest, it would be important for Kathy to assess her personal and professional risk before choosing to expose her vulnerability. In the future, it may be helpful for Kathy to decide whether the risk of being vulnerable is worth the possible payoff. She must determine if she is strong enough to deal with the consequences if the encounter goes sour.

Sometimes a matter can be so important that self-expression is justifiable, even when the risk of being understood is modest and the likelihood of rejection great. In the case of Keith, he was important enough for Kathy to be willing to run the risk of acting awkwardly and being rejected in order to straighten out her relationship.

Keith seemed to be a fairly safe person with whom Kathy could discuss the nature of their relationship. The result of the conversation was that Kathy felt relieved of her concerns. In addition, she felt stronger and wanted to take her new direct and gentler communication skills to yet other relationships. This was very different than her contact with Robert, who never returned.

PROJECTION   There is another communication issue that Kathy raises in her narrative regarding Robert, "Suddenly I went into that kind of thinking. I had something tied up in running him...to get this thing worked out." She then concluded, "Lots of things that come out of my mouth are things that I need to hear." Kathy recognized that she was putting her psychological head on Robert's shoulders. This is clinically referred to as projection. She unconsciously perceived within Robert, traits that were unacceptable within herself. She then became ego-involved in changing those traits in him.

As Kathy became aware of projecting her issues and needs onto clients with similar struggles, she opened the possibility for her own change and growth. From her new awareness, she could then choose to focus on and respond to her own problems and she could consciously choose to stay focused upon Robert's dilemma. In either case, she would no longer feel compelled to rush in and do something about Robert. Kathy was beginning to recognize within herself a new capacity to restrain from giving advice. "You want to have an affair with someone? Fine, go ahead! If you want to talk about it later—fine." Perhaps, at some point she will possess a third alternative: being present with her knowledge and her feelings of acceptance for her clients and their struggles without having to say anything.

MARITAL DISHARMONY Kathy's story does not reveal information that would lead to understanding the nature of her own marital disharmony. Her interest in the relationship problems of her clients is not surprising given her own marital Achilles' heel. Indeed, the dissonance of her own love life may act as a magnet to draw similar issues from clients in similar circumstances. It might be helpful for Kathy to know that relationship problems are difficult to resolve even for the most skilled psychotherapists. For the issues of attraction and romance to no longer compromise Kathy's professional relationships she needs to understand and appreciate the complex issues of selecting, developing, and maintaining a healthy love relationship. Without this understanding and appreciation of one's own stumbling blocks to successful relationships, it is all too easy to leave one troubled relationship only to encounter the same dilemmas in another. One may then incorrectly surmise that the problem is in the nature of relationships rather than within an unfinished piece within oneself.

MULTIPLE FACES In Robert's case, he would remain conflicted between two women no matter which one he chose. It is not just the relationships which are problematic, but Robert. The resolution to his dilemma resides within the strata of the deeper faces[1] of his personality. Robert would need skilled, patient, psychotherapeutic support to work through the emotional levels of his struggle. Until these inner levels are resolved, he would find himself having difficulty with either relationship.

PROBLEM-SOLVING That a person with a life-stressed body will begin to verbalize the events that are stored in her or his knotted tissues when she or he is massaged is not at all surprising. It requires strength on the part of the bodyworker to assume the role of confidant without jumping in with simplistic answers to dilemmas that may have been decades in the making. Some problems may appear to be easy for an outsider to solve. Simplistic solutions often do not work. The presenting problem may be a solution to yet another issue that is far less obvious.

As we have seen, these problems may be branded into the deepest levels of personality by powerful emotional bonds, family rules, religious beliefs, or work ethics. Some problems may appear easy to resolve for an outsider, yet resolution may require emotional, social, economic, and/or spiritual support that is absent. The solution may call for understanding, skills, self-realization, or actions that will be painful beyond the clients' willingness or ability to tolerate. The naive bodyworker, advising or insisting upon what her or his client should or should not do only adds additional expectations and pressure.

If a person rushes in to give advice, as Kathy did, the growth issue for her or him is not one of judging or berating her or himself for doing so. The issue is to recognize that giving advice may be more harmful than helpful. If a client asks what the bodyworker would do in a similar situation, and, if the body worker chooses to share, then it is appropriate for the practitioner to share her or his thoughts. A final note regarding giving advice: advice is most readily received when the giver of the advice is not personally involved in the client's taking it.

SUMMARY

Kathy was freely able to verbalize her thoughts and beliefs when her task was to prescribe for her clients. Communication was far more difficult when the task was to directly recognize and express her own feelings and struggles. Complicating the issue of communicating with her clients was the fact that Kathy was having difficulty with her own marital relationship. Keeping a client's struggles and decisions separate from one's own is particularly difficult when the client is struggling with similar issues. In such cases one may try to close down the client's struggle by moralizing or providing a quick fix because of one's personal discomfort with the issue.

Kathy painfully recognized that though her clients may talk to her about their life struggles, they do not come to her for advice. She wisely chose not to complicate and compromise her already shaky marital situation by acting upon her own romantic feelings toward a client who had a crush on her. However, by not seeking support for herself with her own personal relationship difficulties, she did not recognize how complex relationships are, what is involved in promoting a harmonious marital relationship, and what is involved in choosing a more appropriate partner. Understanding the complexity of the marital relationship may help Kathy appreciate the importance of maintaining critical distance in her clients' personal affairs and contribute to her own personal growth.

END NOTES

[1] **Multiple Faces** Romantic relationships are comprised of multiple levels. Each of these levels is like an alternate face. We can quickly become attracted to the visual appeal of the physical face or body. Beyond physical attraction, people possess a social presence. Some people are outgoing, friendly, bubbly, talkative, or charming. Other people are more pensive, standoffish, introspective, emotional, or quiet. Appearances and superficial social characteristics usually make readily available entrees for relationships. Socioeconomic background, educational achievement, or recreational interests also contribute to an initial sense of attraction. However, a true perception, recognition, and appreciation for another's psychosocial dynamics or inner face may take a considerable amount of time and experience.

A deep sense of another's inner psychological face may not arise until a major conflict is encountered with that person. A more complete picture of who they are can only materialize when the chips are down, rather than when she or he is wearing the charm of romantic attraction. The most accurate picture may emerge in the problem-solving task of overcoming conflict. Problem-solving in the face of adversity provides the clearest sense of a partner's personality, as well as, whether successful problem solving will build the strength of a relationship and contribute to its growth and love. Unfortunately, many relationships are solidified before this aspect is ever perceived.

Attraction or infatuation may just happen. Often our attraction or infatuation to another's surface levels are labeled or mislabeled as love. Love, unlike attraction, develops over time. Love grows as a result of mutually respectful and supportive interaction. What then becomes more apparent over time is whether or not a couple is compatible. Compatibility includes similarity of expectation, tolerance of differences, and a willingness to work out the issues or differences.

Often relationships survive the initial romantic phase because one or both partners are oblivious to or ignore the differences that might threaten the surface harmony. The partners blind themselves with the attraction that they label as "love." Or, the differences are superficially perceived: "opposites attract." As a result, the couple is unable or unwilling to see the issues that compromise the compatibility of the deeper faces of the relationship. Over the long term, quality survival of a relationship has little to do with the initial surface attraction. The long term integrity of a relationship depends upon cooperative living, coping with everyday life, respecting of inner wounds, and responding to the unforeseen stresses that inevitably arise. These are the relevant issues that make a relationship successful. With time and strength the couple is able to perceive and confront deeper and deeper issues. With the recognition, acceptance, and embracing of these deeper faces true love develops and the relationship bond is strengthened.

There are a number of issues beneath the surface that reflect upon the long-term stability of a relationship. These issues may neither be recognized nor resolved in the early dating or romantic phase of a relationship. They reflect deeper, less apparent social faces or issues such as: How is income to be distributed? How, when, where, and on what is it to be spent? How is time to be invested? How much time is to be allocated to couple time, individual time, individual work time, time with friends, time with mutual friends? Who will do which household tasks and when? Who is to be responsible for what in child-rearing? How will or will not the children be disciplined, by whom, and for what reasons?

This list goes on. Does everybody walk away from sex feeling satisfied? And is that okay? Does everyone feel sufficiently listened to and heard in conversations? Is one person always initiating social activity? Does someone feel taken for granted? Are one's needs in illness responded to as she or he would like? Are both sets of the couple's families responded to satisfactorily? Does each partner get touched, hugged, kissed as much as they want and the way they want? Is each party's need for affection met exclusive of sexuality? This is not an exhaustive list of the relevant issues involved in a relationship. However, it gives a taste for the issues that a couple must address in order to achieve an ongoing harmony.

A deeper psychological face comes from childhood. This face deals with unresolved feelings from childhood that creep into mate selection, perception, and treatment. This deeper level is often the one that determines the course of a relationship. This face is rarely immediately apparent.

Resentments are created in a relationship when unresolved conflicts or breakdowns begin to accumulate. These resentments build and fester over time. Even superficial happenings in the relationship may trigger these latent antagonisms. A major blowup can occur over someone's squeezing the toothpaste tube from the middle rather than rolling it up from the end, or vise versa. The actual conflict may be over one person feeling that her or his needs or wishes are chronically ignored. The tooth paste tube is a symbol of that struggle.

At this point, a deeper face that was less apparent during the early phases of the relationship is revealed. Given that everything in the dating phase went smoothly, the partner's inner psychological face was obscured.

With conflict, breakdowns occur in the superficial levels of the relationship allowing the less apparent latent personality traits and expectations to emerge. The initial, superficial levels become irrelevant. The underlying dynamics ultimately materialize into the significant factors of the relationship. Rather than recognizing and responding to these essential personality dynamics, many people are likely to get stuck in clinging to their memories or yearnings for the good old romantic days when the relationship was new and more simple.

Differences in relationships will exist to the extent that it is unlikely one can find a partner who is a perfect match. These differences are likely to emerge with time, even if no specific crises surface. Differences, in and of themselves, are not an issue nor are they necessarily bad. Differences can lend to the depth and richness of the relationship. They only become an issue when a couple is unable or unwilling to recognize or agree upon how to address or resolve them. These unresolved issues can then lead to incompatibilities. The incompatibilities make for emotional distance.

Perhaps marriage contracts should speak to the many faces of the couple. Each person could enumerate what she or he specifically wants and does not want to receive from the other. In addition, it could spell out what she or he is willing to lovingly give and not give to meet the other's deeper needs. Once this contract was drawn up there would have to be a clause which would state exactly how problems were to be resolved. People equipped with such a contract might become more selective before they consented to sign on the dotted line. They might be more successful resolving conflicts after they have signed.

15

CRYING ACROSS PENNSYLVANIA

Sherry is a gentle, petite woman, in her early forties. It felt special to be in her presence—quieting, comforting, healing. She cocked her head down just a fraction of an inch, like the proverbial ram about to punch a hole in the dam. Then she launched into her story.

I went to massage school because I could never find something that I wanted to do with my life. I would do something for a year, then I couldn't hold my attention. The school I went to focused on growth rather than technique. I was high when I came out of school. I was 35. I had been away from my family and immersed in bodywork for seven months. I found my life's work. I felt ignited by polarity therapy.

(Sherry spoke rapidly.) I returned home ready to work. I had a friend, Angie, who was an oncology nurse. Angie was looking for someone who could do bodywork for some of her terminal patients who wanted to take an alternate approach in addition to their mainline medical treatment. Massage was not appropriate for these cancer patients. However, polarity work was. I had everything that I wanted. I was floating on energy from massage school. I had my life's work. I had patients to work on. And, I thought polarity therapy could do anything.

Working with cancer patients made sense to me. I suffered from cancer when I was 26 years old. My cancer was treated surgically. I was ignorant about my condition. A woman prayed for me. I had no pain, no discomfort. A scar was the only physical aftermath. But I perpetually live with the anxiety of the cancer's recurrence.

I could readily identify with my young dying patients. My patients could empathize with me because of my history with cancer. These patients were in their 30's and 40's, open-minded, and not ready to die. Several could not lie still because of their agonizing pain. These people were receiving all kinds of medical procedures, surgery, and experimental drugs. The procedures weren't working. Several went to Sloan Kettering. Many did not return. I believe many of these people suffered from trying to live longer. Their emotions were continuously subjected to the ups and downs of believing maybe this time it would work. *(Sherry's memories and feelings came back to her as her story unfolded. Her speech was extremely rapid. Emotion was hard to detect for the intensity in her voice.)* I'm just remembering this stuff. I didn't think that I stuffed it, but it's hard sharing this story. All of a sudden, I feel flooded with old memories and feelings that have been buried for years.

The last night…*(Sherry's voice trailed off into silence. She began again.)* Dory was the closest to my age of several women I worked with. She had a daughter, husband, good job, and an interesting career. She went to a big hospital in the mid-west. She had just come back from a horrible operation. They didn't close her up properly. She was wired up internally and the wire poked out of her abdomen. She was stapled rather than stitched-up externally. Her physicians didn't expect her to live, so they were not concerned over the cosmetics of their stitches.

Dory suffered from intestinal cancer that had metastasized. Her prognosis was grim. Her condition was expected to deteriorate rapidly. She was in constant pain. Dory clutched for her pain medication every two to three hours. I had worked with a terminal patient using a particular technique to ease pain. It focused his awareness out of his body. He soon died a painless death. So, when Dory asked if I could do anything to remove her from her body, I said, "Yes."

I was prepared to work with Dory. But the first thing I did was to knock over a coffee table with drinking water on it. That's not me. I was extremely embarrassed. After cleaning up the mess, I gathered myself together to begin again. "Kaboom!" Just as I started there was a tremendous clap of lightening that came down outside of the window. Dory and I laughed together over being startled by the thunder. I began again. "Kaboom!" There was no storm outside and no storm in sight. It was as if someone was sending a metaphysical sign. We agreed to stop. After that, I continued to work with Dory in a gentle manner to help manage her pain.

Dory lived another four months. Her doctors could not understand how she could have lived so long. The last four months were a wonderful romantic time for Dory and her husband. They both made each other happy. There was no agonizing, they parted like soul mates.

Not long after Dory's death, I had driven east and had just completed a course at the Omega Institute. I then drove down from New York to visit my family who also lived in the East. I had time to talk with my father who had had several heart attacks. He was an active man who had his first heart attack not long before he was to retire. He then became depressed and lost his zest for life. Nothing interested him. He leaves the room if you try to talk to him about it.

Ever since he had his first attack when I was twenty-eight, he has been trying to die. But he feels that he has to be here. He wants to see my sister settled. But she won't be settled. So, he hangs on.

He is strong on the outside, mushy on the inside. He came from a farming family in the old country. I learned from my aunts, that in their childhood, family life was extremely hard. Their father was physically abusive. But dad would never talk about it. He is strong. He holds it in.

I was driving across the Pennsylvania Turnpike on my way home. I don't know what triggered it. I started to think about how heavy my life was. I was aware of how negative my thinking was. For example, I was feeling guilty for having low blood pressure. Instantly, I began to sob. It was a horrible thing to drive and cry at the same time. My sobbing didn't stop.

As I drove, waves of memories, thoughts, and tears flooded my awareness. I remembered Osama, a terminal patient I worked with. I saw him on three separate occasions. He was a sixty-seven year old, educated man with a distinguished accent. He had pancreatic cancer. He was frustrated with his nurses who pampered him and told him that everything was going to be all right. The first time he met with me was enjoyable. He just talked. The second time he met with me, he talked and then allowed me to do some work with him. The third time I met with Osama I spent more time focused on helping him respond to his pain and death. Angie later told me the last session frightened Osama. He wanted to live and feared working with me would hasten his death.

I got a call from my nursing friend. Angie told me Osama was dying and asked to say good-bye to me. I went into the hospital to see him. I did not recognize him. He was filled with fluid. His face and body were bloated. He seemed to be out of it. I held his hand and talked with him. A minister then came in and rushed me out of the room. I told him I had to say good-bye.

As I started to leave, Osama's hand tightened. He struggled for hours before dying.

I drove and thought. I compared Dory to Osama. I thought to myself, "Struggling against death reinforces suffering. It is futile to struggle against death." Then I became angry. The whole business of how people are treated makes me angry. Looking at that wire poking out of Dory made me angry.

I drove and cried. I cried for the suffering of humanity. I hate pain. Why is it so hard? I hate the only way we can grow is to suffer. I hate on this planet we have to learn through suffering. It's stupid. It's just stupid. Cancer is supposed to be a cleanser. It is a way of releasing tons and tons of karma. But I just feel antagonistic toward suffering. I began to struggle with my motives to work with these dying patients. When Dory asked me if there was anything I could do, I should have said, "No!"

After I returned home to my work, I became more gentle. My patients died faster. I continued my work for another four months and then decided to give myself a break for several months by not working with cancer patients. But, even with these non-cancer patients I became involved.

Something happened to me over my trip across Pennsylvania. When I returned home, I realized, "I am burned out. I hesitate touching anyone. I need more time to rationally deal with the energies that go through me in this bodywork process. I'll never attempt to extricate my patients from their bodies again."

I never returned to working with dying patients. Soon I reached the point where I said, "I can't take it anymore! I have to get away from it all!" Then I quit bodywork altogether.

The time I cried across Pennsylvania, I realized that I had a number of pieces to a puzzle in my hand. I knew regarding Dory that I helped her with her pain control and her fear of death and dying. These people put their life in majestic perspective when they don't fight it. For myself, my orientation was to fix the outer body. But, I had no experience in verbal therapy and was not prepared for people with life and death issues.

The maturity has to be there. I've decided, I am not old enough. I am so ignorant of the powers that go through me when I help people. I need to have a lot more maturity before I try to access this energy again. I need to know my motives completely. It is just too strong! You can't do bodywork with your ego. You do more harm than good.

DISCUSSION

RIGHT BRAIN Sherry spoke of her own cancer surgery. She said that a woman prayed for her before her surgery, and she "had no pain, no discomfort". This experience has particular significance. Prayer encountered experientially is a right-brain intervention. Any right-brain intervention has the potential to allow for muscle elonga-tion, reduced tension, diminished pain, boosted immune system functioning, and enhanced recovery rate. Some right brain interven-tions include guided imagery, hypnosis, art therapy, music, and meditation. These techniques promote an altered state of conscious-ness which in turn triggers physiologic changes which facilitate the healing process. These interventions are more rapidly incorporated for those who are amenable to right-brain interventions. Sherry assisted in the success of her surgery and recuperation process to the degree that she opened to and accepted the prayer offered for her. Beyond the right brain effects, Sherry may have been assisted by divine interven-tion to the extent that the woman who prayed for her was able to invoke the assistance of a higher power.

IDENTIFICATION   Sherry's identification with her clients was a double-edged sword. On the one hand, she could be present with a sixth sense to support her clients in their struggles. On the other hand, her own personal boundaries were not sufficiently strong to keep her clients' pain from pulling her down. Their struggle and suffering over life and death triggered unresolved issues within Sherry: feelings toward her own life and death and perhaps that of her father's.

Her strong identification with her clients' tender cores allowed Sherry to become intimately close. Her identification might have been more helpful if it had alerted Sherry to protect her own tender core. She could have provided protection for herself by increasing the amount of support available to her; maintaining emotional distance, processing her psychological reactions as they emerged with herself and/or with a confidante; increasing the number of supportive events she participated in such as exercise, recreation, social contacts and/or spiritual enrichment; increasing the amount of recognition, apprecia-tion, and love she received from her family. The involvement in support activities could have better matched the amount of stress she was under. When one works with chronic stress or illness, it is helpful to have many or all of these supportive techniques incorporated into one's lifestyle.

ACCEPTANCE VS. DENIAL   There is a continuum which ranges from acceptance to denial that we all encounter when facing developmental growth hurdles. We face and leap these hurdles to the extent that cer-tain prerequisites are in place including: awareness of the concerns, placement of the concerns sufficiently high on our list of priorities to be responded to, motivation to respond to these issues, and possession of the abilities, skills, knowledge, and resources to accomplish the task. We may choose to postpone our response to these concerns to the degree that any or all of the above prerequisites are not in position. If the concerns outstrip our ability to contemplate them, we may repress them. In this repression, the concerns are relegated to that part of our cognitive process for which we have no awareness—the unconscious. Stored there, we are safe from their troubling presence. We must use additional energy, however, to maintain both their storage and our lack of conscious memory that we are storing them. Perhaps the strain of this extra energy requirement is what makes death so painful. The person is actively dying while some part of the person is struggling to keep the dying a secret.

Beyond the issue of acceptance of one's death, is the issue of how one chooses to die if she or he is fortunate enough to be able to make that decision. Sherry taught a process of pain relief that may, in addition to the easing of pain, have given her clients more choice about letting go of their life. The first client that Sherry used this technique with, died quickly. She and Dory chose not to use it at all. Osama was unwilling to use it. Dory was not in denial about her impending death. Dory was very aware of death and what she was requesting when she asked Sherry, "Is there anything you can do to remove me from my body?"

Perhaps Osama was in denial. Yet he was irritated with his saccharin nurses who pampered him with a false sense of security. This proud man of foreign birth, like Sherry's father, may have derived part of his sense of masculinity and dignity from fighting off death to the very end. If pain was the price Osama had to pay to maintain himself in the battle, he chose to pay. Perhaps he simply wanted to have sincere, caring, feminine, comfort in the process. He may have been "out of it" as Sherry suggested. However, he was not so out of it that he did not know to clasp her petite, firm, caring, hand. Osama held that hand more tightly when the minister informed Sherry that she would have to leave her dying client.

Just as there is not a single acceptable way to live life, there is not a single acceptable way to die. The best that any health care worker can do is to bring the latest information to their patients' or clients' attention and then facilitate as best as possible the choices of the dying person.

INCONGRUENCE Sherry was thrust into a full blown identity crisis driving across Pennsylvania. As a result of this crisis, she chose to give up her "life's work." Something, however, was unresolved. Sherry was sufficiently intuitive to recognize some important factors: the extremely powerful experiences that ran through her body as a result of her interactions with her dying clients, the recognition that she lacked experience with verbal therapy, and the recognition that she was emotionally overloaded from her work experiences. She was "burned out." There were ongoing emotional stress issues related to Sherry's work and her inability to maintain protective boundaries. As a result, this young woman handled these problems the way emotionally stressful events were handled in her family: she stuffed them until there was no more room to stuff. She abandoned her "life's work." Seven years later when she told her story, this talented woman had yet to find employment that provided the same level of satisfaction.

CHOICE   Behavioral coping skills, like other skills, are most slowly and arduously learned during hard times.[1] Unfortunately, the motivation and stamina needed to develop these skills may be unavailable in times of crisis.[2] Then an individual may succumb to denial, anger, bargaining, or the helplessness and hopelessness of depression, or even shock. This is probably what happened to Sherry's father after his heart attack. This is probably what happened to Sherry after her drive across Pennsylvania. Dory, on the other hand, did not succumb. When confronted by fate's lightning bolts, she chose not to volitionally end her life.

A person is fortunate when faced by a life crisis if she or he has a caring person like Sherry available to provide support through the transition. Supported or not, though, we all retain the choice of whether or not to consciously and deliberately face our nemesis.

REENTRY PROBLEMS   Sherry left her training program after seven months away from her family and home. She returned eager to employ her new skills in a promising field. She had no problem letting go of her training program. Nor did she speak of difficulty returning to her family. However, Sherry suffered from reentry problems after leaving her Omega program.

Reentry difficulties are not unusual after leaving a retreat facility which provides safety, support, and intense, intimate social and spiritual contact. The difficulty arises as a result of the lost support of the temporary community. Though brief, such contacts allow for deep sharing, attention, and understanding. After all, the people who go to retreats are self-selected by their interest to participate in these growth events. They chose to go to a specific program because of their experience, knowledge, and interest in the area. Group members may easily identify with one another as spiritual siblings. The work group represents an instant community or a supportive substitute family. Leaving such a supportive family can be exceedingly upsetting especially if one did not have such an experience in her or his childhood or does not have such a supportive environment to which to return.

Another cause of reentry problems arises from the kind of learning that occurs in her or his retreat experience. Learning, growth, and change are taking place whether one brings her or his own personal struggles into the focus of the group or is merely in the presence of others who are genuinely grappling with their dilemmas. Reentry shock can be most severe when changes take place but the individual does not consciously recognize or understand the changes or the implications of those changes. The participant may return to the life she or he left and no longer belong or fit.

Even though the growth experience was positive, the individual may still feel unfocused or overwhelmed by the contrast with the home environment. After having a wonderful, emotionally nourishing time, she or he is thrust into confusion without the benefit of support from her or his instant retreat community.

Sherry threw herself into a vocational field propelled by her new skills and enthusiasm, but she lacked psychotherapeutic grounding. She had unresolved family issues regarding death. Her father suffered from heart problems and wanted to die. He said that he had to stay alive to take care of Sherry's younger sister. Sherry loved her father. She wanted to help him, but, he was macho and tough, from the old country. He was beyond her help. Sherry, emotionally open, went to visit her family after her retreat, where she had been supported by a nurturing temporary family. When she returned to the reality of her biological family, the disparity between the two may have been exceedingly painful for her.

As Sherry left her parents' home, alone in the existential void of her car on the Pennsylvania Turnpike, it was as if a tornado swept down striking her—like Dorothy being swept away to Oz. When her car touched down again at home, Sherry was no longer the same. She could no longer simply step back into her life as if nothing had happened. She could no longer pretend that all was well and just return to work.

IDENTITY CRISIS   Driving across Pennsylvania, Sherry may have had an "identity crisis" or a "spiritual emergency." The dam-burst of imploded emotion was a cathartic release. What was the turmoil that Sherry experienced as she crossed Pennsylvania? Was she simply feeling all the pain and suffering that she had been buffered from experiencing as she assumed her care-giving role? Was Sherry struck by survival guilt? She lived while the patients she worked with died. Was Sherry overwhelmed with guilt because she became aware that she was deflecting a need to gain acceptance from her suffering father by giving to suffering others? Whatever the underlying truth of this turmoil, Sherry was unable to live comfortably with her actions.

Without understanding what it was about, this intuitive woman recognized, "Something happened to me over my trip across Pennsylvania." Sherry's life experience had provided grist for her philosophical mill. Taking herself to a growth institute for continued training provided her with the critical distance and support for the material inside herself to begin to take meaningful form and expression. The issues of personal meaning and Sherry's life path were further stirred by the visit to her parents' home. Explosive chain reactions of experience, affect, and cognition occurred as the elements interacted in the caldron of Sherry's awareness.

Sherry developed a new sense of clarity about her personal truths. "Struggling against death reinforces suffering." She concluded, "It is futile to struggle against death." She became clear about the health care establishment, "The whole business of how people are treated makes me angry." The integrity and dignity of people who Sherry cared for and loved was compromised by a system that disregarded the quality and the integrity of individual life. The job was far greater then Sherry could tackle single-handedly.

Sherry continued gaining professional clarity upon her arrival home. While she was angry about the lack of dignity the medical system demonstrated toward dying patients, Sherry was overwhelmed by the anguish from the responsibility she personally assumed for her clients. "I realized I am burned out. I hesitate touching anyone." Sherry knew she needed more than the youthful enthusiasm of discovering her "life's work." "It is just too strong! You can't do bodywork with your ego. You do more harm than good." "The maturity has to be there. I've decided, I am not old enough. I am so ignorant of the powers that go through me when I help people. I need to have a lot more maturity before I try to access this energy again. I need to know my motives completely."

Sherry had the integrity to acknowledge that she could no longer continue with her work until she integrated who she was with what she was doing. And, Sherry may have been mistaken in stating that she was not old enough to participate in the work she was doing. Although she may have felt too immature, years alone do not create maturity. Maturity is created by what a person does with the experiences she or he has over those years. Sherry was bright, intuitive, and had many rich experiences from which to draw.

Sherry gained valuable information from her experience in health care. She had the skill and knowledge to ease the discomfort of those who suffered. Rather than finding a way to successfully utilize her knowledge and skills, she internalized her anxiety and pain and followed her father's role model. Sherry withdrew from the relevant issues of her life. Withdrawal was one possible solution to her discomfort with her work, but it did not provide for a resolution of Sherry's discomfort. Sherry soon discovered that her "burnout" encompassed far more than working with cancer patients. She discovered that any involvement in a helping, bodywork capacity became toxic for her. Sherry felt compelled to leave the health-care field.

Alternatively, Sherry could have prevented her psychological drain by building up a strong internal and external support system. Part of this support would have been of a psychological nature so that Sherry could have recognized, confronted and resolved issues of past as well as present concerns. Other aspects of a support program could have included bodywork, physical exercise, and right-brain activity such as imagery, artistic creativity, and/or prayer. It might also have included a request for more expressed love, support, and recognition from her family.

CHRONIC ANXIETY Another factor in this story: Sherry had cancer when she was 26. She had successful surgery. A telltale scar was the only outward sign of the ordeal. It sounds simple, and it sounds over. As with many cancer survivors an invisible psychological scar had become a permanent part of Sherry's reality. Her chronic anxiety remained as a perpetual reminder of her close encounter with death and the ever present potential for the reappearance of cancer. In addition to eroding Sherry's peace of mind, this chronic anxiety could readily become physically draining, leading to fatigue, and depression.

For Sherry's psychological and physical well-being it is essential that she learn not to internalize her work-related stress. This internalized stress intensifies and complicates the already existing anxiety over her medical condition. This anxiety may also have masked other unresolved psychosocial conflicts.

Psychotherapeutic support can greatly assist cancer patients who are amenable to it. It can provide specific skills to deal with issues of anxiety and pain. It can provide understanding and legitimization for the psychological distresses encountered throughout cancer treatment. Anxiety of relapse can remain years after the end of successful treatment. Psychotherapeutic support can provide for normalization and anxiety reduction. Untold psychological duress is created when the roles people play run contrary to their true nature. Psychotherapy reduces emotional tension as cancer patients distinguish who they are from the roles that they have been playing. The medical condition is often aided as the underlying psychological conflict is resolved.

KARMA Karma is part of Sherry's belief system. It is essential that she address it. Karma is believed to be a behavioral pattern which destines the individual live out that pattern over and over again until it is spiritually transcended. The pattern could have originated in the past or the present. It can be constructive or destructive. Overcoming karma is essential to the degree it is destructive. Sherry speaks of cancer being a karma cleanser, "It is a way of releasing tons and tons of karma." If Sherry is correct and her karma was not surgically removed along with the cancer, then she may also believe she still has karma to work out. This chronic duress is something that Sherry can overcome far less stressfully than by suffering from cancer. It is not having cancer per se that is the karma-buster, but the way that the individual confronts her or his cancer that may bust the karma.

The issue of resolving karma is essentially no different than the issue of maintaining emotional health. Whether or not a person believes that her or his karma arises from a past life or lives, in order to resolve the issue of karma, she or he must identify the behavioral pattern that has to be transcended. She or he must overcome the resistances to changing her or his life-patterns and she or he must develop a healthier alternative life-pattern. That pattern must then be acted upon. These are also the steps of personal growth.

LEARNING THROUGH SUFFERING   Sherry's family background of internalizing the pain of past traumas stopped Sherry from identifying and resolving her issues. This legacy of suppression may also obscure the potential paths that could help Sherry transcend her "behaviorally inherited" patterns.

Sherry has been sensitized to the difficulty and hardship of learning from life experience. She resents that the only way people can learn is through suffering. Perhaps because of Sherry's familial experience, she learned to hate pain, the hardships of life, and the stupidity of a society that has not yet learned a more benign way to teach its members the messages of living an emotionally healthy life. Unfortunately, many people do not learn in spite of their pain and suffering. They remain stuck in their karma.

It is not true that the only way people can learn is through pain, suffering, or loss. Many people learn through trial and error, didactic teaching, role modeling, brain storming, problem solving, schooling, apprenticeship, reading, popular media, and consultation. The issue of learning is not whether pain and suffering are necessary, the issue is whether or not there is motivation, dedication, and perseverance to change. Most people want things to be better. However, many people are not willing to take the necessary steps to improve their lives. One's own suffering and the inadvertent suffering of others may be a preferable alternative than facing the pain and fear of her or his internal and external realities. For those who genuinely want to change, making contact with a supportive, caring mental health professional can make the difference as to whether they remain in painful suffering and withdrawal, or choose to discover and create a new, gentler, freer, less painful alternative way of living. Having a supportive bodyworker can make the process even more nurturing, comfortable, and healthy.

ASSISTED DEATH By definition, the conscious and deliberate taking of one's own life is what we call suicide. When Dory asked Sherry if there was anything she could do to remove Dory from her body, was Dory asking Sherry to help ease her pain or end her life? Clearly, Sherry believed that she had a skill which if taught to Dory, would significantly ease this patient's pain. Sherry also believed that her "energy" analgesia would be provided at the price of hastening Dory's death.

Dory was a terminal cancer patient in great pain. The medical establishment had already written her off. Her surgeon left a surgical wire sticking out of her. The surgeon must not have believed Dory would live very long and was not concerned how the wire was left. If Sherry provided her service to Dory, would she have been assisting her death? Sherry's motive and actions do not relate to death per se. Sherry's concern was solely to provide comfort and ease for this cancer victim's suffering. Was part of her anguish driving across Pennsylvania unconscious guilt over assisting in the death of patients with whom she worked?

Death is an issue that Sherry understandably might not have resolved yet. It is an issue for society at large and one with which each of us must come to grips. In general, we prolong people's lives at the expense of their comfort, peace of mind, dignity, and finances.

Angie knew that Osama's death was imminent. Osama must have known that, too. Osama knew what Sherry meant to him. She was someone who could ease him through the agony of the inevitable and help him face his mortality. Sherry provided Osama with her presence, comfort, and truth, easing his physical pain and perhaps hastening his death. When he asked to say goodbye to Sherry, he surely must have known what he was seeking.

In assisting Osama and her other patients, was Sherry guilty of assisted death? If so, isn't anyone whose presence, support, or prayers that lend to a patient's comfort also lending to the possibility of that patient's death? If God is omnipresent, then is it not true that God must be in Sherry as well as in Osama, and the priest? Was Sherry simply acting upon the Divine Spirit that lay within and moved through her? Or, was Sherry projecting and superimposing an unconscious wish onto the patients with whom she worked of wanting to help her father end his life pain? Was she psychologically trying to help him by giving to others what he wanted? If Sherry was doing the right thing for the patients she worked with but for the wrong reason, was she doing the right thing?

Where is the line drawn between accepting one's natural death and committing suicide, between providing comfort and assisting death? And, even if we can legislate, license, or ordain who can provide comfort to the dying and who not, will that ultimately be a moral resolution to the issues of when, by whom, and how the termination of life is acceptable? And, how can anyone who is providing comfort to the dying know that her or his actions are appropriate?

There is no single correct answer to these questions. Perhaps there never will be. This does not mean we are absolved from wrestling with these questions. We will all face death one time or another. If we do not have a sense of our own beliefs and desires about confronting death, we may fail to make the best decision for ourselves, or, by default, turn the decision over to someone whose decision is radically opposed to anything we believe in or may have chosen for ourselves.

SUMMARY

After drifting from job to job, Sherry discovered and became excited about polarity therapy. And, thanks to her friend Angie, she had a practice handed to her. Sherry worked with a clientele with whom she could identify—cancer patients. She, too, had suffered from cancer. If there were any psychogenic antecedents to her disease, Sherry was unaware of them. She reported that she was "ignorant about her condition." Yet, almost a lifetime later, she would recognize that through cancer there may be some kind of karma that the body is dealing with physiologically.

As she told her story, to her own surprise, she recognized that she had stuffed her feelings. She spoke of past troubling work encounters for which she never allowed herself emotional release. She recognized that her feelings for her father's health, suffering, and longevity had something to do with her work.

After taking a vacation at an East Coast growth retreat and having a brief visit with her parents, Sherry returned home. In the sanctuary of her car on the Pennsylvania Turnpike, Sherry began to experience how overwhelmed she was feeling by her work, the patients she worked with, the needless suffering of the dying, and the suffering of humanity. Not long after Sherry returned home, she recognized that she was burned out and decided that she could no longer perform bodywork. She also realized that without far more maturity and far greater psychological skills, she was not equipped to perform the work she was performing. "Working out of her ego did more harm than good."

Sherry's withdrawal from her stress laden work may have been the most pragmatic thing for her to do at the time. The issues of this story, though, remain unresolved. Sherry provided her care, concern, and support to people in the most difficult times of their lives—their final letting go. Seven years after Sherry's Pennsylvania trip, crying "for the suffering of humanity," giving up her bodywork career, the pieces of Sherry's life puzzle have not yet come together.

END NOTES

[1] **Five Stages** Elisabeth Kubler-Ross, a physician who interviewed dying patients, discovered five stages that people often pass through, or in which they may get stuck, in coming to grips with their death. These stages include denial, anger, bargaining, depression, and acceptance. The first stage is characterized by being unable to deal with and accept the fatal information. Denial, pushing out of conscious awareness, is the coping strategy utilized to confront the overwhelming information in this first stage. Anger and rage characterize the second stage. Often there is an acting-out of this anger toward those who are close and those who will continue to live. Bargaining is a process in which someone tries to make a deal with life, attempting to buy health or time. Depression follows as an individual realizes that there is no bargaining with reality. Finally, there is acceptance. The patient accepts the status of her or his physiological health.

Kubler-Ross' stages are similar to the identity achievement process, in that not everyone systematically works her or his way through all of the stages. Some people fight for life until a bitter end.

The process of working through cognitive-affective stages as one grapples with loss does not belong to the dying patient alone. Relatives and friends of the dying may also go through a similar process. These stages of coping with death can be identified in anyone experiencing loss. And, some of the losses that people must cope with are metaphorical deaths: loss of opportunity, health, youth, or peace of mind. The grieving process can be triggered by any loss.

[2] **Choice** Illness has the ability to snatch one from her or his everyday roles and thrust a person into face to face recognition of her or his vulnerability, mortality, and/or self-meaning. If a person is unprepared with a repertoire of psychosocial coping skills, any or all of these confrontations can overwhelm a person, putting her or him into a disabling 157.

16

HEART-TO-HEART TALK

Patricia is a gentle, perky, spiritual, and caring woman in her early forties who had been in an unhappy marriage with a wealthy but non-supportive husband. She asked for no alimony or settlement. She simply left. Her wealthy husband made no attempt to provide Patricia with on-going economic support or an economic cushion to ease her transition.

Well, huum, huum. My nice friend referred Georgia to me. Georgia was sixty-seven. She had cancer. She had breast cancer. It was localized, with a tumor about the size of a golf ball under her right arm. It was right at a lymphatic drainage point for her whole arm. When I began seeing her, she had had it for two years. She had one round of chemotherapy when it first appeared. They said that they couldn't operate on it. They wanted to do chemo and radiation. They told her that radiation would burn her badly and there was no guarantee that it would help her. Anyway, she took one round of chemotherapy, and this is what she related to me.

She said that she lost her hair and it made her so sick that she didn't want to spend her life over the toilet bowl. And she felt so bad that she decided she wanted to try alternative methods to get well. That's when I met her.

It was two years after chemotherapy and the tumor was about the same size. Chemo really hadn't touched it, and she was looking into every option that she knew about. So I jumped right in there and looked for every option with her. They were options outside of herself rather than inside. I talked with her a lot, but we were really…I didn't know how to get in-depth with Georgia. I recommended that she go into psychotherapy, but, eh, that wasn't an option for her. She didn't think she had any psychological problems. And she just kept looking to me and looking to me, and I wanted to help her. I wanted to see someone beat cancer. I bought into it!

It was a challenge to me because she...I could tell she was depending upon me to find an answer for her healing. And I was real into looking for it, just like *(chuckle)* she wanted me to. For a while she did a lot better. In fact, her tumor reduced in size some. I thought, "Hey, this is working." She had two doctors...a holistic physician and an oncologist. Both told her to keep seeing me, to keep on doing whatever it was she was doing.

She was taking a supplement that was supposed to cure her cancer, and she was on a diet with fresh juice and things like that. She did anything nutritionally that might help her heal, and she came to me for almost a year and a half.

Then she decided to go to this cancer clinic in Mexico. That was last Christmas...and they had a sixty-five percent cure rate with terminal cancer patients. She took every kind of treatment that they had down there...from colonics, to shark cartilage, to chelation therapy, to live cell treatment, every possible alternative cancer treatment. She wrote me letters about how terrible the treatments were making her feel and how she was not feeling well.

One of the treatments she had down there...I felt like it must have been the live cell treatment. It is where they take cells from living calves. For instance, if your problem is liver cancer, they'll take cells from the liver of a calf, clean them up, and inject them into you. And it is supposed to help your liver regenerate, and the cancer goes away. Actually, it is what I felt made the cancer go crazy. It went crazy because when she came back, I could feel a couple of nodules here around her clavicle, and I could feel a couple in her neck that she didn't have before. It was like the whole Mexico treatment speeded up spreading the cancer rather than curing it!

And I said, "I still think you need to do psychotherapy." But I wasn't sure who to send her to, 'cause I thought, "This is going too fast, and I think she's going to die." And I didn't feel like she was ready to hear it, and I was too chicken to talk to her about it...until I really knew that she was going to die, 'cause her arm was all swollen up. These were in the last few weeks of her seeing me. Her arm was probably three times the size that it should be. Her neck was swollen clear up to her ear and face.

I used to come home and cry, "What else am I going to do for Georgia! I can't think of what else to do!" As a bodyworker, you can't offer a physical cure. You can't. You can't. But that is what I tried to do in my own screwed-upness...I don't know. I know there's probably a lot of stuff going on behind my screwed-upness. I think I have to go to therapy...and find some thread.

(Having shared this much of her story, Patricia returned to work with her client Georgia once again. Several months later, after returning from a trip abroad, she finished telling this story. At the time, Patricia was troubled by shoulder pain which had been problematic for several weeks. Her own work and that of her bodywork friends had been unsuccessful in releasing the pain. Her resulting strain was evident from an emotional dullness and a sense of being burdened in her voice.)

The next time I saw Georgia, I finally "got it" that I couldn't do anything for her. She was saying, "No!" now to everything that I would suggest as far as counseling. It took all my strength to look at her and say, "I love you, and I don't think you are going to make it." And she really surprised me because she said, "Oh, I know." She said it very casually, "Oh, I know." And I knew that she did know.

Then we finally had the heart-to-heart talk that we should have had in the beginning. I felt like I had made a mistake; I should have had the conversation in the beginning. The conversation was, "You might not make it." We were just trying to pull the same cart to, "You are going to make it," instead of, "You know, there is a possibility you won't make it." But, I was too afraid to talk to her about it. I wasn't ready. I had never handled a patient like that before. I never had a terminally ill patient before...in my practice of almost twenty years. I never had a terminally ill person.

So I said, "Well, are you afraid?" "No, I'm not afraid," she said. "I'm not afraid at all." I said, "Well what is keeping you here? You're in so much pain." She said, "Well, I don't know how to get out of my body." And, I didn't know what to tell her. *(Nervous chuckle)* I said, "What else is holding you?" "Harold," she replied. "He depends on me a lot, and he'll be lost without me." And I really felt like I wanted her to get to the point where she was so okay inside that it didn't matter what her body was doing outside. If she knew that everything was fine, her soul was okay, she could surrender; she could get out of her body more easily and not suffer so much. I don't feel like she ever got to that place. She just ended up dying a really horrible, painful death.

I was on vacation when she finally died. I felt guilty that I didn't get her to therapy, that I didn't do or say something to help her with her inner process myself. I don't know what I did with that guilt. I hope I learned for the next time. Next time I would probably say, "Lots of times we don't think that we have any problems until we talk with someone who is more objective...and can hear us talk and can pick up a little something, a thread that we might need to weed out,"...that's probably how I would talk..."something might be weeded out that might be a real important part of your healing." That's probably what I would say now, that I didn't say then.

I hope that I've learned to be more honest and not afraid I would pull the team in the wrong direction...that it could go either way. I have to be more honest than just do what I think she was wanting me to do. I really felt like she wanted to live so badly, and I thought, "If I wanted to live that badly, I sure wouldn't want to be going to someone who thought, "Well, you're not going to make it." I'd want them to have a complete mind set that "I was going to live..." But, I don't know, I don't have it all figured out right now.

When I look back on it now, even though Georgia was so sick and telling me that she wanted to live,...I don't think that she wanted to live. She wasn't open to anything else, like therapy.

She was divorced from her first husband. I said, *(in a gentle, pleading voice)* "Well, Georgia you have probably read all of Louise Hay's books, and sometimes cancer can come from past stuff." She said, "Well, I think I've done all that. I've forgiven my ex. I've done all that. I don't think that could be my problem."

During my last conversation with her I said, "Well, when you do pass over, would you try to let me know you are okay?" She said, "I sure will if I can." The day that she died I was on vacation. It was a Tuesday afternoon; I was in Portugal. I was driving to a holy place. It was kind of mountainous, and I rounded a curve and I was real excited about going to this place. As I came around the turn, it looked like it was going to rain. Dark clouds were sort of descending on these mountains. And there was a rainbow. And, it just...um...struck me. I said, "I've got to stop and take a picture of this because this is significant to me." For some reason I could feel it. So, I stopped, and I took a picture of it. As soon as I snapped the picture, it was gone...just gone...just total black clouds!

So, when I got home the following weekend, the first thing my daughter said when she met me at the airport was, *(clearing her throat)* "Mom, I'm sorry your friend Georgia died on Tuesday." I called her husband, Harold. He told me the time Georgia died and it was exactly the same time I saw the rainbow. So, because of what I felt when I saw it, I know that was Georgia letting me know she was okay. The picture came out, and I had it blown up and gave one to Harold and his daughter. I was so grateful that she let me know she was okay. I couldn't believe that she stayed alive during the first week I was on vacation. She knew that this trip to Fatima was special for me, and I think she waited until I was on my way there so I would "get it" that it was her, and she was okay. If I had seen a rainbow in Lisbon, I wouldn't have thought much about it, but on the drive to Fatima it certainly got my attention.

After Georgia died, I thought, "No more cancer patients. I don't want any more cancer patients—ever!" As soon as I said that, that's when Gina came in. She was a good friend. She was my first patient when I moved to this town. I hadn't seen her for probably a year. Gina called me. She told me she had been very sick, but I didn't know how sick she had been. I hadn't seen her for a long time, and I was looking forward to seeing her. I saw Gina probably three weeks after Georgia died. With Georgia I always prayed for her to be healed. She wanted to live so badly, and it took the stuffing out of me. I knew I couldn't do that again.

When Gina walked in my office the first thing she did was take her wig off. Then I realized, "Oh, my God! She has no hair. She's had chemotherapy. She has cancer!" I was in shock. I looked at her, and she looked so sick. I said, "Well, obviously you have had chemotherapy or something like that." And, she said, "Yes." And, I asked her, "How bad is it?" She told me she has a rare form of ovarian cancer that had spread all over her inside…to everywhere. They had taken out her uterus, but they couldn't do anything else. It had metastasized everywhere. She was real thin. She looked terrible.

She laid down on my table. As soon as she laid down, my insides were saying, "Oh no, another cancer patient!" And my insides were saying, "Now, don't get so drawn in to her like you did with Georgia! Do this differently." I said, "Well, are you worried you won't make it?" I would never have said that to Georgia, 'cause I was always, "You are going to beat this." She said, "I don't think I am going to die. Not yet anyway." And I didn't know, because she looked so sick…it looked like she might to me.

She was going to start with the last round of chemo, and…it felt like she really wasn't strong enough to go through any more because the last round had just about taken her out. That's what I felt, anyway. She was just one week post her third chemotherapy treatment. That's when she came to see me. She hadn't eaten anything for two weeks; she'd only had water. I told her that she might not make it. She said, "I know that. I've been pretty sick, and I don't know what's going to happen. But I don't think I'm ready to die."

She said to me, "Do you think I ought to go to therapy?" I said, "Yes!" I didn't think she had a very good relationship with her husband. Gina said, "First of all, I don't think I'm ready to get a divorce through all of this." I said, "Nobody said you have to get a divorce. But if you could get clearer about things, maybe in some way it would help you to heal this."

Gina is really very sensitive. *(Patricia got a catch in her throat and had to clear it.)* I really love Gina. She has always been able to feel whatever kind of therapy I would do with her. She could feel subtle energy and was very sensitive to cranial work. She told me she could actually feel her cerebral spinal fluid moving when she was having a treatment.

Well, here she was in my office… so sick…and I had no idea what to do for her. She was in a lot of pain. I asked her, "Where do you hurt the most?" She said, "Over my liver. I just had a CT scan. They were trying to see if the chemotherapy had done anything, but it hasn't. Now I have cysts in my liver, like about a dozen or so." So…I sat down beside the table, and I put one hand underneath her liver and one hand on top of it, and I started to pray…silently. I said, "God, why are you doing this to me again? *(Then in a whisper that started to vibrate as if breaking into a cry.)* You know I don't do well with this. I didn't do well with the last one. I want to help her though, Lord, she's my friend." And I just sat there holding her liver between my hands. I just said to God, "Well, *(Patricia spoke in a whisper. Her eyes turned red and filled with tears that rolled down her cheeks. Then she sniffed and wiped her tears on her sleeves.)* just help me to be with her Lord, and help me to know what to say."

Then I felt something. I opened my eyes, and Gina was crying. Only she wasn't crying because she was in pain or sad. I could tell that something had touched her. I could feel how much she loved me. She seemed to be moved by this overwhelming feeling of love for me. I still had my hands on her. I was looking at her, and she was so touched. The whole room seemed to be filled with love. She told me that she loved me. It was hard for me to take it in. I just sat there being with these feelings the two of us were having. Both of us were crying. Then I felt her liver just sort of rotate, and it felt like something released, and it got lighter. I said to Gina, "It feels like something eased up… did your pain get easier?" She said, "Yes, it feels different…it feels better." After that I did some cranial work, and altogether the whole session took about an hour.

When I was finished, she said, "Do you want to go out for lunch?" I thought it was strange that she was inviting me out to lunch since she hadn't eaten in many days, so I asked her, "Are you hungry?" She said, "Yes, I'm hungry!" So I was thinking quickly what someone should eat when they haven't eaten in days. I said, "How about Chinese food?" I thought she could eat soup, but when we got to the restaurant, she ordered beef lo mein. I thought it was kind of greasy looking. She ate everything on her plate! I ate soup!

I didn't hear from her for several weeks after this. I didn't want to call her. I was afr..., I thought, well, she is probably worse. It was about a month later that I did get my nerve up and called her. She told me she had just gotten out of the hospital. She said, "The doctor had wanted to do exploratory surgery." I was ready to scream, I thought, "Surgery! What else can they do to this poor lady! She's got cancer. She's suffering. She's had chemotherapy. Now, they want to cut her?" She said, "They hadn't seen any change on the CT scan, and the doctor wanted to see if there was anything else he could do. And, Patricia, something wonderful happened...when they opened me up...*(Patricia again whispered and then burst into tears.)*...I don't have cancer."

Her cancer was gone...none...anywhere! We both knew that the moment we had had together was significant, but I didn't heal her. She healed herself. I think she raised her own vibration by the feelings of that love we felt. Diseases can't exist in that state. *(Again, wiping her eyes and her nose on her shirt sleeve)* And that's how it is.

(After telling about her experiences with her clients, Patricia spoke of her struggle with her shoulder pain. Several of her friends and colleagues, as well as she herself, worked on her shoulder. It only provided temporary relief.)

I have been waking up at night and have been unable to get back to sleep. I wake with fear. I'm afraid of not being able to work because of my pain. My pain is magnified by my fear. At night the fear paralyzes me. I think to myself, "How will I pay for everything? There is no buffer-zone if I can't work. This is a high expense week, and I'm feeling bad."

It makes me think of getting money from my ex, so I can have a safety net if I can't work. But I don't feel strong enough to get in a fight and stand up to him. And I want to be spiritually correct. Should I try to get money from my ex, or is there a "higher" way? I'm not feeling calm enough to meditate. I feel like I'm stuck, and I'm not calm enough to feel what's right. I just feel confusion and fear.

A nightmare woke me up, and I felt afraid, and the fear magnified the nerve pain in my shoulder. I don't like being this self-absorbed and so incapacitated that I can't move! I don't like to take drugs, but the drugs help the pain. *(The drug Patricia was taking was ibuprofen.)* I couldn't stand the pain if I didn't take something. I know that the pain has been with me a shorter time than the fear. It seems like I've been afraid of one thing or another my whole life!

It feels like I can't relax. I have to stay tight to protect myself. I can still breathe, though. But if I had money for a safety net, I wouldn't have to worry about trying to work while I feel this way. Then perhaps

I could slowly unravel the constrictions in my shoulder, instead of having to do it fast so I can still work. I feel pushed to get through this fast!

EPILOGUE

Several days after sharing this story Patricia called up her ex and told him that she would need financial assistance to make it through her transition to singleness. He was noncommittal. However, after putting her concern out in the open with him, her shoulder pain went away.

She also explained, "It also became clear to me what the struggle with Georgia was all about. It was about my father. My father died unexpectedly of a heart attack when I was only four. It was frightening to me. After that, death frightened me. I fought to keep Georgia alive so I wouldn't have to face death."

DISCUSSION

ACCEPTING A REFERRAL: A PROBLEM-SOLVING DIALOGUE If Patricia had an inner consultant, and this inner consultant said, "Your good friend is making a referral to you. The woman whom she is referring is suffering from terminal cancer. This woman is willing to go through the risks and discomforts of unconventional treatment in Mexico, but she is unwilling to continue with the discomforts of traditional medical treatment in the United States. It will quickly become clear to you that she does not face or deal with her emotional issues, and she is adamantly opposed to enlisting psychological support. As her condition deteriorates, she will become more oppositional toward obtaining outside psychological support, and she is likely to be more demanding of relief. If her condition turns sour, the weight to rescue her will be solely on your shoulders. Would you be interested in taking this referral?"

If so, the consultant continues, "Issues will arise with this client that you have never faced before because you have never dealt with a terminally ill person. Will you be able to identify and know how to deal with the central psychosocial and medical issues that arise? And whether or not this woman chooses to obtain traditional treatment, do you have psychological backup to help support yourself, to confront the concerns that are sure to arise? And, if this woman chooses not to follow your guidelines, which in the course of treatment could occur, do you know what you will do? She will test your limits, do you know what your bottom line is? And, if you do know your bottom line; do you have the courage and strength to stand behind it?" You have to know how you would answer your inner consultant to be prepared for this client.

PSYCHOTHERAPY Both Georgia and Gina are disquieted by the prospect of seeing a psychologist. There is something that feels frightening about meeting with a person who may shed a psychological ray of light on their existence. By avoiding being evaluated psychologically and perhaps being recognized as being "imperfect," both of these women are willing to forego the teaching and healing gifts that can come from psychotherapy. The dreaded nausea and pain could have been eased for Georgia if she had availed herself of a right-brain intervention such as guided imagery. Discussion of Georgia's fears and anxieties regarding her illness and her treatment would have further reduced her anxiety and the discomforting side effects of chemotherapy. If Georgia had opened to exploration of and catharsis of unresolved past emotional wounds, her pain and nausea could have been reduced even more. This might have made chemotherapy a viable option for her.

If Georgia had had an opportunity to discuss with a supportive, caring psychotherapist the issues of body-image change that were going on for her, she would have had an easier time dealing with the pain in her swollen arm and the trauma of her temporary hair-loss. Just having the opportunity to express troubling internalized feelings can promote well-being and healing. Professional therapeutic support can help make a frightening and uncomfortable treatment regimen easier to tolerate. Physicians lack the opportunity for the kind of in-depth psychosocial exploration and support that are the hallmarks of psychotherapy.

Georgia and Gina may have projected onto a yet-unmet psychotherapist, their anxieties of being judged, shamed, rejected, or abandoned. This may be a monster-in-the-closet situation. From childhood, they may have locked their internal emotional monsters in their own secret closet. Like most people, they may have been afraid, in adulthood, that their psychological gremlins would be as terrifying as perhaps they were in youth. In fear of a psychotherapist opening that emotional closet, they avoided the dreaded encounter and maintained a psychophysical stance of withholding. It might have been this very process of investing energy in holding the door to the closet shut that set the stage for the compromise of their immune systems and allowed the potentially lethal cancer cell to become such a monster.

Psychologists are trained to be warm, empathic, and positive. They possess the skills to help transform lifestyle patterns that may contribute to disease. It is ironic that the psychologist was perceived as a threat to the wellness and integrity of these cancer patients.

Psychologists, like bodyworkers, do not make physical cures. They do not even make psychological cures. Their work may, though, facilitate the healing process. If a medical cure is not possible, and a patient avails her or himself of psychotherapeutic support, a concerned psychotherapist can help ease the emotional trauma for the patient, the patient's family, and even the healthcare team. An effective relationship with a psychotherapist can facilitate a patient's ability to die with dignity.

GUILT Patricia lamented that she did not have the clinical skills to go deep enough to release Georgia's emotional discomfort. This caring, intuitive bodyworker knew what had to be done, and she knew who could do it. She was unable to give Georgia what she knew was essential. Patricia, a kindly, gentle woman who believed that her client only wanted to hear good news, did not possess the emotional fortitude to face her client's possible death. Perhaps in Patricia's bodywork training she never experienced or witnessed a successful demonstration of the communication skills needed to tell her "patient" that additional support on the healthcare team was essential. Maybe, in her childhood, at the time of her father's death, she lacked a role-model who demonstrated adequately how to cope with loss. Patricia had not received the necessary professional training she needed to know how to stand behind her personal-professional convictions.

Patricia put herself down and was punitive with herself for becoming psychologically enmeshed with Georgia's drive to live and her own inability to provide a psychological referral. Punitiveness leads to avoidance and dysfunction—neither of which are productive or helpful in overcoming personal growth issues.

Successfully confronting a manipulative, avoidant patient is no small feat. The fact that Patricia did not succeed in her first attempt to provide a referral for a cancer patient may not be significant. What is significant is that Patricia recognized: "What could I learn from my experience so that I will do it differently next time?" Of course, there would be a next time! When Gina called for an appointment, Patricia had already decided approximately what to say. She also had a greater conviction to say it.

DEPTH Patricia's inability to move into any depth with Georgia, Georgia's unwillingness to go into psychotherapy, and Georgia's belief that she had no problems are likely different faces of the same thing—denial. Patricia encountered something that she was unable to overcome.

There is no guarantee that, even if Patricia had convinced Georgia to see a psychotherapist, after six and a half decades Georgia would have chosen to be open to overcoming her lifetime patterns of conflict avoidance. Even if Georgia did not directly benefit from such an opportunity, Patricia's consultation with a psychotherapist might have helped her to manage her client more effectively and to work with her dying client without guilt. Patricia already had good rapport with Georgia. A psychotherapist might have helped Patricia in understanding her "patient's" behavior more clearly and to respond more effectively.

AN ACCEPTABLE ALTERNATIVE   Many people are unwilling to talk out their problems with a psychologist. However, some of these people might be willing to talk with a minister, a priest, a rabbi, or a pastoral counselor. Spiritual support may be an acceptable alternative. Trained clerics are often able to provide therapeutic support. They routinely deal with issues of death and dying. This could be an alternative or additional referral to include in a health-care team.

COME HOME CRYING   Patricia works from her heart. This, beyond any physical intervention, is what this caring bodyworker provides her clients. Indeed, this may be the critical variable that helped to turn around Gina's condition.

It would be helpful for Patricia to choose from where her caring energies emerge. Patricia may find herself burning out or becoming overwhelmed if she takes this energy solely from her heart-center with a client such as Georgia. Georgia was oppositional when it came to taking command of her own psychological integrity. She wanted emotional and physical miracles from Patricia, and because Patricia was so deeply caring and loving, it was making an emotional mix-master out of her. Though Georgia did not do it consciously, she was callously placing Patricia in the position of "feeling so responsible."

Georgia's denial closed her to her own heart-center making her unable to respect Patricia's intuitive wisdom. For Patricia's protection and Georgia's benefit, this bodyworker's "recommendations" might have been more easily accepted if they came from deeper in Patricia's power center—her gut.

As a result of Patricia's encounter with Georgia, and her putting the encounter into words, she became more knowledgeable and willing to take action in the future. Patricia recognized that she "bought into" Georgia's manipulation, but could not yet recognize the "thread" connecting her inability to stand her own ground to Georgia's avoidance.

FINDING A THREAD   Patricia believed that there was a relationship between unresolved psychological problems and physical drains on the body. She believed that, if Georgia could discover and externalize her psychological stress, she would have more energy to fight off her cancer. She also believed that, if Georgia had help, she might have been able to "weed out something" that would make for an easier transition rather than "suffering a really horrible, painful, death."

Patricia joked about not understanding the "thread" that might reveal her own inability to take action with Georgia: "I think I have to go to therapy." The thread to which Patricia alluded might have revealed an understanding of her reluctance to be honest with and to respond to a client who was in denial. Patricia might have reflected upon her reluctance to confront her former wealthy, but non-supportive husband and ask for the alimony that was due her. Psychotherapy might have provided the support and skills to take a stand and then take action on her own behalf.

Patricia did not seek psychotherapy to deal with her concerns. Yet, talking out her experiences and sharing her feelings with a trained listener *(this author)* allowed her to examine her stance with her problematic client and with her former husband. In each case, she was able to design an intervention strategy and put her strategy into action.

SELF-PUNITIVE Punishment may temporarily, or even permanently, stop an inappropriate behavior. However, punishment fails to suggest appropriate alternatives and reduces energy necessary for explorations of alternatives. Patricia, who is so gentle and understanding when it comes to others, calls herself "screwed-up," contributing to her own low self-esteem and negative self-image.

When Patricia calls herself "screwed-up," she judges all of herself by a tiny part of what she did. This distorts her self-perception, deflecting her awareness of being a fine person. Patricia is a woman who provided Georgia with love, care, hope, support, and comfort. She gave Georgia something that money cannot buy. Patricia's love may also have contributed to healing Gina.

PROBLEM-SOLVING: A PROBLEM-SOLVING STRATEGY The issue one encounters when she or he believes a mistake has been made is how to problem-solve. To problem-solve, one must be aware that something is awry. Then, one must find out exactly what the problem is. Next, constructive alternative interventions must be developed. And, one must choose the most appropriate alternative. Then, one must assess the outcome of the alternative intervention. The problem-solving process must be developed, and repeated if initially unsuccessful. Whatever the outcome, it is essential to provide oneself with credit for what has been undertaken. Punishment does not figure into the problem-solving equation. Recognition and appreciation of awareness, earnestness, and efforts must be provided at each step in the problem-solving process.

FULFILLING A PROMISE   How could Patricia have known when Georgia died? Perhaps she is clairvoyant. Using some extrasensory ability, she was able to perceive the passing of a friend. Or, maybe after working with Georgia so intensely and for so long, Patricia became entrained to Georgia's metabolism. This may have left Patricia, a sensitive body-worker, with an intrinsic sense of Georgia's body rhythms.

Some combination of clairvoyance and entrainment might explain the phenomena of Patricia's awareness of the time of her client's death. It does not explain the rainbow that Patricia saw. The fact that she was looking at a rainbow at about that time might have been just a coincidence. The rainbow's disappearance after the picture was taken could have been the result of air currents, or coincidence. On the other hand, Georgia may have been fulfilling a promise to her loving friend by giving her a sign of her well-being from the other side.

THE MIRACULOUS   If receiving a sign from the other side sounds like a miracle, it is no less miraculous than the connection this loving body-worker made with Gina. Gina was in pain. She had not eaten for days. A recent CT scan revealed a dozen cysts in her liver. The third round of chemo had no effect on Gina's cancer.

Patricia placed one hand under her client's liver and one above. This bodyworker pleafully turned herself over to prayer. Patricia "...felt something." Gina was touched by the love that she was receiv-ing from Patricia. In turn, her own love poured forth. Patricia told herself, "Don't try to do anything. Just be with her." Amidst the love and crying, Patricia felt a shift between her hands. Gina's pain changed. Immediately following the session, Gina invited her body-worker for lunch. This appetiteless woman then consumed her entire plate of beef lo mein!

A month later, following exploratory surgery, Gina's physicians found no signs of cancer. Now, that sounds like a miracle! This event was not miraculous for Patricia. Someday medical science may be able to empirically demonstrate what Patricia intuitively knew: in the expe-riential presence of love, cancer cannot exist.

PAIN IN THE NIGHT   Gina discovered healing in the loving presence of her bodyworker. Patricia, however, was experiencing pain in the shadow of her loveless former husband. Work and daily life-events provide a distraction from injuries, pain, and worries. During the mid-dle of the night, though, when there are no distractions, those nocturnal monsters of fear and worry emerge from the recesses of awareness. Uncertainty about the future is a genuine concern. Patricia's bodywork practice had down-side economic protection. While she was married to a successful businessman, she could easily make it through seasonal fluctuations in her business cycle. Without her ex's support, she was living from week to week solely on her own cash-flow. This readily leads to anxiety no matter how successful Patricia's practice might have been. If she had expenses that had accrued while she was still married, she would have the additional worries of paying off past as well as present creditors.

Patricia, as the sole support of herself, is dependent upon her body's health and well-functioning. Incapacitating shoulder pain must have been terrifying for her. Unfortunately, terror leads to tightening muscles and exacerbation of the incapacitating pain and sleeplessness. The anxiety of not making it financially, the lack of distracting daily activity, the feeling of being alone in the world, and the unresolved feelings of abandonment by a mate all contribute to the nightmare that magnifies discomfort into "excruciating nerve pain" and fear into "paralysis."

Perhaps, because support was so lacking in Patricia's life, she strongly identified and empathized with her client, Georgia. Patricia threw her heart and soul into her work with her dying client. Both must have surely touched and changed each other in their contact. Georgia may have had an increased longevity that resulted from Patricia's loving, healing energy. Georgia's death might even have been far more painful had it not been for Patricia's presence.

FEAR OF DEATH Each time Patricia was able to share and reflect, she made a step forward in her own personal and professional growth. Patricia realized that she was not prepared to work with a terminally ill patient. She recognized that she was trying to provide her client with a physical cure. And she identified her own denial, the "stuff" behind her unprofessional behavior. Finally, she was able to tie off the loose threads personified by her experiences with her cancer patients.

Georgia's cancer and the threat of her death confronted Patricia with her own dread of death. Patricia was prepared to promise the unpromisable and to attempt the undoable to stop her client from dying and save herself from re-experiencing death. Unconsciously, Patricia was anxious that dealing with death as an adult would rip the scab off her emotionally unhealed childhood wound and would be the same traumatic experience she had experienced as a child when her father was suddenly gone.

After Patricia was able to build herself up emotionally, she became sufficiently strong to recognize and deal with her hidden psychological "stuff." This intellectual understanding emerged after, if not as a result of, her emotionally and behaviorally confronting both her clients and her former husband. This is an important point because many people believe that, in order to take meaningful action, they must first understand "why a situation is the way it is" or "why they are doing what they are doing." Patricia demonstrated that meaningful, successful action can be taken before the "why" is known. In fact, the significant action must often be taken before the "why" can be known. And, Patricia's decision to take action was the critical ingredient in allowing her shoulder pain to heal.

SUPPORTING HER INNER CHILD: A PERSONAL-GROWTH EXERCISE Now that Patricia knows "why" she had so much trouble dealing with terminally ill clients, there is still an unfinished task remaining. Inside of Patricia is an emotional "inner child" who was pained and terrified by the death of her father. Many people believe that children are resilient. They believe that children can go through trauma without being detrimentally affected, blemished, or scarred. "They'll get over it." This simply is not true. Adults may not see the damage done by trauma and may not probe to determine the depth of the injury. Just because a child is not crying or acting-out does not mean that she or he is unmarred by tragedy. What more important time could there be for a child to know the comfort, support, understanding, and nourishment of others than with the loss of a parent?

Patricia's emotional child still needs to be touched, comforted, supported, and commiserated with over her losses. And now, in her adulthood, it is she who must pledge her love and support to her inner child who was neglected in her time of need. This grieving and support is not an event that will occur just once. The pain of grief may need to be re-visited time and time again with the reminders of life's seasons.

SUMMARY

Patricia tells a long story which accurately demonstrates the interweaving of the body and mind: the professional and personal, the past and present. Her story begins with the referral of Georgia, a kind of client that she had never before worked with in her twenty-year career, a cancer patient. From the beginning, Georgia blocked the avenues of intervention such as psychotherapeutic release that Patricia believed were necessary. Patricia may have experienced resistance similar to that which Georgia's traditional physicians experienced in working with her. In spite of the thwarting of her wisdom, Patricia continued to dedicate herself to "pulling Georgia's wagon" in the same direction as her client...towards a cure.

Patricia pulled Georgia's wagon because she wanted to support her. She pulled because she was flattered to be so important to Georgia. Unbeknownst to herself, Patricia pulled also because she feared dealing with death. Without direction and riddled with anxiety, Patricia pulled until she had the opportunity to unburden herself by telling the troubling story. Then Patricia found the strength to face the stark truth: Georgia's death was imminent. At this point Patricia stopped pulling the wagon and had "the heart-to-heart talk" she realized that she should have had at the very beginning.

Patricia did not respond to this particular situation by merely having an honest conversation about what could and could not be accomplished; she established how she wanted to handle the issue of treatment with potentially terminal patients. She would no longer promise what was beyond her capability. She would confront the issue of death and let her clients know when additional support was needed. When Patricia's next cancer patient presented herself, Patricia was prepared and put her new policy to work.

Beyond the problem-solving with a professional listener, this experience helped Patricia to build up her internal strength and integrity. As a result, she was able to confront her former husband in a way that she had not confronted him in the past. She requested financial help in her time of distress. He was as unsympathetic and non-supportive after divorce as he had been in marriage. Patricia's gentle and courageous confrontation had no effect in influencing this financially well-established businessman, but did have a profound effect on her.

Pain from an injured shoulder had been exacerbated by Patricia's fear of economic insolvency. She would be unable to survive if she could not count on her shoulder for work. In all likelihood this fear somatically locked the holding pattern into her shoulder muscles. By standing up to the economic Goliath of her former husband, Patricia discovered the strength she needed to "shoulder" her own economic uncertainty. Armed with this knowledge, she broke the chains of her muscular shackles.

Part V

MEN

17

ALL SCREWED UP

Matt is a solid, gruff sounding, burly, personable body worker in his late forties. He spoke as much with his hands as he did with his words.

There was a woman, Nina, who I was in massage class with. I opted to go on and become a massage therapist. I took the AMTA test and passed that. She backed out of it. She became a buyer. But it was the very first time I worked with her that it happened. And, I almost didn't go into massage because of it.

I worked on her probably fifty times. It was basically a regular mechanical massage. Ya know, nothing out of the ordinary. But this first time I was working on her, and a...a, it was the diaphragm. I started working around the rib cage, *(Matt lifted his hands tentatively to demonstrate that his touch was light.)* more just getting ready to work. Then she started crying. And I mean just letting go!

At first I thought, "I must have used too much pressure." I asked her if everything was all right. She said, "Yeah." She says, "I feel so bad. I got this enormous grief."

And, I...really...I felt like shit. Because, my God, what did I do? I hope I didn't...like...ya know, the liver is there.

And I say, "Are you feeling all right?" And she says, "Yeah. There is just this enormous grief." And I say, "You want me to keep working on you?" And she says, "Yeah. I think it would be really good." So, I started working again. I didn't talk. It seemed like an hour; maybe it was five minutes or something, because I just got done with the stomach.

She started talking about her and her husband were in the process of getting a divorce. And she said, "I've been holding it in. I have been very rational and very fair." And she says, "This isn't fair; we have been together for twenty years." And, I didn't do anything because I didn't know what to do. I just kept doing the bodywork. And, so, basically, I say, "Did I miss anything?" And, she says, "If you could work on my chest, *(Gesturing)* I put my hands between the scapula, and propped her up a bit. And she started crying again but a different kind. And then she started smiling and all.

But, ha...when we were done, she was all right. But I was all screwed up! I thought, "Ya know if this is going to happen, this isn't for me. I'm not a psychologist. I don't know what to say!" And I was this far *(Matt boldly demonstrated the distance of a quarter of an inch between his thumb and index finger.)* of literally backing out of it.

I didn't know if it was an emotional response, or she just had it in her and this was an opportunity to get it out with somebody she knew, or whatever, or I accessed where she was holding it or whatever. I don't know. But, the tonal quality of the sob, I still remember. It more than...the fear..."I'm supposed to help people. Here I am...ya know, screwing them up!"

People called me up to get worked on, and I actually turned them down. People that I had been working on. Although a week later Nina called and asked if I could work on her again. She said that she felt so good and this and that. To be honest, I don't know why I did it. But it was an immediate, "Yes!" She called. She was on the phone. And, then I did her again. And, I felt *(Matt rapped twice on a table top with his knuckles.)* Right on there! So, I guess you could say, "Getting back on the horse that throws ya...ah." But, if she hadn't called back I wouldn't have done it again. It was like...Jesus! I am supposed to be helping people and here I am...ya know. But I do believe I stumbled through it okay.

But if she hadn't called back, I may never have done, ya know... bodywork...again. For sure, I never would have done around the ribcage. That was the first and most influential emotional event I had in bodywork. Until then, it was fun and it was happy and it was this and that. And that was like the dark side of it...which turned out to be therapeutic. But I never knew that until years later. Now, I realize, "This is what bodywork is. If you break a leg, your body is not going to forget it."

Ya know, I never thought of this until now, but I think there was a place in me that I could put Nina's cry. It was locked up and could-n't...but, kinda had to come out. Now that I think about it, that was the time space that my dad passed away.

After that, I had people who had minor ones, but it was never to this extent. Ya know it was a real low cry. Like someone who was really sad who has lost somebody. It is a real low cry. It was that kind. And, it really bothered me. Ya know, my brothers and I...ya know, we had to be tough and that bull shit. Until just now when I verbalized it, I never realized that that potential is in me and it probably still is. I just don't give it an opportunity.

I really didn't have much to let out when my father died. He died of cancer. It was a horrible process. When he was alive, I took him to the doctor. On the drive, I would start crying. He'd say, "It's all right, Matt." Then afterwards it was out before it happened. I was very fortunate telling him that I loved him. But, we were close and I always told him that. It was like seeing the cancer and the pain he was in and saying good-bye...saying good-bye wasn't as hard as seeing him suffer.

I didn't think I had that bottled up...Ya know, I think, like everybody else...the little angers build up. Sometimes, I think they are worse. Everybody thinks there is one big thing. But it is the little things that pile up every day. And, they are as important as the big ones. The big ones we are aware of...the little ones that we don't acknowledge pile up.

It was a different trauma. The cancer was more traumatic than his passing away. Ya know, the grief was shared with him while he was there, ya know. I don't know if it was a conduit when I worked with Nina, but I don't think so. I think it was more an openness to the feeling. Ya know, if you don't know what to do with it...but once you learn how to read, it can change your life. But, it was a surprise. It was a surprise.

DISCUSSION

AN EMOTIONAL EXPLOSION   Often people unconsciously inhibit their breathing to avoid experiencing uncomfortable or painful feelings. Bearing down, swallowing, or inhibiting the respiratory process will suppress painful life experiences. This is the physical side of suppressed emotions. As one holds down more and more feeling, more and more emotional explosive is packed into the casing of the body, and an emotional bomb is created. Nina's diaphragm was the detonator of her emotional bomb. With Matt's gentle contact on Nina's abdomen he released the internalized emotional explosion.

INTENT   Matt wanted to give his former classmate and friend support. Much to his dismay, his trustworthiness, caring, and gentleness toward Nina triggered the emotional explosion of her internalized pain. Matt was successful. Rather than the mechanical intervention, it was the "quality" of Matt's presence that effected Nina. The experience of his slightest touch triggered Nina's release.

It was to Matt's chagrin that Nina "just let go!" Perhaps Matt's solid gruffness is a message to people saying, "Don't get too close! Don't feel too comfortable. Don't 'just let go' around me." If this was Matt's intent, for the most part, it worked. No one in a decade had ever had the intense emotional release with him that Nina did. On a non-verbal level Matt may have been sending the message, "This is just bodywork. I am not a psychologist. This is not for feelings. It is just for muscles."

COMFORT WITH ONE'S OWN FEELINGS   In order to work effectively and comfortably with another's feelings, one must know and be comfortable with one's own feelings, otherwise, emotional distress or emotional intensity may be obstructed. The bodyworker's own emotional reaction may block out the unwanted feelings, as we saw with Matt, or, the bodyworker's reaction may put a disapproving lid on her or his client's emotional expression. Another intervention that blocks a client's unwinding process is to rush in with a solution to her or his problem. The cognitive solution interrupts being with the emotional experience. This too, leaves the client alienated from her or his own emerging sense of self. In either case, the client is emotionally abandoned in a moment of need.

The type of self-awareness that would enable a person to comfortably and effectively be with another's catharsis often takes specific training and psychotherapeutic experience. Matt had the intuitive wisdom not to attempt to fix something within his client that was beyond his own emotional comfort level. He set a limit, "I am not a psychologist," though he did stay as physically and emotionally present with Nina as he could.

FEEDBACK   Nina became acquainted with Matt and knew him in a non-work related context. In a sense, they had a dual relationship. Both were students and friends together at massage school. Nina may have seen the vulnerable, personable, and affable sides of Matt as they fumbled to learn the techniques of kneading, vibration, percussion, joint movements, and as they memorized anatomy and physiology. In these circumstances Nina may have seen Matt's sensitivity and grew to trust him with her feelings. Nina may have seen strengths within Matt that he himself had not recognized. In spite of Matt's external burliness, Nina knew of his internal acceptance and caring. So, on the first session, almost before Matt actually made physical contact with Nina's emotionally explosive diaphragm, Nina felt safe with Matt. She could be open with her feelings without feeling vulnerable or threatened.

With little warning, Matt found himself in the vortex of an emotional maelstrom. Amidst this emotional shrapnel, he was uncomfortable and perplexed. Not knowing what was happening, what to do, to precede or to stop—he kept checking in with Nina.

It is not necessary to know what is happening with a client all the time. Nor is it necessary to know exactly what to do all the time. But for a man who defines his task as a mechanical one, not knowing what to do is tantamount to being out of control. Nevertheless, Matt kept checking in with his friend to get feedback about how she was doing. Letting Nina know his concern for her and asking about her experience probably made this event more grounded and safe for her.

RESPONSIBILITY With Nina's emotional explosion, Matt immediately felt overwhelmed by a sense of guilt. Whether Nina's pain was physical or psychological Matt felt "eaten up" inside by a sense of responsibility for this trauma. But Matt was not responsible for the pain that was inside of his friend; her pain was a result of her own life struggles. Matt was responsible for supporting Nina's somatic, psychological system. Nina was able to release her suppressed feelings as a result of Matt's gentle, caring, supportive touch. Matt was responsible for providing his firm presence which allowed Nina to cry and discharge suppressed feelings. He was equally responsible for the smile that followed the release.

When Matt began his career in bodywork, he did not realize that his actions upon the people with whom he worked would be sufficiently profound as to produce psychological change. To become a bodyworker, however, was to become a change agent. This role also entails a certain amount of responsibility. Matt just wanted his work to be "fun and happy." He would have enjoyed seeing all of his clients walk out of his office feeling good and smiling. With experience he learned there is a "dark side" to the work. Sometimes, as a result of a particular release, clients may walk out with an awareness of previously unknown internalized pain.

Matt stumbled upon this responsibility when he worked on Nina, and it was disconcerting for him. Matt did not go into the bodywork field to become a "psychologist." After nine years as a bodyworker, Matt had become more philosophical about the issue. He had come to realize that life comes with certain insults and injuries. And, "the body is not going to forget." These insults and injuries may be reexperienced when the bodyworker touches the anatomical places where they are stored.

INTERNALIZATION Nina was smiling, her troubling feelings catharted, as she climbed off Matt's massage table. Matt's feelings were far from catharted: he was "feeling like shit."

Unprepared for Nina's emotional reaction, it caught Matt by surprise. He remained in shock. Matt was uncertain as to how to deal with the haunting feelings of hurting his client and friend. He internalized this distressing experience.

Internalized feelings often are stored in a different emotional form than they occurred. Internalized anger may be turned into depression. Internalized resentment may be transformed into guilt. Internalized low self-esteem may be stored as fear or suspicion of others. Matt's internalized sense of responsibility and concern translated itself into guilt.

In the process of holding in his feelings, Matt sent himself on a guilt trip. He then turned his experience into a greater catastrophe by imagining that he "screwed up" Nina and his other clients. His confidence in his ability to massage plummeted to zero; he "actually turned down" further work. Matt's experience with Nina was sufficiently traumatic that Matt considered dropping out of his bodywork career altogether. Matt was so shaken, he could have become phobic about working around any client's rib cage again.

SHARING: A PROBLEM-SOLVING STRATEGY   In all likelihood, sharing his experience with Nina, or someone else with whom he felt comfortable, would have externalized and aired out Matt's feelings, as it had for Nina. But Matt held in his reaction to Nina's emotional release. Perhaps internalization is the masculine thing to do. This middle-aged man probably was inexperienced in sharing feelings. Verbally sharing his distress was not perceived as a possibility without losing some of the machismo with which he and his brothers were raised.

INTIMACY   Matt clearly believed his task as a bodyworker to be a mechanical one. His job was simply that of easing stress from the musculature. He wanted Nina to feel relaxed when she walked out of his office. He was neither prepared for, nor wanted to deal with his client's emotions or the psychological traumas from which they originated. The "tonal quality" of Nina's sob placed him in direct contact with her core emotions. This psychological intimacy was disconcerting and overwhelming. Matt could not figure out what happened. And the psychological starkness that Nina revealed, left Matt unglued. The usual distance that he maintained in their social and even professional relationship was broken. A new and emotionally intimate level was exposed—Nina's raw feelings.

When the event occurred, the significance of the sound that emanated from Nina's depths did not consciously register with Matt. However, eight or nine years later as Matt told his story, he realized that "there was a place in me that I could put her cry." Matt had unconsciously identified with Nina's cry of loss. It "…was a place that was locked up." Matt had not fully allowed himself to grieve his father's death.

UNRESOLVED GRIEF   At the time, the death of Matt's dad seemed like a blessing. His father had been suffering for so long. At long last, the pain came to an end. "Saying good-bye wasn't as hard as seeing him suffer."

The death had been coming about so slowly that Matt had time for anticipatory grieving. Little by little, Matt shared his cry with his father in spite of the messages he had learned about being macho. Matt counted himself as lucky for letting his father know that he loved him. Because he considered this a "blessing," Matt did not realize the depths of his grief. And that was the sound that he heard emanating from Nina. The sound of this woman's loss, like a tuning fork, began to vibrate this gentle, gruff, sensitive man's heart strings. Matt became a conduit for Nina's feelings. In the depths of Nina's cry was the echo of Matt's loss for the father he loved. But at the time, Matt did not know how to "read" the message.

Matt quickly felt overwhelmed by Nina's intensity, and in the absence of knowing how to interpret his or Nina's message, he began to withdraw. To his credit, he continued to check-in with Nina for feedback as he continued the mechanical task of providing a massage. But he was so distraught by his client's expression, that he was not seeing or hearing her relief. When the session ended, Matt was so upset over the intensity of Nina's feelings that he was unaware his friend had walked out smiling.

The power of being with the expression of another's true feelings is that they are capable of opening us to our own emotional truths. It would be almost a decade before Matt realized that "reading" Nina's message required him to acknowledge a "locked-up" place in himself, his memory of the enormous grief he felt over his father's suffering and death.

We all have many levels to our lives. Each one can be viewed as a life in and of itself. We have a physical life, a social life, a psychological life, a religious life, and an anatomical life. We also have a marital and a family life. For Matt, when his dad's physical life came to an end, it was a blessing. His father no longer had to live in pain. Because of the blessing of the end of his father's suffering, Matt may not have grieved all the other deaths and losses in his relationship with his father. The pain over losing the father he loved so deeply may have been too much for Matt to bear at the time so he unconsciously locked up his traumatic, emotional memories. Not only did Matt push away the memories, but he pushed away the memory of locking up the painful information. Matt did not consciously know that there was any pain to release.

Grief is not a one time thing. What we truly love, we are pained about losing, not just once, but over and over again across the span of a lifetime. We must be prepared to revisit our loss with each age, with each new discovery, with each reminder. We must be prepared each time to shed our tears as we remember the richness of what we had, what we lost, and what we will never again be able to share. When we actively grieve our losses, we no longer need deflect our energy from our present life. When we consciously confront our pain, we need no longer divert our energy to protect ourselves from remembering and feeling our loss. Though the pain of loss may never totally leave, as a person actively grieves, the intensity gradually diminishes.

FORGIVENESS It was not until a week later, when she called back asking for another massage, that it finally registered for Matt, "Nina was all right." Matt made a spontaneous reversal of his decision to abandon bodywork after hearing Nina on the phone, though he could not consciously answer, "Why?"

Matt realized on an intuitive level that he had not damaged Nina's body or her psyche. Indeed, Nina experienced the release that Matt intended his client to receive. There was no reason for him to avoid the work for which he had trained. Nina was okay; they were still friends and Nina wanted him to work on her again. Matt freed himself from reproach and his avoidance of bodywork.

After years of experience, Matt learned that his clients could occasionally experience emotional release. He recognized that this was a phenomenon related to the practice of bodywork. There was nothing that he had to do about it. It would happen as an integral part of the process.

SUMMARY

Matt shared a story from early in his massage career when he worked with a former fellow student, Nina. To his surprise, he hardly touched her, and she went into a deep emotional release. Matt became frightened by the intensity of her release and believed there was something he had done that hurt her. In spite of his shock, Matt continued to check-in with his friend and client to see how she was doing and whether or not she wanted him to continue with the session. After releasing a deep and enormous amount of affective grief, she told of the pain and unfairness of her divorce. Cognitively, Matt did not know what to do with this material. He simply remained present.

After the session, Nina left feeling rejuvenated, but Matt felt "screwed up." It was then that he made his first decision. If he were going to subject himself to the possibility of that kind of emotional intensity, Matt was backing out of bodywork. Nina phoned back a week later asking to be worked on again. As if having a second chance to climb upon a horse that had just thrown him, he said, "Yes," and reversed his decision.

Years later Matt discovered that there was what he termed, "a dark side to the profession." From time to time a client might have a therapeutic reaction in which a somatically stored emotional wound would be recalled and released. Matt put his first influential experience together with his discovery. He then concluded that this is, in part, what bodywork is about. Bodywork can help clients remember and deal with these unfinished emotional pieces.

As Matt verbalized his story through the lens of time and distance, he recalled having had his own deep feelings. He noted that he had worked with Nina about the same time that his father had died of cancer. His father's death was not as emotionally troubling for Matt as having to witness and endure his father's slow, horrible, degenerative suffering. As a result, Matt had not fully released the insults of deep anguish and pain he felt over his loss. These insults accumulated inside of him.

When Matt inadvertently released Nina's pain, he unconsciously identified with the intensity of this pain. Perhaps, it was for this reason that Matt felt guilty for inflicting such pain on Nina. Although Nina experienced catharsis and release and left the session feeling better, Matt did not have a similar release. He felt dreadful. Matt shared the metaphor of a client's body being like a book and being unable to "read" it. It was a book that told about the deep unresolved grief over the loss of Matt's dad. At the time, he was unable to read the words. Matt concluded that when you learn how to read those experiential messages, "…it can change your life."

18

A VERY COMMON BOND

Carl is a gregarious, energetic, part-time bodyworker in his late thirties.

I was at this Healing Touch workshop just doing my thing and feeling the energy fields, and I had no idea what was about to happen. I could feel the different levels of the fields working and was really in touch with what was happening. I was really there with it. The next thing I know was my partner's body, her whole body, was just convulsing. She literally had a whole body release of very early…I guess it was child abuse. You probably have heard this same stuff before, but I mean it was so intense that I…it was just real…I had no idea how to deal with it.

These old emotions and this old fear and anger that she has stored in her outer bodies—years in her emotional body and in her energy bodies…and she started dumping it just like that! *(snapping his fingers)* She was just ready to let it go. And it just so happened that I happened to be there working on her. When I felt the energy of her field, sensing what was going on, I felt a real, real, cold spot in her emotional field. It was…it just threw me like an electric charge. I was just thrown back by it. My hands got numb.

I asked my instructor, "I have no idea what's happening here. This is frightening to me. This is frightening!" So, she said, "Just stay with it." And the instructor came to help me. And my partner's body was just going through this whole release, and she cried and cried. And I cried. It was like I was experiencing it with her. And at the same time my instructor looked at me and said, "Dear!" She said, "…let it go." I said, "Let what go?" She said, "What you are holding on to." She said,

"You are sharing this with her." And it was really empathic. And at the same time I realized I was letting go of a lot of old stuff. It wasn't whole body, but it was on a heart level. And old hurts that I had inside of me were opened up immediately. By doing that, I just started sobbing immediately.

With all of my bodywork, all of my energy work that I have worked with people, when there is old stuff in the field, I feel it completely. At that point her arms and hands were just...she went into a fetal position and stayed there for a long, long time...sobbing. She was very ill through the entire process. She was vomiting. It was a major release. This was on a very early level, somewhere in her childhood, apparently. It was some sort of physical or sexual abuse. She did not share with us what had happened. Though later she did talk with the instructor.

I just really connected with that. I released a lot of stuff I was carrying with me. It has been like that every time that I have really connected with people who are having those releases. I clean my field every time I go through these experiences...because it has happened three or four or five times since then that I have had these experiences. What it did for me and every time, like I previously mentioned, it is such a cleansing.

What it helped me to do was to open my mind to more understanding and more acceptance and less judgment of people...and how I deal with them. Because I know that we are all wounded. I used to be real judgmental, a lot, on people and what they did in their lives...because of my own experiences. I was so hurt. I got judgmental because I saw the people like my brothers. They're doing this stuff, their vices...drinking and anger. They were angry in themselves and then directed it at me. And I'm real judgmental of that. One of my brothers was real jealous of me and my relationship with my father. I caught a lot of shit from him.

Sometimes it is hard for me to put things in words. They are just feelings. Sometimes it just comes to me, and I have clarity. In working with this woman at the training, I recognized there was no sense in being judgmental. Once I got my feelings out, I had ascended to a new plateau. Then I was able to be forgiving.

Well, in learning and experiencing and perceiving all this, I learned that everyone goes through things, and then has a very common bond. I learned from that experience not to be...I have learned and am learning not to be judgmental, as judgmental, against people who experienced the very same thing. That has helped me to deal with my clients more effectively.

I haven't let go of my judgmentalness completely. But now it is a conscious choice. It is because I became aware. See, I became aware of why I was judging people. Because I was holding onto old patterns of energy, old fears, and old angers because of my father. The emotion was there, and I was angry, and I didn't really know why. I didn't know why. I didn't know why I was angry. I didn't know why I was judging people...for what they did or what have you. Well, when I got in touch with her feelings at the workshop, I realized, "That is what it was. That is exactly what it was." It is old energy and fears and anger. Through that, I held onto a lot of judgment.

So, by that, I learned to start letting it go. We are all into this together *(laughter)*...and we really are. It is not just that someone is bad, or someone doesn't have the stuff to be a good person. A lot of people's negative energy goes back to earlier problems, right now...I would say ninety percent of all that...probably more than ninety percent. But that's nothing new, doctors and psychologists have known that for years. It's just that everybody is starting to wake up to it.

I got in touch with a lot of abuse with my dad. My dad and I, we were always very close. But he was just a workaholic. And he expected all of his boys to be exactly like him, and achieve all the same dynamic results at work. My brothers were so *(Matt struggled to gain clarity of his thoughts.)*...my dad, he was so incredibly overbearing with it, that they turned to drugs and alcohol and are still in a heavy emotional connected state like that. I did too, for a short time, but I was so sensitive to all the emotion that he just...I just turned off. I turned everything off. I just started storing all of it. Well, I didn't know how to release it, up until that point.

He wasn't physically abusive. He just expected so much out of his boys at that point. He pushed so hard. I think a lot of people go through that on many levels—in competition, in sports, not just in work. And they have to deal with that at one point in their life. I was real thankful that I got a chance to get in touch with those feelings and let it go, and I still have a lot of work to do with it.

My dad started his own business that he had to start from scratch. He had to push hard because he had a big family, but he pushed us kids too hard, and expected way too much from us. Now, *(laughter)* I am doing the business, but I don't expect anything out of my boys—my nine year old...so I've learned. Because when I was six, I was already out there working hard. I mean, I wanted to go to work with him and my brothers. But as time went on, he just heaped everything on. He heaped everything on my shoulders. My brothers left, and I was the only boy in there. *(Laugh)* And I had to carry everything. I was the youngest of the boys.

That is one aspect of it. The empathy that I feel, I've always been in touch with people like that. Then my dad, too, there for along time, he was an alcoholic. He kicked it himself. He had that much will...determination. In those impressionable years, I was really abused along those lines by his alcoholism...the fear of being a four, five year old boy. His coming home ranting, screaming, and just crazy with the alcohol, abusing my mother, physically—banging on her, hitting her. He never really, it wasn't such a serious, serious physical abuse, but when he got crazy with it, I can see him literally pick her up and throw her across the room onto the couch. It wasn't like he thrashed her or beat her. She was really fiery, my mother. She wouldn't put up with his stuff. She got right in his face. In doing that, it just enraged him, but it was the alcohol. It was the disease. I really believe that. And my mother has a heart as big as an elephant. It was just that he was going through a hard time, too. He had a real serious childhood. His dad was an alcoholic. And his dad was an alcoholic. And it goes on and on.

I turned all that fear inside. I think that was the beginning level how I started to get in touch with higher energy. I'm a Piscean. So I am very, very sensitive anyway. But with all the emotional abuse that I received, over the years from that situation, I just really looked for ways to escape. That is how I connected with my Higher Source.

I still have work I have to do. I still have self-approval issues that I work around. Where I feel like I'm not good enough. I can't do the work good enough. There is not enough time. I don't have enough energy. I find myself real frustrated because I know that it still revolves around dad, his always pushing. He always made me feel, "Hey, you have to do better! You have to do better than this which is not good enough." So it stems right back to the childhood stuff.

DISCUSSION

CONSULTATION   Carl knew how to use his hands to sense his client's energy fields. He did not know what to do when that energy was unleashed. As his partner began a convulsive discharge of her psychosocial toxins, the immediacy, intensity, and novelty of this event was shocking and intimidating for Carl. He was at a loss as to how to respond. To his credit, he had the integrity to admit his fear, concern, and lack of knowledge. He quickly obtained support for himself and his partner from his instructor. Knowing when to seek consultation and following through is the mark of a professional.

Feeling overwhelmed is an issue that relates to anxiety or fear. The behavioral intervention in such a case is to decrease the stress or increase the amount of available support. Bringing the instructor over increased the available support, though Carl still did not know how to effectively be with his client in such a circumstance.

Unfortunately, Carl's instructor did not provide him with direction. To the contrary, she created more stress for him by raising his awareness of something completely unconscious. The instructor must have sensed that Carl was at the brink of having his own emotional release. She told Carl, "Dear, let it go." He was unaware of his identification with his partner's process and responded, "Let go of what?" That should have been a tip to the instructor to either back-off or give Carl more support. She informed him that he was sharing the experience with his partner, and he promptly did. Carl joined his client in an emotional release. His instructor, having invited this shaken man to open to his feelings, then left. Leaving a person in a lengthy emotional catharsis is neither kindly nor therapeutic.

Carl reported that the instructor later met with his partner. Since he was excluded, he still did not learn what to do. While the instructor made time to talk with his partner, she did not make time to talk with him. Carl, as well as his partner, had internalized childhood trauma. And, the training event with his partner was traumatizing.

The instructor failed to assist Carl in learning what to do in such a situation, and she failed to provide him with support for his emotional release. Perhaps Carl got the message from his instructor, "When your clients are having an emotional release, you should join them with your own emotional release." Carl has done this four or five times. Having an emotional release is not synonymous with resolving the internalized conflict.

DEFLECTION   Carl explains that he engages in his own emotional catharsis when he works with his clients' emotional releases of their energy fields. This becomes problematic from the standpoint of being available to a client who is in need of his full attention. To the extent that a bodyworker is focused on her or his own cleansing process, her or his attention is distracted from the client.

Identifying with a client's struggle is understandable. Empathizing with a client's pain can be supportive and confirming for the bodyworker as well as for the client. Losing oneself in the client's struggle is, however, neither helpful for the client nor the bodyworker. It is essential that a bodyworker be emotionally and intellectually present with a client who is releasing her or his repressed holding patterns. When the client is experiencing a loss of her or his familiar boundaries, the bodyworker must maintain a solid, integrated presence.

SUPPORTIVE INSTRUCTION: A PROBLEM-SOLVING STRATEGY From the beginning of his partner's release, Carl was frightened. His anxiety might have been eased if he had received supportive instruction. He could have been told that clients going through intense emotional releases may become frightened by what is happening to them. It may also be frightening for the bodyworker. This is particularly true if one has never seen this type of release before and is certainly understandable.

A bodyworker, especially a male, might have been helped by being told what to do. When someone is going through such a release, it is important to be grounded so that one does not become overwhelmed. Make sure your feet are firmly planted on the ground. Take slow, easy, deep breaths. Make a mental note of what is happening. "This person has opened up an energy level which was previously closed off. She or he is releasing painful feelings from the past." "This is probably happening now because she or he is feeling safe in these surroundings and feeling safe with you."

While you are emotionally grounding yourself, you also need to ground your client. While you do not have to do anything to your client, you must remain consciously present. That in and of itself can be a major piece of work. Be close enough to your client that she or he is aware of your calming, supportive presence. At the same time, allow yourself enough distance so she or he does not feel smothered or overwhelmed by you. You might be tempted to rush in with a tissue—the interruption may take your client away from the moment of her or his release of feelings—think twice before you rush in. You might be tempted to touch your client at the moment of emotional discharge. Again, touch at this moment may be a distraction or intrusion. If your intuition tells you to make contact, ask your client for permission first and then be prepared to respect her or his answer. You might suggest that your client take some slow, easy breaths to help ground her or himself. If such clients close their eyes and appear to be getting increasingly frightened, you can encourage them to open their eyes and see that they are now in a safe place.

After this reaction is over, you can suggest to your client that sometimes the work you do has a cleansing effect. It allows intense, painful, emotional holding patterns to be released. This is a normal, natural, and healthy process. After it is entirely over, a person is likely to feel tired, but also lighter, freer, and more comfortable inside her or himself. You can tell your client, "If you experienced something that was troubling to you, it might be helpful to discuss it with someone who is knowledgeable and skilled in this area. This type of discussion allows the released event to become more meaningful and understandable."

If Carl's instructor had provided him with this kind of information, his anxiety likely would have been decreased. He would have learned how to respond to such an experience. He also would have been better able to appreciate his own experience. If Carl had followed through and had spoken to a psychotherapist about his experience, perhaps he would have "put things in words" to better describe, understand, and respond to that experience.

DOING MY THING   Carl thought that his presence was accidental when this woman experienced her emotional release. Her release may have occurred precisely because of his empathic presence. In "doing my thing," Carl brought to his work an open, earnest, non-directive, non-judgmental, attentive, confirming support. Additionally, the two may have shared a common psychosocial history. When Carl used Healing Touch on his partner's energy fields, the safety and support in the training environment helped to set a safe and therapeutic stage for the woman's release. She surely must have allowed her dam burst of repressed, emotional energy to convulse through her because she felt safe to do so with Carl.

RECURRENCE   Initially, Carl unleashed his partner's unconscious feelings, then, his partner's release unleashed his repressed feelings. His release, though, was incomplete. Carl's release was not a simple, singular event. He had similar identifications and releases another "four or five times." This recurrence speaks to the depth of Carl's wound. It says that the childhood traumas that created his psychological wounds remained unresolved. Merely releasing his feelings was insufficient for the healing process to occur. Something more was necessary.

Carl needed to mediate his emotional pain with intellectual understanding and behavioral resolution. Verbalization is necessary to accomplish this. While Carl is gifted in intuitive and somatic traits, he struggles in the verbal area. He comments, "Sometimes it is hard for me to put things into words. They are just feelings." The feelings relating to events in his childhood go verbally unrecognized, unconcretized, and unresolved. On his own, Carl does not have the language skills to work through these issues. His psychophysical holding patterns remain until the next time he can identify with one of his clients and he has another emotional release.

In order to resolve these issues, Carl must reach into the emotional depths of his trauma and verbally connect the appropriate emotional labels with the feelings he encounters. With his discoveries, he must then problem-solve as to who he is and what he needs to do to take care of himself. This process goes beyond working a body. It requires bodymind integration. Just as proper bodywork requires a competent professional so, too, the work of intellectual integration calls for a qualified professional. This is the emotionally arduous work that people undertake in psychotherapy.

DENIAL Carl began to get a clearer picture that his "negative energy right now...goes back to earlier problems." He also knew that he "still has work to do." The psychological scars remaining from his early family life left him with feelings of inferiority, fatigue and depression. Carl did not know how the pieces to his life's puzzle fit together. Nor was he aware that he continued, at his own expense, to project a halo on the image he maintained of his father. While he was getting closer to working it all out, he remained in a denial stage. Denial is that unconscious psychological state in which a person is unable to perceive a situation which is too painful to accept. This denial can be seen in the lack of integration of Carl's perceptions of his father.

Carl portrays two pictures of his father. One is of a terrorizing, demanding, hateful, rigid, unappreciative, resentful, blaming man. His father was unable to recognize, appreciate, or treat appropriately a loving wife who "had a heart as big as an elephant." He could not recognize, appreciate, or treat appropriately three sons who were willing to invest their childhoods and adolescences into the family's livelihood. Carl's father lacked the clarity to recognize and appreciate each of his sons' special talents, skills, and abilities. He lacked the strength and integrity to give each son the necessary support to achieve his own unique destiny.

Instead, the father attempted to superimpose his will and domination onto each of his sons. In his attempts to replicate his "dynamic results," he crippled their initiative and marred their self-confidence. He recreated his own pathology, the pathology which was passed down to him by his father—feelings of inferiority, alcoholism, perfectionism, projected anger, and blame. Carl describes his father as "a workaholic, who expected his boys to be exactly like him, incredibly overbearing, pushing too hard, expecting way too much, ranting, screaming, crazy with the alcohol." The father provided the model of a husband who abuses his wife, bangs on her, hits her and throws her across the room in the presence of his terrified children. He may have also failed to demonstrate how to express tenderness, concern, compassion, appreciation, intimacy, and love.

The second picture of Carl's father is of a man who taught his sons the skills of survival. He started his own business from scratch. He taught his sons the business from the ground floor up and provided them with the potential for a livelihood. Carl shares, "My dad and I, we were always very close." Then Carl begins to make excuses for his father, "but." The "but" is part of Carl's denial which probably began in childhood. "Little Carl," the internal emotional child, is unable to accept that the same father he loves, can also be a tyrannical, alcoholic father who terrorizes, intimidates, belittles, and emotionally traumatizes the entire family. "Little Carl" explains away the horrible damage to the family caused by his father's behavior. His father was not really physically abusive; he just had high expectations and became frustrated when he or others did not live up to them. And the father never did any permanent physical damage to his wife when he beat on her. And if it were not for her getting in his face, he would not have been so provoked and explosive.

"Little Carl" tells himself that it was not his father who was making the choice to drink and to act out his frustration and self-loathing on the people who loved and depended upon him, "But it was the alcohol. It was the disease." The emotional child believes that his father should not be held responsible for his actions. After all, he had had a terrible childhood. The father had alcoholic parents. And "he single handedly, out of sheer will power, overcame generations of alcoholism."

This sensitive Piscean child, perhaps in order to protect himself and the image he maintained of the father he loved, denied to himself his feelings of terror. "He wasn't physically abusive. He just expected a lot. And lots of people go through pressure on lots of levels. And there are lots of times in people's lives when they must confront hard times and painful confrontations." This is true. However, people generally, when facing hard times, do not violently throw the ones they love across rooms. Perhaps, in order to feel safe in an unsafe environment, Carl chose to identify with the aggressor. To do this, he had to deny his father's violent, alcoholic behavior and then become "judgmental" of this same behavior in his brothers and others.

DISPLACEMENT Carl's brother, unlike Carl, did not consciously identify with his aggressor—father. He may have copied the behaviors his father role modeled for him, but the brother did not like his driving father. He did not make excuses to explain away the father's behavior. The brother resented the way he was pressured by his father. The middle brother may have identified with his victimized mother. Possibly Carl's brother was not angry or jealous of Carl's "close relationship" with their father at all. He simply displaced and took out his anger and frustration on Carl because he was unable to release the rage he felt onto the person to whom it belonged—his father. A safer target was his younger brother, who identified himself with the father. Without recognizing or intending it, "Little Carl's" naïve identification with his abusive father may have been an additional irritation to his victimized middle brother.

Whether or not the brother consciously identified with his father, he learned from him how to treat those in a position of inferiority. The brother, like his father, simply displaced his anger and frustration onto someone smaller, less powerful and less able to defend himself.

ACCEPTANCE   One can understand and explain why another person has developed abusive behaviors. This understanding can soften one's reaction to the abusive behavior. This understanding does not negate, excuse or explain it away. Nor does this understanding undo the generations of damage that the abusive behavior has inflicted. Fortunately, by accepting what is, one can determine to create something different.

The circumstances that a person grows up with do not necessarily determine her or his behavior. Carl had a self-centered, abusive, alcoholic father. He even had self-centered, abusive, alcoholic brothers. And he chose not to replicate that family pattern. It is not inevitable that because anyone's parents were one way or the other that she or he has to be. However, it takes a lot of courage, honesty, and work to undo the internalized messages received in one's childhood.

So what is the next step in Carl's growth? Beyond denial is acceptance. Carl has yet to learn that he can both love his father and also be angry with him. He can love his brother and also be angry with him. Indeed, his brother probably loves Carl and may also hate him, too. Carl has reported some very significant information. As Carl's judgmentalness became conscious, he was no longer automatically or impulsively judgmental. As Carl was no longer unconscious of his judgmental feelings, he was able to consciously understand and accept his feelings. He was able to consciously choose how he would respond to them. Carl's conscious, rational, healing adult was gaining command over his unconscious, wounded child. This new awareness was assisted by his emotional release.

IMPRESSIONABLE YEARS   Whatever the motivation for the brother's and father's behavior, the silent wounds of those early life traumas remain locked inside Carl decades afterwards by "Little Carl's" psychomuscular holding patterns. Now in his late thirties, Carl continues to struggle with self-approval issues. He perceives himself lacking the time, energy, and finesse to do the job "good enough." His father's voice echoes, still demanding and demeaning.

Carl has decided that he does not want to repeat his father's mistakes with his own children. When Carl was six he was already working hard with his father and his brothers. He does not want his son to grow up with feelings of incompetence because he can never live up to his father's expectations, never have his father's approval.

Carl anticipated achieving his goals with his sons by doing the opposite of what his father did: "I don't expect anything out of my boys."

Hopefully, Carl is not being literal when he says he does not expect anything from his sons. Many children rebel or try not to replicate their parents' mistakes by omitting behavior that was damaging in their own childhood. This omission leaves a vacuum. It is realistic for parents to have expectations for their children. Expectations are best when tempered with reasonability and appropriateness for the children's ages. Otherwise, further damage may result.

In order for a child to experience feeling loved, more than lip service must be provided. Overindulging a child does not make up for the emotional nourishment one did not receive in one's childhood. This simply produces a spoiled, self-centered child who believes she or his is entitled to anything and everything. Overindulgence does not cause a child to feel loved, only entitled. A child learns to be a responsible person when her or his parents express caring through setting reasonable limits, providing emotional support, and demonstrating positive values.

As much as giving of himself to his boys, Carl must also set an example by sharing his unconditional love with his inner child, "Little Carl." Carl must demonstrate to his sons, through his example, that he cares for someone who is worthy and deserving of love—his feeling self.

A healthy alternative to overindulgence is consistent love. Consistent love can be expressed in many ways: with pats, handshakes, hugs, kisses, as well as, applause, laughter, and expressions of joy. Love can be expressed by taking time with each child individually, listening and allowing each child to feel recognized. Love can be expressed by teaching social skills. It comes through supporting and guiding the child to actualize her or his unique talents and abilities.

Love can also be expressed through expectations for children to take on reasonable family responsibilities and through recognition and confirmation of each family member's contribution. Love comes in helping a child to develop as a person. Love comes through teaching children to use tools and machinery safely, through reading and learning together. Love grows with acceptance. No matter what the outcome of the child's efforts, they must be reinforced and appreciated. In this way a child learns she or he is unconditionally loved.

RECOGNIZING AND APPRECIATING: A PROBLEM-SOLVING STRATEGY

Carl chronically suffers from a lack of self-approval. This may come from a number of sources. Some of this self-devaluation is a result of internalizing the role model provided by his father who also must have suffered from low self-esteem. Some of Carl's self-devaluation was a result of internalizing the content of his father's words to him. Another part may have come from Carl's failure to actualize his own dreams.

Carl had already amassed sufficient life achievements to provide him with the self-esteem he desperately needed. He had apprenticed and learned well the tools of his trade. He supported his family. He made a choice not to be an abusive parent and husband. He had arrested and overcome any tendency to drug or alcohol abuse. This earnest Piscean had chosen to nurture his sensitive, caring nature by learning a bodywork discipline. He had already brought his sensitivity and skills to many clients and had helped them to release their buried burden of emotional pain. Carl achieved much for which he could be proud.

What was missing for Carl was the belief that he was both lovable and deserving. He also lacked the knowledge that in adulthood, self-esteem emerges from recognizing and appreciating one's own achievements. Recognition from others may be sweet, but if one is dependent upon external recognition, or is not accepting of recognition, then self-esteem will not be achieved. By genuinely providing heartfelt recognition and appreciation for his many accomplishments and achievements, Carl can begin to turn around his chronic low self-esteem.

STARTING TO WAKE UP It would be nice to believe, as Carl suggests, that "everybody is starting to wake-up" to the relationship between early childhood trauma and "peoples' negative energy." Just as individuals have their ways of denying painful truths, society at large also has its own repressive ways of burying its awareness of painful realities. Society's denial is articulated in the way it chooses or fails to choose to legislate, appropriate, educate, and favor one group over another.

Society is repressive when it naively and simplistically tells people who struggle with dependency issues, "Just Say No." Some people, out of sheer will power, may be successful in arresting their abusive, awareness-numbing, chemically dependent behavior. However, they are left with all the hurtful underlying issues that instigated the chemically tranquilizing or irritating behavior in the first place. They are left with neither the skills to handle the problems nor the artificial support to numb them out. This creates people who Alcoholics Anonymous refers to as "Dry Drunks." These are people who have stopped their abusive drinking, but continue to exhibit all of the other psychosocially destructive traits of someone who is alcoholically or chemically dependent. The repressive myopic thinking "Just Say No," if it works, may stop the overt signs of the problem, but it can only pretend that the covert, causal issues have been addressed. The new "managed" health care system which maximizes profits by curtailing the availability of out-patient psychotherapy may also be an expression of the social repression of the need to support those who could benefit from ongoing treatment.

While society at large may be struggling with its "wake up call," Carl is getting closer to his own truth. He is beginning to recognize and remedy the personal damage that was done to him. He is trying to stop the pattern so that it is not passed on to his children or their children. When Carl has sufficiently dealt with his internalized pain, fear, and anger, he may be able to accomplish two things: Carl will be able to accept the despicable, damaging nature of his father's behavior toward the family during his childhood. And he will be able to release his judgmentalness toward people like his father. This will allow Carl to perceive his father as a total person and truly accept him for who he is rather than a fantasy of who he would like his father to have been.

The scars of Carl's childhood are probably deeper than those of others. More people than realize have been scathed by traumatic events of childrearing. They do not realize the consequences these wounds have on their developmental life paths. Carl is quite accurate when he says, "I know that we are all wounded." Some people are just more prepared and willing to deal with the wounds than others. Perhaps, as a result of the professional-personal growth that Carl is undergoing, he will be better able to support others in their recoveries.

SUMMARY

Carl was at a Healing Touch workshop when he was as profoundly touched by his contact with his training partner as she was by him. Carl left his training with the specific tools of that discipline and with a shift in his personality. At the time, he may have been unable to articulate the specifics of his shift, but Carl knew he felt less judgmental after his catharsis.

Later, as he told the story of his training experience, he realized his shift, "ascending to a new plateau," resulted in being "able to be forgiving." Previously, "old fears and old angers" blocked his ability to be open and understanding toward his brother. Once he had this emotional release, what became clear to him was that he had been angry and "didn't know why." Carl's repression kept him from realizing that his anger and judgmentalness were related and resulted from his childhood relationship with his father and brothers. After the release, he was feeling closer to all of those who had played the role of aggressor. In particular, Carl felt forgiving of his middle brother from whom he reported catching "a lot of shit."

After Carl's release, he became consciously aware of his repressed childhood wounds and how they resulted in his judgmental attitude toward his brothers and anyone else who was alcoholic and angry. As he was able to express his painful feelings, he understood that both he and his brothers had been wounded by their childhood. The wounds were just expressed in different ways. In addition to appreciating that they were wounded by the same events, Carl discovered the internal strength to forgive his brothers for their anger and jealousy. Carl recognized, "we are all wounded." His plight and that of mankind in general are related. "We are all in the struggle of life together." We share "a very common bond." As he brings his new consciousness to bear, Carl chooses forgiveness rather than belligerence.

19

GIVE TO A FAULT

Andy is a massage therapist in his mid-forties. As he tells of his experience with his client, he becomes increasingly forceful and driven.

Well, I could have done a certain thing, but I didn't tell him I was going to do it. I started to think, "I could lose my job over this! I may be angered to a point where I may take an action and something probably very violent could happen."

This client, Hal, has had juvenile diabetes since he was eleven. Now he is in his late forties. I started working with him about five and a half years ago. When he was growing up, he'd party. He was a heavy partier and you don't do that if you have diabetes. He had his insulin pump and the whole bit. He drank, like, a fifth of tequila over the weekend and just got soused. That was, growing up here in this area, these East Side people tend to party hearty. They are like upper income.

It got to his health. He ended up having to have a kidney transplant. When I started working on him, he had had his second kidney transplant. When people are sick, I just...my whole being goes into them. Because for some reason, I seem to be able to place myself in their situation. That's why I kind of grope at it...I want to help, help, help, help.

There are just some things with this disease that you can't take. He had already been amputated below the right knee. He had acupuncture, and his left toe got infected. They had to do surgery and cut it off. His anti-rejection drugs from his kidney transplant gave him a tumor in the rectum. He had to have that cut out and sewn up and a colostomy. That kidney started failing. He had to go in and have a shunt put in so he could have cleansing of the blood. This guy has been through hell. I'm getting through it real quick so we just don't dwell on it.

He had to check his blood and stick his fingers with needles regularly. And from time to time they would get so they wouldn't heal. His artificial leg would put an ulcer on his leg because the doctors would misfit him. He already had a hole in his heel that I worked and worked to get it to heal. It didn't close up for two years.

I got through that with a lot of prayer. A lot of prayer is going in for this person because I think that is the only healing...the only power that can even deal with the situation because he is just rotting away. When he was having problems with the ulcer on his leg, they had to take a two foot muscle out of his back. They put him on crutches, and he fractured his foot. Then, from that, his toes started to get involved. So I got involved with Melaleuca with him, ointments—from the Melaleuca tree. That seemed to soften it up, and I kept thinking, "We are going to save these...positively save these toes." We didn't. They had to cut his foot off. They had to take a two foot latissimus out of his back. Brought it down. Sewed it to his foot. This guy was having veins sewn in so he could have blood to the tissues, both arms...a medical marvel over at the hospital. Great case study! The medical record is a foot long. Phenomenal surgeons.

He puts himself onto Dilaudid drugs and takes himself off of them. I admire the man to a point of loving him—a brotherly love. So I am really caught up into this. So we finally got his foot healing up. It is something he can walk on. It has a potential infection in the bone. I'm thinking, "Don't tell me you've gone through all of this hell to get this stump put on your foot, and you might lose it!" You know? He is doing okay with that. They are giving him antibiotics and so forth.

Hal's firm threw a fund raiser for him. That provided some extra cash for medical expenses, but the fund was mismanaged, and the money was lost. Then there were some really tight financial times.

We got Workman's Comp to pay for his treatments. So I went for awhile where I wouldn't charge him because I knew he needed it. I can't throw somebody out because they don't have money, or set them aside like a piece of trash, especially a sick man. That can come back on me, and I could get sick. I don't know if it could happen that way. But I just...life isn't about money. I think life is not just material. It's...I think you give more of yourself than wanting to receive. I am not in this business to excel materialistically.

I've treated Hal's wife several times. She came in and said, "Hal's doctors tell me what is going on with his body is also going on with his mind." *(Becoming increasingly upset and overwhelmed)* That kind of really shocked me. I wondered whether that was going on, but she confirmed it. His doctors are saying, "Get prepared because his body is decaying, and his mind can snap too!"

There is trouble with the company. Hal is trying to throw his weight around. He is this handicapped person, but he is rugged. I'd like you to meet him. Throughout his working years with the company he could kind of throw his weight around. This handicapped person saying, "I need a rest room all to myself." And he would bring the handicapped corporation in to help him...like to tell the company, "You better do something for this man!"

During this time his wife lost her job. I went to the extent of asking some of my influential clients if they could help her. None of them cared. They just said, "She'll find work. She'll find work." The reason that I divulged this to others about Hal and his family was because they were selling things out of their house to survive. Like having garage sales and things like this because Hal couldn't work well, but he was still making a living. But he was still relying on his wife's professional salary. Do they just drop her and shit-can her? So I'm thinking, "Shit, you are not only sick, your wife is out of work. It looks like you are going down the tubes." I don't understand why, but no one was helping.

They had a garage sale. So I bought a Nordic, not a Nordic, but a walker from him and an air conditioner. And, I gave him some treatments. I could afford it. It was no big deal. She finally found work. And things started going up slope instead of this down side.

So, I told you about the special funds being depleted and my helping him by buying little things, helping him with his treatments, and his wife saying, "What is going on with his body is going on with his head." Then there were changes at the company. A new president was brought in.

Hal went to work when he could...when he was not in the hospital. He went to work one particular day, and the president and his manager had a meeting. You know I am really caught up in this guy. I care about him like a brother. The meeting is over with and the president and the manager come out. The president says, "Hal, I want to talk with you. Will you come to my office." Hal walks in there and the president says, "Your manager tells me you are nothing but a trouble-maker, and if you don't keep your mouth shut and quit turning the company in over these little issues about the handicapped, you are going to lose your job. You are not going to make any money, and...you are going to lose your insurance."

Hal said to me, "Andy...," I think this happened on a Friday, I treated Hal on Sunday. He says, "Andy, if they keep this up I am going to go into the house and get my automatic and walk over there, and I'm going to shoot the place up!" And he says, "I've got an excuse...I can plead insanity."

I said to Hal, "If they make me mad ...," I said, "they are going to have some problems." And I said, "This president of yours is on the verge of doing it." When my brother has problems...I thought to myself, "You know Hal, you don't have to do it. I'll take care of it for you." You know I am a Vietnam veteran. *(With a long, cold blooded look in his now snake-like eyes)* I've been trained to kill!

And that is when I caught myself. I thought, "This is not good!" I thought, "I'm putting up a wall here. This is wrong." I had never gotten involved to that degree with a client—emotionally and in my heart of helping. I said to myself, "I am getting too involved with this situation because I can get my ass locked up!"

I immediately turned it over to the Lord, but I didn't mention the Lord at all to Hal. I said, "Hal, I think it is best for you ..." I said, "Hal, just keep your mouth shut and see what happens. I feel people who treat sick people that way...something is going to happen to them. The company is going to fold or something." Hal doesn't want to see it fold because he is a loyal worker. He still felt bad. It was like, "Okay, I'll keep my mouth shut."

So Hal...when I saw him the next week, I asked him, "How is work going?" He said, "Okay," I asked, "Are you keeping your mouth shut?" He said, "Yes." And that was it. *(For the first time the pressure in Andy's speech ceased and he spoke in long halting phrases.)* The result...it just worked its own self out. There wasn't anything that changed my mind. It seemed like I was as in control of the situation as I am with all my clientele.

I can't say I learned anything new from this experience. I did learn that I can catch myself before doing anything radical. But I am not sure if a guy like Hal came in for my services that I would not play it out again just the way I did with Hal.

I want to see people get better whether they deserve it or not. What goes around, comes around. I think sometimes I run into situations where things are coming into people's lives that they might not deserve. Then I fall into it. I am such a goober! I give to a fault...to everybody. You ought to have one of my treatments and pay me. I'll show you what I give. To everybody...every one I touch.

But I think I did learn where to cut a relationship off. Exactly where, is hard to put into words. Maybe I just know where by instinct. I don't know. You just have to make a decision how far you will let a situation go—how far you are willing to let yourself get into your clients' lives. My decision was a moral decision not to harm anyone. But I didn't know that I could get carried that far.

I was in this workshop. The leader said my presence is enough. I do not have to put my whole being and life into the client's situation where I do my own self harm. I didn't think I learned anything in that workshop, but maybe I did learn something.

DISCUSSION

DENIAL   Denial is the inability of a person to accept some information, event, or trait in themselves or in another and to unconsciously act as if it were not true. An example of this is a person being given a medical diagnosis, without sufficient support or strength to accept and deal with the condition. The person acts as if the condition does not exist, or may even go out of her or his way and act in ways which exacerbate the condition.

A person in denial may engage in secondary behavior which, in turn, contributes to the denial. Alcohol, drug, or substance consumption, acting as a cognitive tranquilizer, is often a secondary intervention used by those in denial. Hal was confronted by his medical diagnosis at a time when teenagers are psychosocially seeking to conform to peer norms for acceptance. The health and dietary restrictions for his diagnosis and the peer norms were in opposition. Regulation of diet and exercise, as well as, support for stability and psychosocial development, are essential in diabetes. Having a medical handicap might have led Hal to feel different from and inferior to his peer group. Rather than succumb to feelings of inferiority, Hal behaviorally overcompensated for his condition. He ignored contraindications of his medical condition in order to be accepted by his peers. Hal, as a rebellious adolescent, defied his medical condition to his own detriment. Some may perceive his bravado as laudable in the face of his condition. Yet Hal's "partying hearty" may have allowed him to further numb his awareness of his medical identity—his diabetes and the degenerative, debilitating effects of his self-abusive behavior.

As Andy describes his client, Hal is clearly a powerful, determined, and forceful man. From an early age, part of Hal's survival energy was diverted to support his denial rather than to support his self-acceptance and self-preservation. While Andy was investing his "whole being" to help Hal overcome the effects of his disability, the denial part of Hal was working at self-destruction. This was Andy's basic struggle with Hal. Ultimately, this issue brought Andy into his own identity crisis. Andy almost sacrificed his peace of mind and well-being by violating his "moral" values and getting his "own ass locked up" by acting-out Hal's violent fantasy.

Andy had a strong identification with his client who is in denial, and Andy may also have been drawn into that denial. Andy sided with Hal's desire to maintain his rugged lifestyle rather than a healthy one. In doing so he, like Hal, was in denial about the reality of his spiritual brother's condition. From this uncentered, ungrounded posture, Andy was in a poor psychological position to support either himself or his client.

UNCONSCIOUS TEMPLATE   Andy reports being unaware of "the reason that his whole being goes out to people when they are sick." Andy's motivation to "help, help, help, help" is unconscious. This material may be unconscious because it is linked to some painful earlier event in his life. Andy knows that he "gropes" to help, but he does not recognize the dynamic which allows for immediate identification with those he wants to help.

PRAYER   Andy says that there is something special that he gives to everyone he touches. There can be little question of this. The quality of Andy's touch must communicate the grace that Andy experiences when he is in prayer. His client, through contact with Andy, also experiences this grace. The healing potential of this is inestimable. While Andy intellectually recognizes something is special about his touch, he stops short of fully integrating this knowledge. Consequently, he believes there is something more that he must do.

This notion of having to "do" in order to have impact, meaning, or substance may be related to the issue of assuming a rescuing or helping role. Andy's insatiable need to "do" may also be related to his concept of manhood. If Andy accepts the cultural stereotype of masculinity, then he believes the quantity or even the outcome of his efforts proves his worth. This perverts the assessment of healing power. Healing potential is a variable of the wholesomeness of one's state of being, the clarity of one's identity, and the oneness of mind and spirit. Healing power cannot be reduced to measurement in quantitative terms. The part of Andy that locks him into playing a role, also keeps him from further self-integration, self-acceptance, and self-appreciation.

Andy recognizes the significance of prayer for himself and his professional practice. Andy believes prayer is the only effective intervention with a person in a grave condition. However, Andy takes the entire responsibility for praying onto his own shoulders. Without proselytizing, he could suggest its potency to his client. Prayer, like any form of meditation, can promote relaxation of muscular tension, immune system stimulation, increase of blood circulation, and opening to higher consciousness.

SNAP While Andy could cope with Hal's degenerating body, his "mind-snapping" was deeply troubling for Andy to contemplate. Andy seemed willing to take on yet more responsibility in an attempt to ward-off this possibility.

Hal's physicians suggested to his wife that Hal's mind, like his body, could snap. Did those physicians recommend emotional support for either Hal or his wife? Did they provide referral for psychological, psychiatric, or even pastoral support? Very often people who are trained in providing medical intervention do not consider providing emotional or spiritual intervention for their patients.

Andy felt concern for the whole client. And Andy was a networker for his clients. He could have suggested to either Hal or his wife that he or she seek emotional support. After all, both of them were his clients.

Hal was an alcohol abuser in his youth. His adult patterns of numbing can easily be linked to the alcohol related patterns of numbing in his youth. If Andy's information was accurate, Hal self-determined his use of Dilaudid, a powerful pain killer. A physician must have provided him with a prescription for its use. Did the physician know of Hal's denial, his self-destructive acting out behavior, and his alcohol abuse? If Hal and/or his wife were willing to accept a referral for emotional support, perhaps the possibility of his mind's snapping would have been diminished. Andy and Hal's wife would both have had additional support in coping with Hal's condition.

Andy would have benefited from a consultation for support of himself. He was already becoming emotionally overwhelmed. Andy had been bonding with Hal. Hal was on the verge of snapping. Likewise, Andy was on the verge of exceeding his limits. Professional consultation might have lessened the responsibility Andy felt and might have reduced the extent to which he was becoming enmeshed in the turmoil of his client's life.

BONDING Bonding occurs naturally as a consequence of sharing the traumas and triumphs of another's life. Andy's bond with Hal became deeper and deeper as Andy made continuing investments in the physical, economic, and occupational welfare of Hal's life. Andy bonded with Hal through his psychological identification. He bonded further with his hands-on work. The bonding accelerated as Andy became ego-involved in attempting, literally, to save his client's life and limbs. Andy realized the depth of the bonding when he experienced the threat to his friend's livelihood as a personal challenge. Andy reacted with thoughts and feelings of homicidal rage.

FANTASIES OF VIOLENCE Andy and Hal were enraged by Hal's new company president whose leadership style was emasculating, treating a man as if he had no rights, no say, no dignity. Understandably this led to resentment, anger, and rage. The fact that Andy and Hal were driven to fantasies of violence is not surprising. These men had been raised in a culture which values competition rather than cooperation. Crisis intervention is the solution of choice rather than prevention. Watching violence in the media is a socially sanctioned form of entertainment. And the Army trained Andy to use violence as the ultimate solution.

Certain interpersonal aspects of the work place can create an unhealthy psychophysical arena. Gross psychopathology in one employee or employer can create an emotionally toxic air for others to breathe. When people learn to accept, or are forced to compensate for this psychosocial pollution by redirecting their energies, this process compromises the worker's productivity and personal integrity. The higher in the organizational ranks this pathology occurs, the greater the number of people who are infected by the poisons as it trickles down.

As a self-employed bodyworker, Andy is spared all of the potential indignity of such a work place. He is…"not in business to excel materialistically." If he chooses to be altruistic and to provide services gratuitously to a needy client, he does not have to obtain permission. He just does it.

Andy will encounter clients who do not share the luxuries of being self-employed. It will be his job to help those clients to release the physical tension that they build up as a result of psychosocial stressors in their work environment. If Andy does not set realistic limits or boundaries to his involvement, however, he may burn-out in his attempts to help others.

POST TRAUMATIC STRESS Andy, through his identification with Hal, experiences the impotent, seething rage that many experience when a relative or loved one is the subject of mistreatment in the workplace. When scarce jobs, tight funds or medical problems make change difficult, a worker can feel trapped in such a situation. There is often little one can do as a caring, concerned onlooker other than sharing that concern and caring. In the short run, this affective support may provide understanding and solace. In the long run, it may provide the other individual with the strength to take corrective action or find a better work alternative.

There is usually no one who provides effective recognition and support for the empathic caregiver. For many caregivers like Andy, their affective needs regarding troubling cases go unmet if they do not specifically seek out or create healthy support for themselves. Andy's stress grew little by little as he failed to recognize his needs.

Andy, like others who have work-related frustrations, found that the intensity of his present frustration removed the affective lid from a past frustration. Andy may have returned to the life or death reality of wartime in Vietnam. This is an invisible and unhealed post traumatic wound he continues to bear.

PRAGMATIC STEP Hal may not have intended to take violent action. He might only have been "talking" of taking vengeful action, as one man might verbally do, venting to another. However, as Andy and Hal fantasized together, Andy's sense of vulnerability was alerted. He recognized something was going too far. Solution by violence was neither a solution nor an acceptable means in Andy's value system. Andy believed in Divine justice, not vigilante justice, "What goes around comes around." He believed every one should be given support "whether they deserve it or not." Andy stopped himself and Hal from entertaining any more thoughts of violence. Andy was turning this problem over to a higher arbiter of justice—"The Lord."

Andy was impressed with Hal's strength of will. He explained that Hal was a "rugged" individual who developed a work style of "throwing his weight around." There must have been people at the company who did not like Hal's brash style. In spite of Hal's handicap, someone mismanaged his "special fund." The new company president was no longer willing to put up with Hal's manipulative demands. Hal did not request handicap accessible facilities to be installed; he demanded his own personal restroom.

With this new president on board, Hal's machismo had run its course. Hal could no longer get his own way at the office. Andy recognized that there was a pragmatic step Hal needed to take in order to ensure his economic and medical security. Hal needed to stop making waves in order to keep his job and medical insurance.

PHILOSOPHICAL STEP By putting his story into words and telling it, Andy, for the first time, had to cognitively formalize what had happened to him. As he took the philosophical step of exploration, he was hard-pressed to say what he learned from his encounter with Hal. He had not contemplated or deliberated sufficiently to gain enough clarity to develop a plan of action to check his giving "to a fault."

Andy was contradictory in his experience with Hal. At one point he stated, "I had never gotten involved to that degree with a client— emotionally and in my heart of helping." At another point he said, "It seemed like I was as in control of the situation as I am with all my clients." Which statement is the truth? Was Hal an exceptional client, or does Andy have difficulty maintaining his professional boundaries with all his clients? Andy again waffled, realizing that it is important to have limits. However, he admitted that should a similar situation arise, he might again play out his experience the same way. The situation might have to reach similar proportions before Andy could recognize and establish his limits.

Andy planned by crisis intervention rather than by design. If Andy would like his business to run more smoothly, he has his work cut out for him. He must tackle the complex task of clarifying his feelings, establishing his limits, identifying when he reaches them, and taking appropriate action to maintain them. He must also clarify the aspects of his practice and his relationships he values most. He must set limits to what he will or will not engage. He must assert himself by taking action.

Establishing boundaries and setting limits is almost impossible without a clear sense of one's identity. One can not have a sense of identity without a clear recognition and understanding of one's own directional orienting system — the feelings. Verbalization with others is often valuable in this complex process. If Andy is like many men who do not verbalize their personal thoughts and feelings, this material may go unintegrated and parts of Andy's identity may remain out of focus.

PRESENCE Giving advice to Hal was "business as usual" for Andy. Another choice was created when Andy attended a workshop in which the leader told him the quality of his presence, in and of itself, was an intervention. With this thought in mind, Andy began to explore the question, "What is the aspect in this practice that makes this treatment so special?" If Andy believed in the integrity of his presence, he might feel he does not have to "do" so much. If he truly believed and trusted in the healing power that comes through the quality of his presence and his prayer, he would not feel pressed to exceed the boundaries of his professional skills in responding to the needs of his clients. As Andy pursues this issue he might want to ask himself, "How come I give to a fault to everyone?" and "Do I want to keep doing this?" Answering these questions may change the shape of both Andy's practice and his personal life.

Andy's prayers may unquestionably provide for his clients' health and healing. While prayer, in and of itself, does not guarantee a specific outcome, it does provide for a link to a "higher" source of wisdom and power. This linkage benefited both client and bodyworker.

SUMMARY

Andy spoke of an adult client who suffered from juvenile diabetes. Over the five year period Andy worked with Hal, he reported developing a feeling of brotherly love for his client. Andy did not merely offer his client, Hal, massage. He took personal interest in him. As a result, Andy provided networking, economic support, social work services, advice, and prayer. He was personally, as well as professionally, dedicated to providing for his client. Andy found himself increasingly bonded with Hal as he fought to preserve Hal's life and limbs.

Andy's involvement began to go beyond brotherly love. As Hal's medical condition deteriorated and he felt more pressure at work, his psyche became more fragile. When Hal felt his economic survival was threatened, he flew into a rage. Andy identified with his client's feelings and contemplated acting-out Hal's rage for him. Andy was surprised how a situation could move so far, so fast. Actually, it did not happen quickly, but, little by little over a long period of time. Andy was not aware of this process, nor how deep his involvement had become until he realized, he could get his "own ass locked up."

Andy then made two decisions. He turned his concerns over to the Lord. With this distance and perspective, he too advised his client to "keep his mouth shut and see what happens." Andy's advice appeared to work.

Andy faced a crisis in his practice, and he made decisions to deal with it. Long after the decisions were made and the event was over, he combined his experience with Hal with something he learned at a workshop—the quality of his presence with his clients is an intervention. He brought his new awareness to the levels of self-examination and policy-making. Though Andy had not yet made a decision to change, his past experience provided fertile seeds for the growth of both his person and his practice.

20

A WORD OF ADVICE

Max is an athletic looking, mid-forty year old man. At first Max denied having a relevant story to share. However, five to ten minutes later he returned to say, "I have a story for you."

There was a word of advice I got from my massage school that I was compelled to disagree with. I was told, "If people do not talk about it, don't bring it up." "If they don't ask, don't say it."

I was working with Priscilla, a talk therapist, a number of years younger than myself. She was a psychiatric social worker. At one point, I was working on her abdomen. My fingers felt an invitation to work there. I asked if I could continue to work on her belly. There was no response, but, the tissue hung on. It would not let go.

As I continued to work on this woman's belly, I made the statement to her, "Your belly is as tight as a solid door." Priscilla then responded, "I am not prepared to get into these head trips." I did not verbally pursue this issue at her request. I simply continued on with my bodywork. This seemed to be a good session other than the tension in her abdomen.

However, she went home and fell apart. She felt violated. She didn't tell me that she felt violated. This came out several days later after she called up and confronted me.

My first reaction when I heard about Priscilla's accusation was anger. I also felt violated. I was infuriated. She was not honest! We had a contract. *(Max emphasized)* I come from a background where if you make a deal with a person you live up to it. You don't get angry at a person when they deliver what you asked for. Priscilla came to me for bodywork. I delivered what she asked for.

After I got over my initial irritation, I got into a second set of reactions. I didn't realize that my comment had the impact it did. I didn't even think I was into "head trips." When she said that she did not want to get into head trips, I thought that by not talking anymore, I was safe. Though later I learned she meant "it was time to stop the session." But this was incredulous to me. She is a talk therapist! That's her milieu. I can't understand why a person who is into talking for a living couldn't express a simple message. To top that off, she was then angry at me for doing what she asked me to do in the first place. I was amazed because I felt so right-on with what Priscilla's body was saying. It did not strike me it was not good for her.

After Priscilla talked to me, I learned that she has a history of abuse. At first she did not feel safe sharing this with me. I was happy to learn about all of this and resolve it. Though I was not happy when I first learned she said I violated her. If she had not shared her experience with me she might have gone off hurt and angry and I would never have known about it. From where I was coming from, after this event was over I had a feeling of honesty in the relationship. The issue that came up was just a matter of my not knowing what was happening for her. After we talked out the misunderstanding, the "solid door" disappeared. Priscilla continued to work with me on a regular basis.

I need to inquire more often with my clients. Just after this happened I had a string of abuse victims. Then I knew a little more about what I was dealing with. "If they don't ask, don't say anything." That's a mask! If something seemed to be wrong, I am unwilling to be silent about it. After this incident I pursued education in Body Centered Psychotherapy. Now I have a better sense of how I want to approach it. I work by permission. If you have a "locked door," I'm not breaking it in. I have established a rule. The rule is, "You be comfortable. If you are not comfortable, I need to know about it."

DISCUSSION

ASSUMPTIONS Max assumed that Priscilla, a "talk therapist" was above having difficulties articulating her own emotional concerns. Priscilla, however, laid on Max's table as a person not as a psychiatric social worker. And to her, Max was a relative stranger, an older man in a position of authority. He was a person who was seeing and touching her body and identifying her inner secrets and her defense mechanisms. Though he did not perceive himself this way, Max was someone to whom Priscilla was both open and vulnerable.

Social workers, psychologists, psychiatrists, and other helping professionals, like everybody else, are people with their own family struggles, life conflicts, anxieties, defense mechanisms, dysfunctional families, and abusive histories. Though they have studied and worked with human dynamics, they are not above or immune to their own psychological dynamics. Talk therapists may suffer from low self-esteem, lack of confidence, and interpersonal insecurity. While knowing how to identify, treat, and teach skills to others, they may have personal struggles utilizing these same skills in communication, problem-solving, assertiveness, and intimacy in their own lives.

EXPOSING DEFENSES Max's innocent, earnest intuition apparently was accurate in identifying an early traumatic holding pattern in Priscilla's abdomen. His fingers were able to feel the holding in her tissue. He may even have accurately perceived a desire for the tissue to release. The holding was more complex than just tired, overworked muscles. Max was unaware of the psychological impact of his words on Priscilla. He did not know she was psychologically wounded as well as psychologically minded. Furthermore, the trauma from this wound left her unable to communicate the nature or extent of her injury to her male bodyworker.

Max experienced and verbalized his intuitive hunch about the physical level of Priscilla's emotional defense mechanism. Max might have avoided this traumatic experience with Priscilla if he had only said, "Your abdominal muscles are tight." Indeed, if Max had made his "solid door" comment to any of his other clients they might have heard him just making a statement about their tight muscles. Because of her clinical background or the accuracy of his statement, Priscilla interpreted Max's metaphor as a statement about her psyche not her soma. The state of her muscles provided a traumatically accurate psychological interpretation to this "talk therapist" client. She was unprepared to either hear or handle the issue and was unwilling to share it with Max. She was unable to express or defend herself. Though not Max's intention, it was as if he lifted a psychological sheet off of his client's naked, wounded psyche. And there Priscilla laid bare, vulnerable, and ashamed of her exposed, scarred psyche.

Max's intuition highlighted the psychodynamic of Priscilla's protection. Like the Emperor with his "new clothes," no one wants her or his nakedness to be publicly exposed. Psychological defense mechanisms are fragile processes. One must have an exceedingly strong trust relationship and a sensitive respect for a client's limits before bringing her or his psychological defenses into the open. Indeed, psychological interpretation, a very powerful tool even in psychotherapy, is usually best used just before the client is strong enough to have the insight on her or his own, not before she or he is ready to handle the issue.

READINESS A person's readiness for self-confrontation must be respected. None of us can decide for others when they are ready to encounter their defense system. To push someone prematurely can lead to retraumatization and an intensification of her or his defenses. A client may then become implosive, getting depressive and/or dissociative. If the implosive depression becomes too intense, the person may even become suicidal. Or the client may become explosive, feeling angry, enraged, or combative. Priscilla's defense was implosive in Max's office; she became explosive after leaving.

NAÏVETÉ Many people seek out a bodyworker with the expectation of simply having tension mechanically eased from their bodies. They believe that their psyches and lifestyles will remain untouched and unchanged from the contact. What they fail to understand is that body and mind are one. A practitioner cannot make genuine contact on one level without effecting other levels. Going to a therapist of any sort without being prepared for the possibility of personal revelation is naïve. Max discovered that even "talk therapists" have their personal blind spots. As a result of his encounter with Priscilla, Max recognized the importance of briefing his clients about the possibility of unforeseen emerging discomfort.

SEXUAL ROLE ORIENTATION Max was hurt because Priscilla failed to appreciate his dedication to task. Priscilla, a female, might have been more concerned with the process and the quality of contact in the relationship with Max. Max, a male, was more concerned with completing the task of the session. He felt a sense of accomplishment and success when getting the job done, completing the contract.

Neither "task" nor "process" orientation is better than the other. To give a quality session as a bodyworker, one must determine which is most appropriate at any given time for a particular client. For this, it behooves the bodyworker, especially if there is a sex difference, to consult with the client to make sure that there is mutual agreement even though one may intuitively believe the "flesh is providing an invitation."

WISHFUL THINKING Max felt something when he was working on Priscilla's abdomen. When he asked her "if he could continue and she provided no response," he assumed this meant, "Yes, you can continue." Max was correct, his fingers were feeling something. Given no message or an ambiguous message, one can easily believe the message that she or he is receiving is the desired response. This allows a person to believe the message is one that meets one's own inner need, "getting the job done," rather than the external reality. Max's intuition about what Priscilla was feeling was inaccurate. Nor did he know what her response meant. Her failure to verbally respond could have been an indication of her distress. When he continued without receiving explicit confirmation, his relationship with his client was compromised.

DISSOCIATION Abuse leaves many scars. It damages a person's self-esteem. It leaves scars in the form of fears, anxieties, defenses, and even alienation from one's own body. Defenses can come in the forms of depression or anger. Dissociation is another type of defense.

Dissociation is an unconscious defense mechanism in which a person numbs certain parts of her or his awareness to threatening thoughts or feelings. As Max was working on the tissue of Priscilla's belly, she may have been numbing to the memories of some traumatic event which were being awakened by his supportive, encouraging touch. She may have failed to respond quickly or more clearly because she was not psychologically present. In addition to dissociating, Priscilla may have regressed. Without specific training Max could not have been aware of his client's psychological state.

REGRESSION Max's physical contact or the release it promoted may have reminded Priscilla of a similar contact at an earlier age. At the moment of that recognition she may have returned to the identical cognitive-affective state that she possessed at the time the trauma occurred. Priscilla may have been confronted by a threatening adult authority figure possessing the physical ability to perpetrate violence, sexual abuse, and/or abandonment. Priscilla may have become mute and immobilized in terror in this threatened state.

Later, when Priscilla returned home, she resumed her normal adult state of awareness. Her recollection of what occurred at Max's office was remembered as a here and now event, rather than as an altered, regressed happening, an experiential replay of a traumatic past experience.

Priscilla was both wise and courageous to discuss her reaction with Max. Had she not discussed her troubling encounter with Max, it might have become another festering secret violation eating away at her in the form of anxiety and depression, eroding her self-esteem and reinforcing her identity as a victim. Her action allowed her to work through this current trauma and allowed for healing of the older psychophysical wound that Max discovered in her somatic holding.

By confronting Max, Priscilla ran the risk of engaging his defensiveness, anger, abandonment, or abusiveness. How Max would respond to her in a confrontation was unknown to Priscilla. A less integrated person than Max might have become defensive, accusatory, or rejecting. Priscilla risked experiencing possible retraumatization of her old wound. Fortunately, Max's essential integrity, maturity, and personal strength promoted a positive resolution.

SUPPORT Max may have initially been attractive to Priscilla for the same reasons he was a threat to her. He was an unfamiliar, older man in a position of authority. He had the capacity to make intimate contact. He was earnest, sincere, and capable of perceiving, identifying, and releasing her defense mechanisms. While there may have been a part of Priscilla that was reluctant to confront her abuse history, there may have been another part that wanted to overcome her past wounds. She may have felt ambivalent about trusting Max. Difficulty trusting is another scar of abuse. Yet Priscilla may have sought Max out precisely because she needed a trustworthy bodyworker to help support her through the process of overcoming her trauma.

MAINTAINING THE RELATIONSHIP After their conflict, Max and Priscilla continued their professional relationship with a new and clearer understanding. Max did not attempt to perform psychotherapy with his client. Max's supportive presence helped Priscilla to experience a positive conflict resolution with a male. It may have also allowed her to overcome defensiveness, shame, and feelings of undesirability. Max's willingness to remain present in the relationship and work through both his and his client's angry and hurt feelings was surely instrumental in keeping a client and helping her recover from her abusive trauma.

PROJECTION Old somatoemotional memories were triggered in Priscilla as Max undertook his work. Max did not do anything to physically or sexually violate Priscilla. But he did elicit unwanted memories. It is possible that Priscilla projected blame onto Max for either someone else's violation, or she held him accountable for her own unwillingness to confront her scars and defenses. Like the bearers of bad news that Cleopatra put to death, Max became the target for Priscilla's internalized anger.

Max's intent in making his comment was not an attempt to "play mind games." His intention was simply to comment on and describe the quality of the tissue he was encountering. Without knowing what he was feeling, he knew there was something going on with her tissue and its ability to release. If there was a "trip" being taken as a result of this statement, it was in Priscilla's head. And, she was not accepting responsibility for it. She did not tell Max up front about her abuse, and if he did his job well, he would have eventually stumbled onto her secret, which is what happened. Priscilla became angry at Max for doing what any bodyworker might have done. Priscilla then put the responsibility on Max for doing what someone else did to her. She accused him of violating her. She was projecting.

Projection is an unconscious process in which a person places blame or responsibility onto another for something that does not belong to them. This is an especially precarious position to be in for a male bodyworker working with an abused female client. In general, it is a wise practice not to work alone with someone who may lose her or his sense of boundaries. If there is someone else in the office, it helps to provide protection for both parties.

If one works with people who may have suffered from either neglect, abuse, or sexual violation it is essential that she or he is aware that projection might occur. And it is important that the bodyworker be emotionally strong enough not to take projections personally or react defensively. If one does find her or himself becoming overly defensive, she or he may want to explore this. On some level the projection may apply.

ADVICE   Max was unwilling to accept the advice he received from his massage school training. "If people don't talk about it, don't bring it up." "If they don't ask, don't say it." This was not bad advice, especially in light of the experience that Max had. Indeed, there was some wisdom in it. However, it was insufficient to prepare him for his encounter with Priscilla.

Even if a bodyworker is not saying anything psychotherapeutic, it is no guarantee that a client will not project unresolved material onto her or him. The bodyworker could be perceived as a parent or sibling surrogate, an acquaintance surrogate, or a perpetrator surrogate. Projection is a fact of life. A person can project unresolved feelings onto another because she or he is in a position of authority, because of age, sex, height, weight, hair color, a frown, or certain type of smile, freckles, a mustache, or pimples! The best defense is awareness, openness, and honesty.

Max was lucky. Priscilla could have been crying all over town that he had violated her. Those kinds of accusations can damage a person's reputation, creating untold personal torment. After the fact, whether the statement is true or false, it is often difficult to undo the damage left in the wake of such acting-out.

An easy rule of thumb is to avoid comment on a situation unless your client mentions it first. Max was commenting about his client's tissue, not her psychological state. He was unaware that this psychologically sophisticated client would perceive his statement on a psychological level not a physiological one. He was also unaware that there was more than one level to his client's physical holding patterns.

It was for this reason that his massage school provided him with such advice. His schooling, however, failed to explain the personal and professional context of its advice and was consequently unacceptable to Max.

Furthermore, Max felt demeaned when he was told what to do by his school's educational approach. He was not provided the opportunity to grapple with and digest the issue for himself. An autocratic educational style was unacceptable for an identity achiever like Max. The responsibility then fell upon Max to determine what the issue was and to come to a conclusion regarding what he wanted to do about it.

Max felt the advice compromised his integrity as well as that of his client. Certainly, if there were a medical concern he would not try to treat it. He would also not want either himself or his client to be ignorant of the condition. By the same token, he was unwilling to work around an emotional concern and pretend that it was not there. At the time he worked with Priscilla, Max lacked the knowledge and skills to gently and safely maintain his client's boundaries and limits and respond to his own sense of integrity. Eventually, he learned to appreciate the significance of the psychological level of his clients. Most of all, he developed a respect for his clients' boundaries.

CONTRACT   Like Priscilla, Max also felt violated in his encounter. He became angered when he heard of her complaint. He felt that Priscilla had come to him for bodywork and that is what he delivered. Priscilla did not do anything to intentionally hurt Max. Yet in mid-course, she chose to change the bodywork contract.[1] Without making a clear statement of her desire or taking clear action, she expected Max to terminate the session. Max could not read Priscilla's mind. He did not know how she was feeling or what she wanted. For Max, Priscilla had no justifiable cause to accuse him of violating her.

Though unintentionally, Max went beyond his contract with Priscilla when he provided his "talk" metaphor. Responsibility for that belongs to Max. To Max's credit and professional growth, his decision to establish an ongoing understanding of safety and freedom to communicate comfort or discomfort is an essential key to protect any relationship and contract.

SUMMARY

Max worked on a client whom he later learned had a "history of abuse." During his session with his client, he naively verbalized something about his client's tissue that she understood to be a "head trip." This retraumatized the client's old psychological wound.

Max had received words of advice from his massage school that he did not heed. Had he taken it, both he and his client might have been spared further emotional trauma and conflict. Instead, from the school of hard knocks, Max learned that there was a psychological as well as a physical level to his clients. In order to perform professionally he had to be aware of both levels and not violate one while trying to make good on his contract to serve the other.

Max was earnest in his approach to his work. He truly heard his client and the two worked through their misunderstanding. This made Max a safe bodyworker with whom Priscilla could continue to work. It also made Max a safe bodyworker with whom other abused clients could work. After his experience, Max understood the importance of the issue underlying his massage school's advice. Max enrolled in another program which trained him to understand the mindbody connection and to communicate safely with clients.

A bodywork student may not like following other's advice. But if a bodyworker is going to venture out on her or his own, it is important to find out why the advice was given in the first place. Then the bodyworker is in a better position to determine what course she or he wants to take regarding the issue.

END NOTES

1 **Contract** Oversights are made and misunderstandings occur even with the best of written legal contracts. These mishaps are usually overlooked or worked-out when they occur. One party or the other does not immediately call for a lawyer and sue for breach of contract. People try to remedy their concerns. What usually makes the difference between insult and understanding is the trust, respect, and caring demonstrated within the existing relationship.

21

SOME KIND OF RELEASE

Michael is a soft spoken intense man in his mid-forties. His speech is rapid and to the point.

I was at an advanced training session. There must have been around twenty or twenty-five people in the session. About a fifth of the group were men. We were doing table work, and I was paired up with this one guy. The odds were against it—winding up with a male partner. It's funny how things work out. He was solidly built, about my age. Todd, he was a hairy guy.

I know all that stuff about homophobia. I don't want to be one of those uptight guys who is afraid of what might be inside. But if I have to choose, I'd rather pair up with a woman. That's just the way I am. I guess women have their own issues with men.

Anyhow, as I worked, I could hear sobbing and moaning from women at two or three locations around the room. They were having some kind of emotional release. Some of the women were clear on the other end of this big room, and their cries were so intense, they were like, right next to you. Don't get me wrong, I'm not putting down what they were doing. This was just the emotional backdrop for what happened.

I was working on Todd's arm. This guy works out! He was solid. As I was working on him, his forearm gave this brief tremor. His digital extensors went into spasm. Then they were still.

I told Todd what I saw, "You had some kind of release there." And he said, "No big deal." And I thought to myself, "Damn! That could be me. I mean here we are surrounded by these women crying, moaning, and wailing. Without any sounds, this guy has this release, and he blows it off. Well, I think anytime anyone gets any kind of release, it's a big deal. But if I was on the table and it happened to me, I'd probably say the same dumb, macho thing. I mean, I come from a family of drivers. It isn't that they drive cars. They drive themselves for success. And no matter how far you drive, you never get there. I know what it is to have to keep pushing and denying the pain.

I told him, I said, "You may not be crying like the women in this room, but your release is significant." And I decided right there on the spot...in my head, "No matter how small I think my achievements are, I have to cop to it." But, I didn't know if I believed myself.

DISCUSSION

HOMOPHOBIA   Homophobia is an anxiety reaction toward or a prejudice against homosexuals. Phobias in general are anxiety reactions which reflect an inner insecurity. Acting out one's intolerance toward homosexuals may reflect an externalization of one's own inner doubts regarding her or his sexual identification.

In this case, Michael talks about the issue of homophobia. He expressed some concern over working on a "solid, hairy guy." While the reactive behavior of a phobic is overt, the underlying issue is both unconscious and protected by defenses. If Michael were clinically homophobic, it is unlikely that he would raise and discuss the issue. Though Michael may not suffer from clinical homophobia, he does express concern over working with a male. After describing his partner as solidly built and hairy, the next thing to come to Michael's mind was homophobia and preferring to work with women. So some concern exists.

This discomfort in working with men and his preference for working with women may just be Michael's personal choice. It may also be reflective of a more pervasive social ethic for men to avoid intimate contact especially with one another. This is complicated further when the issues of intimacy become confused by the boundaries of sensuality and sexuality. Anxiety may be normalized and reduced by having an appreciation of the difference.

SENSUALITY VS. SEXUALITY   Sensuality is a satisfaction of body appetites or a gratification of the senses. Full contact of any of the senses may provide for sensual gratification. Sexuality on the other hand refers specifically to sexual activity. Many people, especially men, may not make the distinction between the two. They may even sexualize contact by reducing any feeling, sharing, or touching event to a sexual event. It may be anxiety provoking or terrifying to express feelings toward, make contact with, or allow oneself to experience the sensation of contact with a member of one's own sex. The more inner doubts one has regarding the integrity of her or his sexual identification, that is being heterosexual vs. homosexual or bisexual, the more frightening the prospect of touching, feeling, and discovering an unacceptable truth. If a bodyworker is preoccupied by the terror of becoming turned on by her or his experience, she or he may avoid this terror by touching without feeling the contact.

TOUCH VS. FEEL One can touch a client and move her or his limbs and tissue without experiencing contact with that client. One can touch without feeling. This sends a message to the client that her or his body is being manipulated while the bodyworker is withdrawing her or his awareness from sensory contact. This objectifying contact may nonverbally tell the client that she or he is somehow unacceptable, even repulsive or revolting to touch: a person is to be manipulated but not experienced. At best, it sends the message that the bodyworker is limiting her or his contact with the client to mechanical movement.

Touching without feeling is quite different from the concepts of Gestalt "contact," the Trager "hook-up," or holistic "high contact." The former type of contact tends to communicate tension. It may effect the client's sense of trust and limit her or his opening and range of movement. It places an external lid on the client's experiencing her or his full potential. The latter forms of contact communicate the message of trust, safety, nourishment, acceptance, and confirmation.

To facilitate a client's full experience of her or his entire self, the bodyworker must be sufficiently integrated and comfortable with her or his personality. Otherwise, the depth of the bodyworker's personal integration will and should limit the influence on the client's growth. It would be foolhardy for a client to allow her or himself to be guided into deep water by a sailor who is unable to navigate unknown seas.

While this did not occur with Michael and Todd, a bodyworker's incessant talking, problem solving, or joking may be an unconscious verbal means to avoid emotional, sensual, or intimate contact. Mechanical or painful pressure in the name of release, also may serve as a defense against full experience. The fact that Todd allowed himself to release his muscular holding is suggestive of Michael's open supportive touch and inner wholeness in spite of his "preference to work with a woman."

SIGNIFICANCE Todd's release was a silent tremor in contrast to the wailing from women in other parts of the training room. Neither size, duration, nor loudness were needed for Michael to recognize this event. Though driving, denial, and failure to self-appreciate were personal issues for Michael, he had no need to do more than bring the release to Todd's awareness.

AWARENESS Awareness is a powerful tool. It is the first step in the Gestalt Energy Cycle. If one invests in her or his awareness, she or he may mobilize energy which can then be translated into action. The action may succeed in making contact. When the contact is successfully negotiated, there is the rest that comes with withdrawal. After this rest, a new stimulus brings about a new sensation and another awareness. And so the Energy Cycle goes, and the individual negotiates life. Without awareness of the sensation, the Energy Cycle does not continue. Michael's raising Todd's awareness of the release is a significant event.

APPRECIATION Todd originally did not recognize or appreciate the significance of his release. Michael, in sharing his belief of the importance of any release, provided something for Todd that he had never received in his own "driving" family. Recognition through awareness is essential to growth. Fortified with this knowledge, an individual can then utilize an encounter to change in a growthful way. Going beyond recognition, appreciation facilitates the bonding of the new growth within the core of the person. In addition, appreciation of an event provides energy for further growth to occur. Without this appreciation, an event is unlikely to be perceived or recognized. The event and the achievement then become non-events.

ROLE MODELING A role model is a person who acts as an example of attitudes, behaviors, or goals for which others may strive. Todd did not appreciate or express appreciation for his muscular release. By communicating with his partner, Michael provided a positive role model of how to give recognition and appreciation for a client's achievement. This role modeling situation is a significant one. Men often provide competitive, domineering, demeaning, or self-aggrandizing models to one another. In this event, Michael provided recognition and appreciation for his partner.

PERFECTIONISM Michael spoke of coming from a "driving" home. He readily identified with Todd's tension and denial of his achievement. These traits are characteristic of perfectionism.[1,2]

MACHO Todd's denial of his release may have been reflective of a "Macho" masculine ethic.[3] Michael reported being able to identify with what he called Todd's "dumb, macho thing." He was able to recognize within himself his partner's denial. He believed Todd's sense of being a man led to his failure to recognize or appreciate the significance of his muscular release. Without this recognition, the release that occurred became a non-event, as if it never happened. Todd may not have consciously intended to be macho any more than Michael did. Both men were subject to the cultural influences that determine what role behaviors are socially acceptable to be men.[4] If not for Michael's attention, Todd would not have acknowledged his release.

DOUBLE STANDARDS Michael alludes to a double standard regarding self-recognition and appreciation. This man, who comes from a "driving family," believes that others who achieve even small releases should recognize themselves. He does not know, however, if he would recognize his own achievement. This indicates a lack of integration.

Michael believes that everyone should acknowledge her and his achievements. Todd should recognize his achievement, and Michael must recognize his own. Perhaps this struggle is another symptom of Michael's perfectionism or his machismo. Whatever the cause, if he is unable to overcome this inability to self-recognize and self-appreciate, he will hold himself back from recognizing future success. This is the heart of Michael's identity struggle which the encounter with Todd brought to his awareness. As he faces, decides, and follows through for himself about how he wants to handle this issue of achievement, he will truly become his own man—a total man.

Another issue reflective of a double standard is Michael's preference to work with women. Perhaps Michael believes that he will not receive the same kind of reception, recognition, and appreciation from a man that he would receive from a woman. Perhaps he believes that there is a certain cultural ethic of macho or competitive behavior which males will automatically trigger in each other. When it comes to receiving bodywork, Michael does not want to receive or offer treatment from someone who internalizes tension and denies appreciation of release. Michael may believe that self-denial is normative behavior for men. This stereotypic belief reduces the possibility of Michael's growth in his interactions with men.

SUMMARY

In sharing his experience at a training session, Michael told of encountering two major issues. This first issue reflected Michael's stand on homophobia. It was not his preference to work with men. Rather than denying the issue by pushing it out of his awareness, he spoke overtly of the concern. Michael actualized his inner strength and normalized his potential anxiety by dealing with this issue openly.

Michael then broached the second issue, also related to masculine identity. Michael shared the struggle of being his own man in a culture which dictates that his identity be equated with self-denial, internalization of stress, and drives for perfection and success. This issue materialized as Michael's partner experienced a muscular release. Michael, as a result of his partner's release and subsequent denial of the significance of the release, experienced an awareness of his family's "driving behavior." In all likelihood, what the partner expressed in his muscular holding and what Michael expressed cognitively were expressions of the same thing on two different levels.

The partner's release was a contact event for Michael. Michael was working on himself, as he worked on his partner. In a moment of contact, something changes for all parties. Perhaps both men shared some essential part of themselves which helped each of them transcend some of the social stereotypes which shackle so many. Stereotypes derived from social training prohibit men from fully actualizing their masculine potential. As a result of their work, Michael and his partner could have "some kind of release" and take further steps toward overcoming their cultural training.

Michael recognized that he no longer wanted to deny his achievements. He also recognized his task would not be an easy one. He did not know if he would be able to achieve it. Perhaps his awareness, clarity, and honesty will support him in making his desired changes.

END NOTES

1 **Perfectionism** Perfectionists are not people who are perfect. They are not even people who believe they are perfect. They believe that they are not perfect. They have feelings of being imperfect and unacceptable. As a result, they strive and drive themselves for perfection. This drive to compensate for a perceived deficiency is often unconscious. Like many unconsciously motivated behaviors, it can be a psychological defense. If confronted, perfectionists might rattle off the names of several people who are far more accomplished and far more driven. They provide this information as proof that they are not driven, that they ought to be more accomplished, and should push themselves yet further.

Perfectionists are likely to come from families that were not emotionally accepting or confirming of the "wholeness" of their children. These families provided recognition and/or reinforcement for what their children accomplished. These children did not experience love and appreciation from their parents for who they were. As a result, these children were likely to perform because they hoped to attain recognition of their productivity. This attention or recognition may be called "love" by either the parents or the children. However, neither attention nor recognition for performance will produce the warm, caring, accepting, and nurturing feelings of love. This conditional love is not true love.

Directly or indirectly, by the model they provide, perfectionists are not only hard on themselves, but they are likely to be relentless with others. These people usually have a difficult time recognizing and praising others for accomplishments because they project their own inadequacies onto them. Inadvertently, perfectionists may "drive" others to greater and greater success, accomplishment, and perfection. Though often hurtful to others, perfectionists can be insensitive to others' feelings because they have become callous to their own feelings.

Some perfectionists intellectually recognize that they were wounded by their distant, driving parents, but are unable to break the emotional bond of low self-esteem. While driving themselves, these perfectionists bend over backwards to be fair and supportive of others. Still, they treat themselves as they were treated in childhood. Like many childhood wounds, those of perfectionism are borne for a lifetime if not confronted.

2   **Muscular Girdle**   The perfectionistic drive can lead some to success. Perfectionism in excess, rather than driving a person onto greater and greater achievements, can also drive a person to a grinding halt. On a psychological level, the expectation is often so great it seems impossible to achieve.

In this case, the psychological drive of perfectionism has an additional behavioral component. Rather than running the risk of failure, the person internalizes the drive and backs away from the challenge. On a physical level, this redirected driving energy, like an isometric muscular girdle, can be experienced as tightness, aches, pains, or even illness. Contained and arrested by her or his own musculature, an underachieving perfectionist may suffer from profound feelings of helplessness, failure, and inferiority.

3   **Macho**   Often, the cultural expectations of a man imply possessing certain stereotypic traits: being tough, strong, fearless, and achieving. It is weak to be sensitive, emotional, expressive, or creative. If a male has not achieved the stereotypic traits, he may feel compelled to "act like a man." This involves superimposing the image of being strong, fearless, having no feelings, showing no pain, and touting accomplishments. To be male is to tighten, to hold on. Loosening and letting go certainly is not macho.

In the process of wearing this mantle of masculinity, the genuine person is lost. Along with the genuineness goes true experience, creative feeling, enlightened thought, and sensitive touch. Underneath the muscular girdle can only be self-doubt that cannot be reached, aired out, cleansed, or liberated. Externally, it drives the macho man to greater and greater strivings in the social or professional arena to attain a perfect image. Internally, this person remains alienated, insulated, and unaffected by his feelings or those of others. Buried inside is the nagging doubt, "Am I a real man?"

4   **A Total Man**   Experiencing, feeling, and expressing are culturally perceived as feminine traits. In order not to appear feminine, men deny, joke about, or demean feelings. This leaves them numb to both their own feel-

ings and those of others. In this process of numbing, they shrink from their fullness. Only a part of the available knowledge is present for a balanced decision making process. Decisions are made rationally. Sensitivity, compassion, love, expressiveness, vision, spirituality, and creativity are culturally extracted from the "real man's" problem solving process.

To be a real man is to be a total man, a thinking, experiencing, feeling, and expressing man. It is to incorporate all of oneself, including the pained, troubled, doubting, insecure, anxious, and fearful parts. To be a real man means one must be courageous enough to stand against the social stereotype of the materialistic, power driven, insensitive "real man" model. It incorporates the knowledge that comes from insecurity and failure, as well as knowledge that comes from success. A man must exercise the strength to be open and reveal his true self to others. To achieve this goal, the total man must incorporate the willingness to face and transcend the terror of losing both his image and the potential acceptance of others.

Part **VI**

RECOVERY

22

KNOWING YOUR STUFF

Nancy, a thirty year old, speaks rapidly, taking thin, shallow breaths. Her words are not supported by her feelings. She has been in practice for three years.

This past week I did energy work for the first time in a long time. Karen is about my age. She came in for bodywork. Every time I work with her, I have to go back and take a moment to ground myself as a professional. Knowing that on a personal level I have to be doing "clearing." Clearing is the way I clear away self-doubts. I must know that I am personally okay in order to present myself as a professional.

I have worked with Karen monthly for almost eight months. She is "recovering." She was sexually abused. There was also alcohol abuse in her family so she is dealing with the "isms." Karen challenges my sense of being personally okay with the difficulties that she has with trust. Karen does not discuss the specifics of her abuse. However, she thought that it was important for her masseuse to know that she was abused. She didn't have to tell me anything. I knew. Karen was already in a 12 Step Program, or I would have provided a referral for that or counseling.

Karen allows me to explore all facets of what I learned in massage school...polarity, craniosacral, and energy work. When I do energy work, I place my hands near a person who has difficulty trusting. This closeness then produces a warmth and safety. After the trust is developed, I am then able to make hands on contact.

When I work with Karen, physically she is lying right there on the table. Mentally and emotionally, she is not there. Her tissue is not warm, supple, or flexible. She is thinking, "I am in my mind. Do what you will with my body." I put together what I am experiencing. Suddenly I think to myself, "This is really scary. She's not there! And she is like a reflection of me on the table!"

When I'm that way, I feel like I'm in a room by myself and feeling empty and lonely. Seeing that from my client, I could perceive myself doing the same thing and that's scary. Through her I am exploring my own personal aspects. I can see how my own recovery is affecting me and my own self-esteem. Then I forget what the next piece of my massage routine is. Then I think to myself, "Am I okay with this?" Then I realize, "Oh my God, I am forgetting how to do all of this!"

I have come to recognize with Karen that I can't do energy work. She really challenges me on a professional level. *(Nancy's otherwise controlled, affectively flat voice quivers.)* I am afraid she reflects my personal level. Then I am left wondering, "Am I grounded? Am I clear in my thinking as far as where I am at? Can I say, Yes, I am okay as a therapist?" My personal esteem reflects upon and influences my professional performance.

Internally, there is a scared little girl in me not knowing what she is doing, where she is going. I was latching onto everybody and everything, wanting to win their approval. Just trying to soak them in. Just trying to let them fill me. Then I would feel okay with myself. Then I would be able to go on.

I was not busy for the first two years I was in business. I didn't have a steady clientele. I wondered why my business was not picking up. Then I realized that my own personal life was totally chaotic and unmanageable. Even when I thought I was in control of things, I was in control of nothing, including my own emotions, and I thought, what do I want to do? How do I want to do a massage? How can I stay firm and go with it? I was tap dancing all over the place. Trying to do lots of things with massage. Yet I was not sure I could do anything. Oh! I don't feel good with that. Let's go this way. Let's go that way.

This past year I realized that I had to become grounded. I had to gain a sense of my spiritual being. I had to develop an internal strength so I could say and mean, "Okay, you are a good therapist. You are not the best and you are not the worst. That's okay. Just do the best with what you've got." So then I would take that and present it on a professional level.

I talk to myself with an open mind. *(Suddenly in a slow, gentle, deliberate, nurturing voice)* "Let's try this." Then the techniques, movements, and procedures all start to come back to me. That in turn reflects back on the personal level. "You know, (going back to a personal dialogue)…you're okay. You know your stuff."

Next week I am going to counseling with my husband. Things have been shaky with us. He is self-employed, and his business is seasonal. He sits at home a lot and drinks. It's just too much! I am the only one bringing in money. I have to take care of our child. And I have to take care of him. My first husband was alcoholic also, and he would become physically violent.

Daddy was the alcoholic in the family. When he was steady at work he was okay. But he would go on binges. He would lose his job and owe his pay checks to the bar. My mother would kick him out of the house. When daddy was there, it was neat because he would overrule mom. That was neat!

EPILOGUE

(Several months later) I just sent out an announcement of the expansion of my practice. The marriage still has its problems. However, we are working together more effectively. My husband has not abandoned his own business, but he has taken on a full time job which provides both challenge for him and steady income for the family.

DISCUSSION

TRUST Nancy often performed "energy work" on clients who had difficulty trusting. It helped her to create a warm safe rapport. After trust was established, she could then perform hands on work. Establishing trust is the first step in any significant relationship.

Trust lays the ground work to support deeper work. The converse is also true. Lack of trust creates a barrier beyond which deepening of a relationship can occur only with difficulty. Trust is not automatic. It is built up with time as a person demonstrates she or he is worthy of being trusted. Trust reflects how well a person has created a safe psychological atmosphere. Nancy does well to attend to the trust issue as she begins her work.

IDENTIFICATION When Nancy performs "energy work," she must focus on and become acutely aware of her client. A new dimension of awareness is brought into focus as soon as this massage therapist uses "energy work." It requires her to be present and aware of her client as a person, not merely a collection of anatomical parts. Nancy uses her tactile senses to confirm her client's dissociative state. The temperature, elasticity, and flexibility of Karen's skin confirmed Nancy's suspicion that Karen was dissociating.

An interaction occurred between Nancy and her "energy work" with Karen. As Nancy recognized Karen's state, she began to identify with her client. Nancy may or may not have been accurate about what Karen's body was saying. She read her client's body language and intuited, "Physically she is lying right there on the table. Mentally and emotionally, she is not there." As Nancy recognized Karen's detachment and began to identify with her, she became frightened and began to dissociate. Nancy became one with the client she perceived as dissociated.

Nancy identified too closely with Karen's lifeless flesh and cognitive withdrawal. She began to imagine herself lying on the table. She even assumed some of the characteristics of her client's insecurity. The result of this negative identification was that Nancy lost sight of her strengths and reduced her sense of identity to that of her client's weaknesses.

PANIC ATTACK   Nancy experienced a sense of panic while working on Karen. Panic attacks can occur when encountering problematic individuals or stressful situations. They can also occur randomly without any specific, apparent trigger. They vary in length from moments to hours. A panic attack is both a psychological and a physiological phenomena. The symptoms can include: sudden anxiety, shortness of breath, palpitations, chest pain, choking sensations, dizziness, feelings of unreality, tingling in hands or feet, hot and cold flashes, sweating, faintness, trembling, and fear of uncontrolled actions such as going crazy or dying.

At the point Nancy allowed herself to become enmeshed with her abused client, she triggered a panic attack. She became so anxious and overwhelmed that she became professionally impotent. Nancy lost sense of her own accomplishments and abilities. She forgot her massage form. Her various techniques became scrambled. "What is the problem? What is needed? Which is the technique that addresses that need? How do I do it?"

SUPPORT   The intervention for anxiety and panic is always support. This support may be comprised of any one or a combination of: systematic desensitization, guided imagery, cognitive retraining, role playing, or bodywork. When panic attacks are sufficiently severe, medication is also a standard method of treatment in conjunction with behavioral intervention. Use of medication or alcohol without behavioral intervention may promote drug or alcohol dependency. This would be a particular concern if there is already a history of drug or alcohol abuse in the family.

Support may come internally or externally. Nancy had already recognized that she becomes "ungrounded." She realized that there was a relationship between her personal insecurity and her professional performance. Nancy knew she needed to "clear" her anxiety. Whether she labeled it as such or not, Nancy had already begun to perform affirmations. "Okay, you are a good therapist. You are not the best. You are not the worst. That's okay. Just do the best with what you've got."

Affirmations interrupt the negative thought process. These positive statements replace the negative ones. This could change Nancy's perception of her reality. In addition to speaking to herself positively, Nancy talked with gentle confirmation. This right-brain effect also helps to interrupt the anxiety attack. Nancy's actions created a safer psychological environment from which she could then perform her work.

Nancy did something else which is extremely important. She changed the rate and rhythm of her breathing. Rather than taking her usual fast, shallow breaths, this young bodyworker took slow, deep rhythmic breaths. She oxygenated her body, allowing her muscles to elongate and relax. As her muscles softened, she took in deeper breaths. Her more fully oxygenated blood then flowed more freely through her relaxed and widened arteries to all the cells of her body. These reactions promote a profound relaxation response, breaking the feelings of panic on a somatic level. Nancy could become even more self-confident if she were to recognize her excellent interventions in her anxiety reaction. This would facilitate breaking the panic attack on the cognitive level.

SELF-APPRECIATION: A PROBLEM-SOLVING STRATEGY While there may be similarities between Nancy and her client, Karen, the two women are not the same. Nancy's anxiety prohibited her from differentiating her own identity from that of her client's.

As already suggested, self-recognition promotes self-esteem. It is extremely important for Nancy to recognize that she has established a firm foundation of personal growth in her own life journey. One of Nancy's strengths is her recognition of the relationship between her personal and professional growth. Nancy is also able to identify when she is becoming overwhelmed. She is also able to intervene, arrest, and reverse her disabling panic attacks.

Another strength was Nancy's willingness to face with honesty her own insecurity and her need to find external confirmation. Nancy knew there was a scared little girl inside who did not know what she was doing or where she was going. Nancy was able to admit, that because of her self-doubt and "chaotic, unmanageable, personal life," she was unable to inspire confidence in potential clients during her first two years of practice.

Though Nancy suffered from low self-esteem, her self-recognition and self-appreciation allowed her to reinforce genuine growth. Nancy could achieve her desired goals through her self-acceptance. And, she had developed sufficient strength to confront her husband in a constructive way to get help for their floundering marriage. Conscious and deliberate self-recognition, appreciation, and celebration of her achievements would take Nancy even further in her growth process.

COMMAND   Nancy had the strength and courage to admit, "Even when I thought I was in control of things, I was in control of nothing." The growth alternative to control[1] is "command." When one has "command," she or he is able to perceive the entire picture, not just with what they are familiar and comfortable. The individual has sufficient strength to be aware of the many alternative paths that might be taken. She or he flexibly chooses the path that makes the most sense.

The person in command has transcended compulsivity, perfectionism, and stereotypic self-conditioning. She or he has achieved the freedom of awareness and choice. Nancy learned to accept that she was "doing the best she can with what she has" for the time being. "... with an open mind," she was able to present this spirit of self-appreciation "on a professional level." "You know, you're okay." "You know your stuff."

REPETITION   As a child Nancy perceived herself as having a "good" parent and a "bad" parent. Her fun, alcoholic "daddy" was the good parent. Her demanding, structuring, resentful mother was the bad parent. Parental relationships are rarely as simplistic as a child's black and white thought processes make them out to be. As a child, adolescent, and even an adult, Nancy did not understand or appreciate the psychology and politics of her parents' relationship.

Nancy did recognize that her husband's seasonal job left her feeling financially insecure and burdened by the responsibility of having to carry the entire family on her shoulders when her husband was out of work. The husband's drinking further complicated their relationship by rendering him unresponsive to family responsibilities. This saddled Nancy with additional stresses and burdens.

As a child, Nancy thought her daddy's overriding her mother's authority was "neat." As an adult, Nancy takes her own family responsibilities seriously. Nancy has completed a three hundred sixty degree turn around since her youth. She took over the role she disdainfully observed her mother play. She even married two alcoholics. From her mother's pattern Nancy had learned to be the kind of woman she deplored, thus, perpetuating the model.

STOPPING THE CYCLE Unlike her mother, Nancy's resolution to her marital problem was not simply to kick her husband out of the house when he went on drinking sprees. She had the courage, strength, and wisdom to seek help with her husband. Nancy did not belittle, reject, or abandon a man who was already suffering from low self-esteem. She attempted to deal constructively with the problems in her relationship. Nancy had chosen to work with her husband to transform her family's life. Nancy's differentiation is a sign of developing her own person rather than merely repeating the victim role that her mother modeled for her. This is yet another sign of Nancy's transcendence.

Fortunately, and to his own credit, Nancy's husband responded to her request[2]. He was willing to confront his own part in the family problems rather than deflecting his awareness by retreating into alcoholic denial, minimizing, excuse making, or blaming. This investment in marital counseling was a testament to both this man's courage to confront himself and also his earnestness to improve the quality of his family's life.

SUMMARY

Nancy highly identified with Karen, a client in recovery. Nancy discovered that when she did energy work with this client, she used Karen as a mirror of herself. She saw in Karen, a woman unable to maintain contact, one who could easily dissociate. As Nancy saw this aspect in Karen, she, too, began to dissociate and forgot her "massage routine." Nancy recognized that her personal esteem effects her professional performance. When she was not feeling solid about herself, her work suffered. In the past Nancy looked to the solidity in others for confirmation. Karen, the client, was unstable and insecure; she, ironically, braced herself in order to receive the massage which was intended to relax her. Karen could not provide the structure her massage therapist lacked. Instead of Karen internalizing Nancy's solidity, Nancy internalized Karen's diffusion. Nancy recognized the same pattern of diffusion in managing her practice and providing a session. Not surprisingly, this same pattern repeated itself in her childhood home life as well as in her marriage.

Nancy was a survivor in the truest sense of the word. She did not allow her overwhelming feelings to incapacitate her. She turned a crisis into a growth event. She recognized that there had to be some changes made, and they had to start with her. She began by accepting herself as she was and doing the best she was capable of doing at the time. Rather than demanding, draining, or nagging herself, she talked, in gentle, supportive, and confirming tones. As she did this, she overcame her anxiety and self-doubt. As Nancy learned from her encounter with her client, she brought strength to her personal identity. As her personal identity gained strength, she brought this new strength to her marriage. Her marriage strengthened. In all likelihood this same momentum added to the growth of her stumbling practice.

END NOTES

[1] **Control**   Control is an illusion of having inner strength and power. It is what people who do not feel powerful do in order to reassure themselves that they are in control. To be in control is to be compulsive about some thought process or set of behaviors. Workaholics strive for perfection to overcome their basic feelings of inferiority. Anorexics and bulimics create eating rituals which give them an illusion of control over caloric consumption, masking the lack of genuine command in their psychosocial lives. Alcoholics tell themselves and others they can quit drinking any time they want to quit. They simply do not want to quit. This gives them a sense of power over their drinking. At the same time, they are developing more and more of a dependency on a chemical substance. This dependency numbs the stressful lives that they have not yet found the courage and/or skills to master. All of these people are compelled to act in rigid, compulsive, unconscious, defensive, and stereotypic fashions. They must act in these ways to maintain an illusion of control.

[2] **Spiritual Union**   Couples may come together for many reasons. In a true spiritual union, one brought together by love, mutual trust, and respect, relationships develop the potential for comfort from life's stresses and challenges. These relationships encourage and support on-going growth and development. They provide for deep healing of past as well as present wounds. A spiritual relationship allows for bonding in which each partner listens to the other without accusations, explanations, defenses, or denial. Each partner embraces and learns from the other's loving feedback. Both are willing to move beyond her or his familiar boundaries. A couple feels a sense of loving, supportive presence even when separated from each other. From the vitality, nourishment, and healing that takes place, an outsider can see these effects in the countenances of the couple. They look healthy and light. They have a glow of well being. They appear attractive, look youthful, and emanate vitality. One can see on-going growthful changes in the couple both as a unit and as individuals.

23

PERPETRATOR

Beth, a bodyworker in her mid-forties, spoke gently, slowly and pensively.

I had a forty year old client who preferred to receive sessions fully clothed. She was referred by a psychologist. *(Beth spoke tentatively as she searched for the appropriate words.)* I gave her several sessions and realized that I was becoming more and more frustrated because she had all these clothes on.

During one of the last sessions, which I believed turned out to be the last one, I began thinking to myself, "I couldn't stand receiving a session while I was fully clothed because I would feel as if I was being mauled...like I was in the back seat of a '57 Chevy, in a driveway with some guy who was always trying to touch me." After all, if she didn't have her clothes on, that would have meant she had chosen to take them off. Then all of a sudden in the middle of the session, I began to feel like I was a perpetrator. I was imagining that she was feeling violated. That wasn't the case, but I couldn't get it out of my mind.

Taking that role really frightened me. I thought it was going to be impossible to do my work if that was how I felt...if I felt as if I was always a threat to someone on the table. Immediately, I called my bodywork instructor and talked to her about the problem. She suggested I look into regression therapy because I had been working through incest issues of my own. They hadn't been satisfactorily resolved yet. I felt impatient about incest, bodywork, and sexuality.

So I did go for regressive therapy. I think for three months, I didn't give a session while I was doing this therapy. I was too tired and too unsure of myself. The therapy had a profound impact on me. It made it possible for me to go back to giving sessions again. It empowered the wounded child within to get past the trauma with my reexperiencing my inner child growing up. There were several noticeable changes in me. One was that I didn't dissociate...automatically...without being aware of it...at the slightest provocation...as I had done for forty years previously. It was exciting to think about the wonderful work I did in that particular kind of therapy...how far and fast it took me in a short time...and be present and be empowered and be introduced to the innocence of those children...me at different ages.

I just started receiving bodywork when I joined a therapy group to work through my incest issues. And it wasn't until I was in that group that I learned about dissociation. I knew that at times I was kind of spacing out and my kids accused me of that, and laughed about it...and my husband too, from time to time. I didn't realize it was so prevalent in my behavior. And I didn't know why, and I didn't realize that it was common to survivors of abuse. It was real helpful to me in group to learn that we have issues in common.

I would essentially leave my body. That was another real problem I was having with giving sessions—staying present. When I would come to a part of the body that I would have issues with, I would dissociate. And therefore,...well, *(clearing her throat)* the idea is for the child...anyway, if you can't see it, it isn't there. And the problem doesn't exist. It was as if I were an observer in some other part of the room. Or, sometimes I would close my eyes, and then I couldn't see the part of the body I was working on.

When I dissociated, my work would become tentative and absolutely ineffective. I would still be touching the client, but I wasn't moving the tissue in a helpful way. In the mid to low back, that's an area of great pain for me. I am beginning to believe it is related to my original abuse...early childhood abuse. I really don't have a clear picture of what that is or why, but in the meantime, it is where I stored much of my tension.

As far as I know, I was four the first time I was abused. I don't have a memory of that. That surfaced in my therapy. I always thought that I was abused by my grandfather first when I was five, and then my father when I was fifteen. The shocking part was this incident at four...involved my father. I was incredulous when I discovered that. But there was no question...I mean I don't doubt it now...because I remembered everything. I mean I had a visual memory.

This woman provided a turning point. Because having to work on her while she was fully clothed, created frustration for me. I kept thinking, "Well, this was a growing point in itself. If only she would disrobe, I could do a better job." Which is...I don't mean it is absurd, but

I believed the session would have gone better. That was the starting point. Then it just developed rapidly from there, until I saw myself as the perpetrator. Well, then I was face to face with my own issues. I realized, "Oow! Wait a minute! This doesn't have anything to do with my client or her clothing."

I don't know what the nature or extent of her abuse was. I do know that when she arrived at my office...I always have my clients sit down and we talk just a little bit before starting a session. So I could get some verbal or physical history...or if they were inclined to show me with their hands where they were experiencing physical symptoms. I had the chairs arranged so that we were...we weren't looking directly at each other. We were...she was off to my left side...so it was possible not to have to look directly at each other. She sat clear on the farthest edge of the chair. And if she could have gotten through the wall, I had the feeling she preferred to sit in the other room.

She seldom if ever looked me directly in the eye. It just surprised me because that's more what I would have expected if...I was a psychotherapist. I mean I seldom look my therapist directly in the eye either. So I am used to the idea of that. But I was surprised she would have that behavior with me because I am not a therapist.

She said to me that she was working through some issues related to her body and she wanted to be able to be touched. And I always give my clients the option to wear whatever they want to wear. She wore turtle necks just about up to her ear lobes with shoulder pads in them. That was the style...and pantyhose and slacks. She was so completely covered up, it really was a frustration. One I think I have outgrown now. But at the time, it really got in the way for me. One of the things she said to me was, "If you knew the issues I was working on, you would understand."

I feel particularly bad about that episode and how it came out. But I am glad it brought me face to face with my own issues. After the session I talked for a little bit of how she might want to think about...see I was still projecting...she might want to think about her issues with clothing and consider the possibility of wearing less. I saw her for about a half a dozen times. I don't remember if she came back one more time or not. But if she did—that was the last time.

The work was going well. It was almost as if I couldn't stand having it go well. That was the other thing. It seemed like I sabotaged it in a way, because even with all that clothing on and with my own frustrations and so on...we seemed to rise above that sometimes. She had some, what I would call integrating experiences where she had a vision of herself as a child. She described where she was outside of the farmhouse where they lived when she was a child...she felt so safe being outside. I didn't delve into it because I was not a psychotherapist, and I didn't ask her what that meant or why that would be particularly...or what it was about being in the house that would make being out of it such a relief. I didn't pursue any of that with her. But it gave her great pleasure to have that experience. So I thought we were doing well. In addition, at the end of each session, I would always ask her if she wanted a hug. And she would accept a hug. And one day she said, "That is the only one I get all week." And I just felt so...so touched by that, and then to have this experience of suddenly feeling like a perpetrator just intervened...and then bearing down on her about wearing clothing.

I called her. I told her that after the session, I realized the problem about the clothing was more mine than hers. She said that she was trying to do something that wasn't possible for her. As if she had given up on herself being able to receive touch...at least at that time. But she did say she neither felt abused, nor, would she have guessed that I felt like a perpetrator. I told her that, too. I just well...I just still have a rotten feeling about it.

DISCUSSION

IDENTIFICATION Beth and her client were the same age. But more than that, both struggled with the issue of discomfort with their bodies, touch, and sexual feelings. Consequently, Beth identified with her client. Her identification was not a warm, empathic, unconditionally accepting identification. It was an unaccepting, impatient, distancing identification. And Beth was not immediately conscious of this identification.

As a result, Beth began to have intense feelings toward Jan which she had not experienced with other clients. Beth was exceedingly frustrated with her client. She imagined that Jan was having a difficult time being worked on while wearing all of her clothes. Beth's logic went like this, "After all, if she took her clothes off, it would have meant that she chose to do so out of her own free volition. However, if she was being touched with her clothes on, then she was choosing to neither take her clothes off, nor be touched. Therefore, touching her would be like violating her in the back seat of a '57 Chevy by some guy ..." Beth imagined her touching Jan would be something like the way she was touched by her abusive father or grandfather.

PROJECTIVE IDENTIFICATION Logic would indicate that Jan had chosen to be touched with her clothing on. However, Beth was in the back seat of the '57 Chevy wearing her clothes, and being touched against her will by a callous, self-indulgent, violating male. Beth lost a sense of her psychological boundaries and projected her vulnerability onto her client.

In projective identification, a person may find her or himself identifying with any one of three perspectives in the abuse triangle: the victim, the aggressor, the ineffectual bystander or parent who fails to protect the victimized child from the aggressor. Beth had experience with all three of these roles in her childhood. Beth could find material related to aggressors and ineffectual bystanders within her experiential memory because she had internalized these parts from both of her parents.

In childhood, Beth was abused. She recognized some similarities between her behavior and that of Jan's. In the process, Beth projected her unacceptable feelings onto Jan as if Jan were a movie screen. Beth then believed that Jan was feeling violated. It was a small jump, from the standpoint of projective identification, for Beth to place herself in the role of aggressor. After all, if Jan were the victim, then Beth must have been the "perpetrator."

HEALTH FACILITATOR: A PROBLEM-SOLVING STRATEGY Beth would be helped by consciously keeping in mind the role of a "health facilitator" while working on Jan. This alternative role requires Beth to consciously bring her caring presence to the work. The "health facilitator" role may enable her to maintain a separation between her childhood wounds and those of the client. This position allows the client to release the psychosocial venom from her wounded soma. As a "health facilitator," Beth's identification allows her to bring more precisely her presence, awareness, concern, and firm gentle touch to enhance her client's healing process. While Beth is actively in this health facilitator role, she will not be a victim, perpetrator, or ineffectual bystander.

ANXIETY Anxiety is the consequence of feeling overwhelmed by some kind of anticipated threat. There are three ways to reduce the intensity of anxiety. One can lower the magnitude of the threat. One can increase the magnitude of knowledge, skill, or support to deal with the threat. And one can combine the two. Beth was so anxious that she was unable to work. She immediately called her bodywork instructor. This sharing provided additional support for Beth. The instructor wisely advised Beth to get professional support to deal with her crisis. Beth followed this advice. As a result, she was able to overcome her anxiety and return to work.

THE INNER CHILD Psychotherapy helped Beth to empower her "inner child." We all have an "inner child." This is the emotional child that we were when growing up. The "inner child" is a metaphor for the emotional storehouse of recorded information about our experiences, decisions, and conflicts. Sometimes our daily behaviors can be the result of executive decisions we made as children or adolescents. When similar events occur in our adult lives, we unconsciously use an automatic, habitual, coping pattern developed earlier in our emotional life.

This automatic coping pattern can be a helpful shortcut in many situations. Useful information can be provided by the "inner child," and negative, distorted information can also be accessed, leading to misperceptions and hasty, inappropriate conclusions. For this reason it is important to resolve old wounds to maintain clarity in adulthood.

DISSOCIATION A multitude of stimuli may illicit traumatic memories from the "inner child." This is especially true for children who have been abused as a result of physical punishment, sexually inappropriate behavior, or neglect. The individual may respond in adulthood as she or he did as a child, acting to avoid a situation in the present that was too painful to confront in the past. The threatening situation is avoided through dissociation or some other avoidance mechanism. This dissociation is an unconscious process of mentally tuning out a memory that is too painful to contemplate.

Beth's family laughed at her when she cognitively "went away" from her traumatic thoughts. They were ignorant or callous to her pain. She needed support from them; instead she received their derision. Often people with low self-esteem place themselves in one-down social positions. When they are attacked they accept the punishment because it is familiar to their "inner child." They believe that they are deserving of it or do not deserve better.

SUPPORT SYSTEM Complicating the road to recovery for abuse survivors are the family and friends who make up their "support" system. One expects a support network to be warm, empathic, and encouraging. In Beth's case, her family was just the opposite: cold, depreciating, and discouraging.

Often friends and family are identified as support systems. If a person has low self-esteem, however, she or he may choose abusive or ineffectual partners and friends. The person with a poor self-image seeking familiarity may replicate what "love" looked like in childhood —an abusive partner. They may alternatively seek the opposite of what was known in childhood—an ineffectual person. The ineffectual person will not be abusive like the parent, but will be incapable of providing genuine, assertive support, and confirmation. This person may become tyrannical in resisting the growth of the low self-esteemed partner. These extreme types appear to be the only people the abused believes she or he deserves. The abused person's children could adopt the role model to not value, respect or support the wounded parent. Friends may likewise provide less than ideal support.

Being a family member or friend is not always synonymous with being a supporter. Ultimately, one's support system is comprised of those who actually behave in ways that are experienced as supportive. The growth task for the abuse survivor is to heal the wounds of the past. In the process, she or he must also develop a support system that is capable of and truly delivers support.

IDENTIFICATION WITH THE AGGRESSOR Children, for better or worse, may identify with the underdog or the aggressor. When a parent is in a one-down position, children may come to their aid, protecting her or him from the abuse of the other parent. On the other hand, a child not wanting to become a victim, may identify with the aggressive parent in an attempt to gain recognition, support, love, or even protection. This may be a futile attempt as the aggressor often is not a nurturer, caretaker, or empathizer. In Beth's case, her children joined often with their father's derision of his wife's dissociative episodes. This made the normalization[1] of Beth's abusive childhood much more difficult.

REGRESSIVE THERAPY When Beth's work was compromised by her overwhelming emotional responses, she found a psychotherapist who used regressive therapeutic techniques[2] which proved helpful and effective.[3] Following her treatment, Beth ceased having her recurring, dissociative episodes.

DISTANCE By the time one is sufficiently trained to give bodywork sessions, it is easy to have forgotten what it was like to be a client for the first time: all of the sensations, thoughts, and doubts that accompany baring one's body to a stranger, the struggle to surrender control, relaxing one's muscles, allowing another to move one's limbs, neck, or head. Receiving bodywork requires a significant amount of trust[4] for anyone, let alone for a person who has been physically or sexually violated.

Beth was aware of the protective distance that Jan created during the initial interview. Jan physically distanced herself in the act of sitting. She distanced herself with the amount of clothing she wore. Her reticence to share relevant psychosocial data created distance, as did her failure to make eye contact.

More subtle was the psychological distance Jan must have internally maintained, prohibiting her from experiencing her own body. She distanced herself from her experience of being touched, fearful perhaps that she would again awaken, remember, and experience violating touch from the past. From the manifest signs Jan demonstrated, it can be assumed that building trust will be slow, on-going, and a major part of her bodywork sessions.

STRENGTH, DARING, AND COURAGE   Jan's lack of eye contact and even her withdrawal from bodywork treatment may stand out and characterize her as fearful, weak, or uncomfortable. However, when these signs are viewed in the context of Jan's extending the limits of her known intrapersonal and interpersonal boundaries, they serve to highlight this woman's strength, daring, and courage especially when contrasted to her previous violations and fears of subsequent contact.

A new growth issue emerges each time an old growth issue is resolved. If one does not stop to recognize and appreciate what has been achieved, her or his experience may be one of having endless problems. Unfortunately, Jan did not recognize her achievement. Taking herself for bodywork was a significant and commendable breakthrough.

TWO DECISIONS   There are two decisions to be made when a person undertakes a growth process. The first decision is a naïve decision. One undertakes the project because she or he thinks its a good idea. There may or may not be a realistic understanding of what is involved in the task. The second decision, an educated decision, comes after one's experiential feet get wet in the endeavor. The educated decision is to continue with the project after knowing what it entails.

Jan, choosing to incorporate bodywork in her growth program, terminated her work with Beth after experiencing the discomfort, emotional pain, and fear of reclaiming her physical body. Beth, on the other hand, knew the pain of psychotherapy and chose to pursue regressive therapy in order to work through unresolved stumbling blocks from her past.

Hopefully, when Jan is feeling stronger, she will decide that the pain of staying stuck is worse than the pain of moving on. Knowing what is involved in bodywork, she can choose to continue her work. She may even return to work with Beth who was honest, concerned, and responsive.

AUTHORITY FIGURE   Beth was struck by her client's inability to make eye contact. She found herself identifying with Jan's behavior. She, too, was unable to make or maintain eye contact[5] with her psychotherapist. This time she was on the other side of the couch, so to speak: she found herself in the role of therapist. Beth was taken aback by this phenomenon. It was difficult for her to imagine herself in the role of an authority figure. She was a victim as a child. She was victimized in her marriage. Beth was perceived as one who went off into fantasy by her children and her husband.

Beth's "inner child" may have accepted her status of "one-down" as all that she deserved. However, in psychotherapy, Beth quietly worked to heal her wounds, to change her self-perception, her feelings of unworthiness, and the role she played in her family. This could be tantamount to a revolution. Overcoming the disparity between Beth's inability to perceive herself as an authority figure and her client's perception of her as an authority figure could provide another pivotal issue for Beth's personal-professional development.

Much to her chagrin, Beth discovered that one need not be a psychotherapist to be the subject of a psychotherapeutic phenomenon. Jan entered Beth's office and immediately treated this bodyworker as she probably treated other people whom she perceived as authority figures and whose rejection or disapproval she feared. This point bears repeating: Not just psychotherapists or bodyworkers, but anyone can be, and is, subject to transference reactions from time to time.

TRYING ON A NEW ROLE: A PROBLEM-SOLVING STRATEGY Rather than being frightened or disconcerted by being perceived as an authority figure, Beth can explore the manner in which she would like to be an authority figure or teacher for her clients. Beth could become an authority figure and partner in Jan's growth process. This subject could be appropriately examined with Beth's psychotherapist. As a professional development issue, it could also be explored with her bodywork instructor or colleagues.

PACING As already noted, Beth identified with Jan's distance and self-protective behaviors. However, she did not simply accept these qualities as signs and symptoms of Jan's low self-esteem. Jan became the screen for Beth's projections. Beth could not tolerate seeing symptoms of her own weakness in Jan anymore than she could tolerate the uncomfortable reminder in herself. As a result, Beth attempted, at her pace, to push her client along in the growth process. Jan was neither ready, nor able, to move as fast as Beth wanted. Beth not only sensed this, but perceived her pace as "bearing down" and violating her client.

People may often dislike or have difficulty accepting others in whom they see their own unacceptable traits. Recognizing these traits and coming to understand their significance is the route to overcoming them. Trying to superimpose change onto others may end in sabotage. Each of us has our own pace for growth. That pace must be respected. Beth discovered with Jan, sometimes to move faster is to move slower.

SABOTAGE Both bodywork and the relationship were "going well" for Beth and Jan in spite of the hardship of working with a heavily clothed, psychologically defended client. Jan was feeling comfortable enough to begin to share with her bodyworker information from her childhood. Indeed, Jan allowed herself to receive a hug from Beth—"the only one she received all week." Beth had succeeded in creating a warm, safe, trusting relationship with her client. The two parties in this relationship were building the groundwork necessary for Jan to achieve her goal.

Beth characterized her final session with Jan as sabotage. Perhaps her work was going too well and the success intolerable, given her past role of being a victim. Perhaps she was unable to tolerate the part of herself that she perceived in Jan. Or Beth may have simply been lacking in sufficient knowledge, pacing skills, and experience to successfully recognize that she had already achieved the next step in her professional relationship. Perhaps a combination of these motives was present. Whatever, Beth took action on her own agenda rather than her client's.

Jan had taken this bodywork experience as far as she could for the time being. When the suggestion to take the work a step farther arose, Jan, overwhelmed, felt incapable of handling more.

FIXATION Fixation is a preoccupation with an act or thought, such as Beth's irritation with Jan's wearing clothes while receiving bodywork. Beth was so concerned that Jan's wearing clothes was a sign that she was violating her, that Beth failed to recognize her own and Jan's achievements. Often people who define themselves as undeserving are unable or unwilling to recognize or accept success when it is present.

There are a number of indicators of Beth's excellent work. Most important, Jan was returning for sessions. Jan was beginning to open up verbally during her bodywork sessions. And Jan accepted Beth's hug—a personal gesture of acceptance. Beth could have been more patient with her client if she had recognized the progress that had already been accomplished, rather than being fixated on what was yet to be achieved.

The fixation ultimately relates to "unfinished business" in Beth's psychosocial past. Jan's difficulty with physical contact interacted with Beth's discomfort over touching a client who was wearing clothes. Beth's anxiety while working with this client proved to be too much for Beth. She was unable to look within and grapple with that unacceptable part of herself. Beth expected her client to be the one to change. Though Jan was actually changing, Beth, unfortunately, was unable to recognize and appreciate the changes.

EARNESTNESS AND INTEGRITY   Beth was uncomfortable during her last session with Jan. She was so uncomfortable that she called Jan and shared her distress and apologized. Beth treated her client as a coequal in their relationship. Beth's honesty with Jan demonstrated her personal integrity and respect for her client. Beth sought consultation from her bodywork instructor and then psychotherapeutic growth work. Both of these acts demonstrate this woman's earnestness and integrity. Beth returned to her practice after doing her personal-professional homework. Her "inner child" healed, Beth had a renewed sense of strength and a firsthand experience with the power of personal growth work.

FORGIVENESS   Beth admitted to Jan that she expected too much of her. If Beth handled herself inappropriately, it was because of this issue of expectation. Her expectations were too high for her client. Jan's experiences during her sessions with Beth were not as Beth assumed them to be. Jan did not sense Beth "bearing down" abusively on her. She did not even feel Beth's impatience. Beth's believing herself to be a "perpetrator" was beyond Jan's imagination. Beth was uncomfortable with her own inappropriate expectations and the possibility that they may have effected Jan.

Beth's perception of herself as a "perpetrator" was gross distortion. She was a soft spoken, self-effacing, empathic woman, overly conscious of and concerned about how her actions effected others. She was touched by the fact that she was the only one to give Jan a hug all week. She somehow felt responsible for hurting her client. And she called Jan to apologize. She also called her instructor to discuss the case. She took herself into special therapy to address this issue. These are not the characteristics of a callous, self-serving perpetrator.

In spite of Jan's assurance to Beth that she was not a perpetrator, Beth was unable to relinquish her sense of guilt. Something remained unfinished for her. Beth had not forgiven herself. Beth may have been unaware of what is required in order to merit forgiveness. She did not know that to gain forgiveness, a person must recognize her or his transgression. Then, one needs to have remorse or regret for the offensive behavior. The individual must apologize to the wronged party. This apology may include compensation or restitution, as well as a commitment not to inflict injury again.

Beth did everything necessary and beyond in order to merit forgiveness. In fact, Jan forgave Beth. Yet even after her work in therapy, Beth was still clutching her guilt. There was no reason in the "here and now" for her to feel guilty. It may have been Beth's misguided projective identification that caused her to feel that she did to Jan what the callous, self-indulgent, adult perpetrators did to her in childhood. What she may have felt responsible for in the past became confused with what she believed she had done to Jan in the present. Beth's "inner child" had internalized the guilt that belonged to her violators—her father and her grandfather, and her mother.

SELF-FORGIVENESS: A PROBLEM-SOLVING STRATEGY There may be a piece of unfinished work for Beth to explore. Beth, the "adult," must turn to Beth, the "inner child," embrace her and say with all sincerity, "Sweetheart, it is time for you to let go of your guilt. A child is not responsible for the deeds of grown men and grown women. You are a beautiful, lovable, deserving child. I love you. And from now on, I will be with you to protect you from anybody whose behavior is inappropriate. You are not a perpetrator. And for any distress that this childhood misunderstanding has caused me over these years, I forgive you." This self-recognition, acceptance, release from self-reproach, and availability for self-support is what constitutes forgiveness.

NON-EVENTS Beth's bodywork instructor did not tell Beth how to handle her problems with her client. She did not probe into Beth's discomfort or offer problem solving advice. After patiently listening to the nature of Beth's concern, she recommended that her student seek professional consultation. The wisdom of this instructor and the strength she demonstrated in not taking direct action merits commendation.

SUMMARY

Beth, a gentle, soft-spoken woman was confronted by a clothed client who reminded her of herself. The client terminated regular sessions after Beth suggested she take off some of her clothes during treatment. Beth faulted herself and perceived herself to be a perpetrator for compromising her work. Beth demanded more from her client than the client was capable of tolerating. She may have made this request out of her own unresolved psychological motives rather than in her client's interest.

Being perfect is not the sign of a professional. Professionals are strong enough to recognize their errors and make good by them. Beth's failure to forgive herself for her fallibility undervalued the healing power of her earnestness, concern, experiential knowledge, and the role model she provided by demonstrating her courage to confront what she believed were her own failings with her client. With the capital investment she had made in herself and her own recovery, Beth came to understand the issues of pacing interventions, respecting client's limits, and valuing the healing power of touch. Consequently, when and if she is ready to do so, Beth will make an excellent bodyworker for any abuse survivor.

END NOTES

1 **Normalization**   One of the benefits of group therapy is the sharing of experiences by the members. They discover, as the sharing unfolds, that they are not the only ones to have certain experiences. Knowing one is not unique or peculiar in having dissociative reactions or other psychologically protective experiences can be comforting. This allows a person to feel normal instead of crazy. Like the post traumatic reactions of a soldier in combat, such protective reactions are normal, given that one has lived through an abnormal situation. One is not at fault or to blame because of her or his quirks. With normalization, dysfunctional behavior can be recognized, addressed, and corrected rather than defended against or denied.

2 **Regressive Therapy**   When performed by a competent professional, these regressive therapeutic techniques safely allow a motivated individual to re-experience or regress to an earlier emotional stage. In the process, a former traumatic event is re-enacted. Rather than being a passive, traumatized victim in the reenactment as in childhood, the client now has an opportunity to utilize the full range of her or his adult knowledge and skills to take positive actions in the traumatic situation.

Regressive therapy provides the "inner child" with the recognition, love, and protection that should have been offered at the time of trauma by responsible parents, family members, or others. This creates within the core of the personality structure a positive set of cognitive and emotional associations from which the individual can draw a new sense of strength, integrity, and esteem. The regressive therapy empowers the "potential child" existing in all of us. The needed recognition, love, and protection now comes from within rather than without the individual. Parenting one's self is the hallmark of becoming a psychological adult.

3 **The Potential Child**   The "inner child" is the emotional child one actually was in childhood. The "potential child" is the creative, energetic, loving child that could have been if not for the abuse or neglect that existed in childhood. The abuse or neglect created psychological buffers to pain and fright. These same buffers also dampened emotional sensitivity, experience, and creativity. When one's "inner child" is appropriately supported by one's adult self, an emotional catharsis or healing occurs. The therapeutic process deactivates this damper and the "potential child" is liberated. The adult now has access to cognitive, behavioral, and emotional potentials previously bound up in the self-protective dissociative process.

4 **Trust**   A bodyworker may assume that trust is automatically present when a client chooses to seek bodywork services. However, it may be foolhardy for anyone to trust another automatically and unconditionally before there has been sufficient time and experience for trust to be established. In establishing the relationship, it may be more helpful for the bodyworker to assume trust must be earned rather than it will automatically occur. In addition, trust may not simply develop with the passage of time; it is what happens over time that creates trust.

Trust is established on the part of the bodyworker for her or his client by a number of factors including understanding, respect, appreciation, and pacing. This trust is enhanced by recognition and appreciation of the courage the client manifests by placing herself or himself in a potentially vulnerable position in the bodyworker's arena. When working with an abuse survivor, the bodyworker needs to check the pulse of this trust frequently by asking the client to assess whether the work is too much, appropriate, or insufficient. Fluctuations of distance with such a client can be interpreted as a psychosocial pulse of progress in the unfolding relationship. Rather than something to get rid of, distance can provide a criterion for either stepping back from the depth of the work or being able to go deeper. If a client's distance is sufficiently problematic, this material could be explored in psychotherapy. Again, the focus would not be to get rid of or analyze it, but to understand and appreciate the significance of the distance.

5 **Eye Contact** Eye contact is an important technique that can be used to heighten awareness and intimacy in a relationship. Eye contact can be a baring of one's soul and psyche to another. If a person is not comfortable with her or himself, eye contact, like many other forms of contact, will be problematic. One can assume in this case, eye contact would be anxiety provoking. The distance created by poor eye contact should be responded to and respected as a sign of a person's level of discomfort. Changes in frequency, or duration of maintaining of eye contact, along with other forms of distancing or contact, can be a helpful indicator of progress in the relationship.

24

SORTING OUT

Fran, an energetic woman in her mid-forties, was a store owner as well as a bodyworker.

Just before I left for my training, I had to fire an employee who was stealing from me. I really liked her, which complicated the matter. It was even more difficult because she denied taking any money. This created just the slightest bit of doubt for me. Her image remained in my mind as I drove to the airport. Repeatedly, I saw the look in her eyes, her tears falling, and her hair flying as she shook her head. These images stayed with me through the flight to my training session.

I try to plan training sessions around my menstrual periods. This time I was unsuccessful. As soon as I got to my training session, I started my period. This created physical pains and discomfort in my abdomen. In addition, I generally felt uncomfortable; my thinking got fuzzy, and I became insecure.

This was also the height of my sexual abuse recovery work. I felt like my whole belly was a bleeding wound. *(Fran paused and then after a long, pressured sigh, she continued.)* I was sexually abused many times. As a child, I was sexually molested by my older brother. I was also sexually abused by several of my mother's boyfriends. I was raped at the age of 18. And my first husband was a sexually abusive man. I have since developed a frame of mind that I will not allow that to happen again.

Early in the training week, I had a trade with a fellow student. The focus for the day was chest work. My partner, in the process of the chest work, touched my abdomen. After my partner touched me gently, I immediately began to tremble. My breathing became shallow and rapid as if I was panting. Tears streamed down either side of my face. I wasn't really crying. I don't know what it was. It was like a spontaneous rebirthing. There was a fantastic energy exchange between us. It was very healing to me. It felt like it began to knit together the wound that I felt in my belly. That night and the next day, I found myself thinking of every abandonment issue I could remember.

The next day I was to have an individual session with one of the training instructors. I got a ride to the house where my instructor was staying. My ride then drove off. I walked up the stairs. I knocked on the door, but nobody answered. No one ever came. In frustration, I had to walk miles and miles back to the house where I was staying. The walk took hours. When I got out there the door was locked. I couldn't get in. *(Fran chuckled.)* I had to pee! It was one thing after another. I called home to talk with a familiar, friendly voice. There was no answer.

The schedule for the last day of the training called for practice sessions with two different partners. I was taking care of transportation business and arrived late for pairing up. I ended up with the one person that I really didn't want to have touch me. She had fingers like hooks. But I didn't feel like I had a choice because everyone else was already working.

My second partner was a thin man about fifteen years younger than myself. I was conscious of not readily being able to establish a rapport as I began to work with this man. Thin men are not my favorite to work with. There is no flesh on them to hold onto. So, I placed myself in a meditative state and quieted myself. Then, when I felt ready, I began to work on my partner.

When the session was over, my partner gave me feedback. He told me he became sexually aroused during the session. This was because, "You came in too close." I knew that I was not physically inappropriate. So I took "coming in too close" to mean that I allowed my sexual feelings to enter into my work. I thought to myself, "There is something wrong within me. I am unable to 'hook-up' *(enter into a therapeutic rapport)* with a client without being sexual."

I left the training session with an old familiar demoralizing, self-depreciating thought, "There is something wrong with me." What is wrong with me is that I am scarred from the sexual abuse that I experienced in my past. Perhaps, I have to turn this into a sexual experience so that I can have power over the man under my hands. After twenty-five years doing massage, I thought I'd quit training. I feared that I would never be able to step up and away from that and be pure and clear and sacred in the work. I was afraid I would not be able to transcend the trauma of my past experience and maintain a professional integrity in my work. "I never will be able to do this work!"

For a month I accepted the responsibility that he gave to me. But after a month of agonizing self-examination, I had a new sense of clarity. I was not responsible for the feelings that he had. I took responsibility as a result of my insecurity from the sexual abuse in my past. I am used to taking responsibility for other people's conduct.

(Fran continued in an earnest tone.) I have since come to believe whatever happened there was not because there was anything wrong with me. In the exchange of a bodywork session, either partner might get in touch with sexual feelings. The rising of sexual energy in either person happens or it doesn't happen. That does not mean that there is something wrong with what the practitioner is doing. It can simply mean that there is sexual energy being released. These feelings are not to be denied, and they are not to be acted upon.

This experience taught me something really important. I want to remain open to question myself and my own motives. I think this is essential with every person that I touch. I came to this conclusion as a result of sorting out my experience. Sorting out brought me to the core of the issue. I did not "come in too close" to him in any sexual way. Even if I had been sexually attracted to him, there is no way I would allow that to enter into what I was doing. I was not responsible for his feelings.

DISCUSSION

LOW RESISTANCE   Low resistance makes a person vulnerable to psychological insult which is difficult, if not impossible, to defend against. Additional stressful events lower resistance still further. Various factors can lower a person's resistance: too little sleep, viruses, bad news, menstrual periods, too much alcohol, family matters, stressful work, poor nutrition, lack of exercise, too much exercise, accidents, losses, constant worry, even social demands. Chronic low self-esteem adds to a person's susceptibility. When one's resistance is lowered, she or he is then more sensitive to psychological reactivity.

In Fran's case, her resistance was initially lowered by the stress of firing an employee for whom she cared a great deal. Traveling some distance to her training in an unfamiliar city, perhaps in a different time zone, was another stress. She then had her menstrual period which presented multiple stresses. In addition, Fran encountered numerous mishaps and let-downs during her training week. These issues, added to a psychological background of sexual abuse and parental neglect resulting in low self-esteem, set Fran up to be less focused, more vulnerable, and more intensely upset.

In her first bodywork trade, Fran experienced a growth event. She paradoxically attributed her intense "healing" response to her "lowered resistance." The conjunction of her vulnerability, and the stimulation of her partner's "gentle touch" on her belly, brought forth many unresolved emotions. Fran's lowered resistance allowed her to get in touch with and work out past emotional trauma. This event was unburdening, healing, clarifying, and growthful.

Emotional growth work is hard work, demanding lots of energy which can leave a person physically, as well as emotionally drained. Until one recovers her or his stamina, she or he is left "open." Relaxation, healing, and growth can occur if the environment is supportive while one is open. If the environment is indifferent, insensitive, or hostile, one then is vulnerable to yet more injury.

By the end of the week, Fran had suffered numerous additional disappointments. She was left vulnerable to becoming overwhelmed by newly-inflicted insults: a mistake in the scheduled time for an individual session, the lack of a ride back to her room, a walk of "miles and miles," and finally the absence of a familiar voice on the telephone when Fran called home. At this low point in her week, Fran "lucked out" in getting the one person that she did not want touching her. In her highly vulnerable state, Fran was extremely susceptible to what might have been her partner's projection.

PROJECTION Projection is a defense mechanism utilized when a person is unable or unwilling to accept responsibility for her or his own feelings or motives. Her or his thoughts and feelings are placed on another. The origin of the reaction is believed to reside in the other person.

Fran's last partner accused her of "coming too close" and sexually arousing him. The issue of Fran's doing something to arouse her partner's sexual reaction is questionable. Assigning responsibility to his bodyworker for his own sexual excitement may have been his projection. If there was something inappropriate about Fran's sexuality or her work, then it stands to reason that more of her male partners would have become aroused by her work. For example, her first male partner should have also become aroused. This did not seem to be the case.

Later, after careful consideration, Fran realized, "Even if I was sexually attracted to him, there is no way I would allow that to enter into what I was doing." There is no reason to believe that Fran might have had unconscious sexual feelings toward her final partner. In addition to initially having difficulty getting in sync with this man, he was a client management problem for her because he was thin. Fran was not attracted to him.

Something else that Fran said puts serious doubt on her acting out sexual feelings. In discussing her self-doubt about continuing in both the training and in her profession, she said, "I feared that I would never be able to step away from that and be pure and clear and sacred in the work." It is understandable, if not justifiable, that a person who was sexually molested and is actively struggling to recover from that trauma might have difficulty with feelings of being "pure" and "clean." To suggest that her work was not "sacred" brings in a totally different element. Fran's work, as much as anything else, is a spiritual expression for her. Bringing unresolved sexual feelings into a spiritual experience was abhorrent for her to even contemplate.

The sexual feelings that emerged from Fran's younger, male partner in all likelihood originated with him. He was unwilling to recognize and accept responsibility for his own feelings when he projected and accused, "I became aroused because you came in too close." Whatever his issue, he failed to accept responsibility for his own behavior.

SEXUAL FEELINGS In Fran's consideration of her client's troubling accusation she said, "In the exchange of a bodywork session, either party might get in touch with sexual feelings. The rising of sexual energy in either person happens or it doesn't. That does not mean there is something wrong with what the practitioner is doing." This stance might be problematic. The problem is not in a practitioner finding a client sexually attractive. Though not true in Fran's case, the problem is if the bodyworker becomes sexually aroused from her or his work and entertains or acts on that arousal.

Touch communicates feelings. If a bodyworker's feelings are supportive, caring, healing, spiritual toward a client, emotionally specific neurotransmitters in the bodyworker transmit that state throughout the bodyworker. Touch then communicates that state. The same type of communication would also convey the emotional state if the bodyworker were feeling erotic. This erotic state of the practitioner would cross and violate the professional boundary of the client. A visual, auditory, or intuitively perceptive client could be touched by the bodyworker's inappropriate state even if the bodyworker did not do anything overtly sexual. This could be traumatizing for a client.

A bodywork session is not for the practitioner to act-out her or his personal needs or fantasies, but to provide a sexually safe, therapeutic environment in which clients may become aware of their experiences. Clients may be wounded if bodyworkers entertain their "rising" erotic feelings. Outside professional assistance may be necessary to address this issue.

BENEFIT OF THE DOUBT People often say that they give someone "the benefit of the doubt." Often there is no benefit in failing to respond to a doubt. There was a question for Fran regarding what her partner meant by, "You came in too close." She knew that she was not too physically close. To what was he referring? She assumed "coming in too close" meant allowing her sexual feelings to enter into her work. After giving careful consideration to the matter, Fran was clear that she had no sexual feelings for this man. It remained unclear as to what, exactly, her partner was referring.

Fran quickly took her partner's words to be the truth. If she had asked him what he meant by "coming in too close," Fran might have clarified her doubts and saved herself an agonizing month of turmoil. Checking this issue out on the spot would have been an appropriate use of her training session.

INTROJECTION   Fran, at first, swallowed the responsibility her partner transferred to her. Indiscriminately taking-in and swallowing such statements made by others is psychologically referred to as "introjection." Swallowing unpalatable pieces of food can make a person physically sick or choke. Similarly, swallowing unpalatable statements or beliefs can make a person psychologically ill.

Low self-esteem and low resistance left Fran particularly vulnerable to accepting this stranger's judgment. His comments were so impactful, Fran even contemplated changing her professional career based upon his insinuations. Fran automatically accepted responsibility for her client's sexual arousal with a sense of complicity and guilt. She thought to herself that her sexually abusive past must surely have been responsible for his sexual arousal. Fran could not conceive that he might have been auto-aroused.

The preventive intervention for introjection is "chewing carefully before swallowing." The remedial intervention is to bring the introjected material back into awareness. Then, material is intellectually "chewed." If the material is appropriate and fits, it can be accepted and swallowed. If it does not apply, it is spit out. That is exactly what Fran did. Though it took a month to get the fallacious, toxic remark and its implications out of her system, Fran finally spat it out.

THE CYCLE   Childhood abuse traumas interfere with the ability to establish and maintain a healthy family climate in which to raise children. For those who are less aware of and disinclined toward healing their wounds, traumatic early life experiences provide the blueprints for raising the next generation of abused children, feeding the cycle of abuse.

Neglect and sexual abuse leave a child feeling as if there is something wrong with her or him. The perception of such a wounded child is, "After all, if something were not wrong with me, surely my mother and father would have been more attentive, caring, protective, and loving." The thought of having a dysfunctional parent is so frightening that the child turns her or his perceptions topsy-turvy. "My parent must be right. Therefore, I am wrong."

A scar is left from the hurts and wounds of an emotionally absent, unprotective parent. The result is low self-esteem, which not only hurts at the time, but is integrated into the structure of the child's personality. Later, it may articulate itself in terms of the person feeling like a second-class citizen, feeling undeserving, and assuming responsibility or blame even when it is inappropriate, as in Fran's case.

A CHILD'S CONFUSION   Fran's upbringing left her vulnerable to introjecting or swallowing her partner's projection. However, Fran did not merely suffer from sexual abuse as a child, she also suffered from emotional neglect. She needed emotional, physical, and cognitive stimulation. And her parents were absent. They gave their daughter neither the nourishment nor the protection she deserved and needed. This lack of healthy stimulation unfortunately leaves many abused children with a misplaced, confused sense of responsibility and guilt for the deviant behaviors which were perpetrated upon them. They believe that because they wanted attention and affection, they somehow caused the inappropriate behavior of another. The "other" was usually an adult.

Children are not responsible for the behaviors of adults. Children cannot make adults take inappropriate action. An adult is responsible for his or her choices. Children often, and inappropriately, take responsibility for the actions of their parents, relatives, and other adults. Consciously or unconsciously, children may later remember deviant sexual actions which they were too young to understand at the time of occurrence. As these children mature, past memories distort the child's sense of self-image, self-worth, sexuality, and desirability. They may grow into confused adults struggling with issues of their attractiveness, worthiness of love, and their sexuality. Such early life experiences become part of the building blocks of the child's personality. Legitimate healthy feelings are linked with deviant ones. The healthy feelings are misconstrued as "dirty," "impure," and undesirable. Feelings of pleasure are associated with guilt, and with being bad.

SELF-DEFENSE   Though Fran was unjustly accused by her partner, she did not become angry. Anger does not seem to be part of this energetic woman's emotional repertoire. Anger is an expansive, explosive, protective feeling. Anger pushes away a potential harm-doer. It protects the emotional core from insult or abuse. Fran holds her anger in rather than marshaling her expansive, protective energy. This internalization or turning of anger back on herself creates depression.

In the case of anger, self-protection comes from pushing the offender away. In the case of depression, self-protection comes in the form of numbing awareness to the insult that has been inflicted. Fran, as a child, was not taught how, or even that she should, protect herself. In addition to lacking supervision, Fran was left vulnerable in her childhood to older, bigger, more powerful males. Her sole defense was to numb psychologically to that pain. In adulthood, Fran remained vulnerable to males. Her defense continued to be an internalization of her thought processes and withdrawal.

SETBACK Fortunately, Fran decided to grow rather than to stay stuck. Once people truly embark upon their growth journeys, they tend to stay on them. Fran suffered a temporary set back. Setbacks are not an indicator of failure on life's growth path, quite to the contrary. Setbacks are to be expected. They are events from which learning, self-definition, and growth can be derived. They can even provide a criterion for growth. All of the following signs can be used to assess progress: the amount of time a person takes to become aware or conscious that she or he has been wounded; the time involved to feel the wound; the period needed to develop a strategy to either defend her or himself and/or to heal the wound; the time taken to formulate an appropriate response; and the time needed before the person takes preventive action.

The fact that it took Fran a month to work through her conflict is a sign of neither strength nor weakness. A month was simply the amount of time that it took her to work through her feelings. What is more significant is that she knew there was something wrong. Fran was immediately aware of being wounded. And, she went right to work trying to set the situation straight. The job might have been easier and faster if Fran had talked out the situation with a supportive listener, someone who would not try to solve her problem for her, but who could be non-judgmental, warm, and empathic. Nevertheless, she "sorted out" the painful encounter and developed a stronger sense of herself.

CONSCIOUS CHOICE: A PROBLEM-SOLVING STRATEGY Fran appreciated the value of prevention. She had already learned from prior experiences that her menstrual period placed her in both emotionally open and vulnerable states. In general, Fran tried to avoid training events in unfamiliar locations when she was having her period. Unfortunately, she was unable to structure the timing of this training to avoid her menses.

A person cannot always control the outcome of her or his life. We can consciously guide ourselves on our growth paths and often prevent injury if we acknowledge our vulnerable states of low resistance. This can be accomplished by choosing a partner to work with prior to the exercise. Waiting till the last moment to pick a partner may offer a novel and challenging experience, but it may be undesirable under stressful circumstances. A safer, more conservative experience may provide far more learning and integration than a more adventurous one.

SUMMARY

Fran began a training session at a time when she was feeling low. Numerous physiological, circumstantial, and psychological situations compromised her sense of personal integrity and strength. During the class, a training partner accused her of being sexually inappropriate with him in her work. Fran at first internalized this comment and accepted it as truth. The comment preyed on Fran's self-esteem and background of sexual abuse to such a depth that she contemplated giving up her twenty-five years of bodywork practice.

Fortunately, Fran took the opportunity of this disturbing encounter to carefully sort out her beliefs, motives, and actions. Fran knew after her examination process that she was not responsible for her partner's sexual excitement. In fact, she recognized that, in working intimately with people, either one or both might become sexually aroused. The professional issue for Fran is not whether a person has feelings of sexual excitement, but what is done with those feelings.

The philosophical stance Fran developed for herself was that she needed to recognize and take responsibility for her feelings, whatever they are and whenever they emerge. She will confront those issues until she feels a sense of resolution. As for sexual feelings toward her clients, Fran knew that she would not take action on them even if they arose. Fran was clear that she was not responsible for her client's feelings.

25

WHY ELSE AM I HERE

Christine is a bodyworker in her late forties. She had just returned from a humanitarian pilgrimage to a Romanian orphanage. She speaks with a driving tenacity. When her speech slows, the fullness of her emotions unfolds.

This may be much more than you want because it is not just one event. It is not just one thing that happened. It is not only one healing experience. The whole thing was a healing experience. As I look on it now, lists of words come out; words like "synergy," words like "synchronicity." Ya' know, things like that come out. But if I look at the whole picture, I think what starts to come to me the greatest is, whenever I go into a situation, I ask, "Why else am I here?" "On what other level am I here?" If I go to a workshop, I go with the obvious agenda to learn a lot of different techniques. But there is another reason that I am there, and I realize that any time I go into an intense situation like that, that I am there for a superficial reason, and I am there for a deeper level. That is the way I invite life to teach me.

So I asked that when I went to Romania, "Okay, I am here as a massage therapist, and I am going to do massage therapy, and I am going to fit in however I can fit in, in this process. And I am here for another reason." And I asked the Universe to show me that reason—because that process serves me. So it kept unfolding like a flower, like this petal. "This is why you are here, and this is why you are here, and this is why you are here." And kind of one whole thing, if I could put all of these experiences under one umbrella, it would be a validation for my whole belief system.

I live my life "diluted," in the sense of being aware of my values. Because I don't have to be aware of my values on a daily basis... because I don't have to make value decisions all the time, a lot of what I do is mundane. Ya' know, you cook...you do your work...you drive your car...you shop, and whatever. But this, this trip to Romania was like a, "This is your life, Christine. We will show it to you in thirty days. You will look at it under a microscope." And all the values, all the belief systems that I think I hold dear were there for scrutiny. I had to ask, "Is this serving me well? Is this something I really want to keep?" So, it was a sifting and a selection process, and a process where it was like, "Oh my God, a lot of the things you really value are taking place, like, right now!"

And one of the things to start out with was the whole thing about synergy. It was, "This is not the time for me to go to Romania." My husband was between jobs. We didn't have the money for me to go. So the first thing that was difficult for me was to end up asking other people for money. I sent out a letter to a lot of different people and asked them if they wanted to make a donation for this trip. I also believe that you get what you ask for. So I knew if I asked, I would get it. But it was difficult for me to take that step.

Now, I talk about synergy, but to live it is another thing. And my value system was saying, "Live it!" So when I did that...when I took the step to do that, the money came in, but it was really hard for me to ask. But the gift I got in return was the feeling that I wasn't going alone to give the gift. It wasn't my gift. It was "our" gift, the gift of all the people who helped me financially to go there.

I had it a few times in my life where I've made snap decisions. More times than not, I think things over for a few days or whatever. However, I was having lunch with a friend who told me about a group called the Free Romania Foundation. People with different specialties were going over there to orphanages for irrecuperable children, handicapped children. The friend explained that she was considering going. That ignited my enthusiasm. I knew right away I was going. I have a background of working with multiple handicapped children and adults. Between my background, massage, and something in my heart, out of my mouth came, "I am going!"

And another little observer part of me said, "What the hell are you committing yourself to? You haven't talked to your family. You don't know how much this is going to cost you, or anything else." But there was a piece of me that knew. I've had that a few times in my life. And I've acted on it and learned how to trust that...You know that intuition. I said a few times, but actually, it happens a lot. But a few times, major decisions were made that fast. But I knew I needed to go. It was a perfect meld. You know I am a massage therapist. I work with special needs children. Ya' know, I have all of those kinds of things in my background. But inside I knew I was going for another reason, too. It was like, "Okay, I trust that. I'm going for another reason."

So, I got early on, that I was going—that "we" were going. It was a collective "we", and we were going because one of our children over there was in pain. Or because a part of us, collectively, needed healing. That is an expression of the way I see myself or what I can do in life. The best thing I can do for the Universe is to work on healing myself. Collectively, I feel that sense of unity. But to have an awareness of how real that really is—how real it is, to take it in at the gut level, to take it in at the feeling level...is what has been just...I mean...*(Christine became choked up with her emotions.)* it has been an extremely moving experience.

I read something by Mother Teresa before I left for Romania. And I had that experience while I was there, and I can feel the feelings start to come up now. She said something about...when you finally open totally to the loving experience, then every child who cries is your crying child, and every poor man in the street is your brother in the gutter. And it was true. That was how it was. And I began to feel like...some people got really angry, for instance, at the director *(of the Romanian orphanage)* And it was...I could feel like he was my brother. It was like...he was a piece of me...don't be angry at him...he does not have an awareness yet. You know he is not awake yet. He is my brother. And over there was this woman working with the children...and she would hit the children with a stick, and it was like...I thought, "My sister does not know any better yet." It was really like she was part of me. And I don't go around having symbiotic relationships like that with people. But it really...it was so moving. It was like, "Oh, my God! We really are all one." And to feel that! And the same way that other belief...I have about how teaching and healing are interchangeable. And I knew, you go there to heal, and you go there to teach, but in the process, you are being taught, and you are being healed. And to feel that, "My God!" *(Christine's voice vibrated from being deeply moved with all that she perceived. She was filled with life. As she spoke it was clear she was deeply alive.)* I could feel the healing take place through that feeling of oneness. The experience is still fresh within me.

All of a sudden the family concept came to me. I was physically abused as a child. And I was sexually abused as a child. And the awareness that "people were doing the best they could with what they had" was coming to me. *(Christine paused from her driving pace. She allowed herself a sigh and a soul filled sob. Then she continued.)* My parents and the men who sexually abused me were doing the best they could with what they had. And if it was an emotional tool or spiritual tool or food that the direct care-givers *(in Romania)* didn't have, they were doing the best they could. And, on some level, so were all the people in my life...who had violated me as a person. I had known that on a cognitive level. I have had psychotherapy and healed it all here, *(Christine explained this in a matter of fact tone, pointing to her head.)* but it got healed here, *(pointing now to her gut. She then repeated her words in a deep vibrating whisper.)* It got healed here.

It, in some ways...it was like having a near-death experience...or one of those experiences where you have a terminal illness and then somehow you make it...then somehow, the quality of your whole life is different because of it. And that's how it feels. The decisions that have started to come from that process. Now I'm not done healing all of those things that were shown to me. You know, like people were doing the best they could with this and this and this. And in some places I had no left-over emotion. Like no place, you know, like; you know, sometimes I cried or did rebirthing work with an issue, and I felt like, well that one at least feels complete. When the sexual abuse one came up, I see...I still have work left to do in that area. But on a gut level I have it in a different place. Now I feel that the work can be completed.

Life there was, like saying, "You have this thirty days," and it was like looking at my life through a microscope. And looking at my values and having to put my money where my mouth was...having to say this belief is an action. It is not just a belief I have in my head. It became an active, living belief.

I was a team leader in Romania. As a result, I had the opportunity to work closely with the director of the orphanage. That was healing in and of itself because I have a whole history of things that have happened with men that make men a frightening thing for me. This is especially true for men I don't know. But walking into somebody who is an authority figure, who is a large man, in a different country, who has a lot of power over how things will be done, and the stories I heard about him were terrible: "He was a raging maniac, a son-of-a-bitch, and all these kinds of things."

But I worked with him and didn't find him that way at all. The reason I didn't find him noxious was because I had this real experience that he was part of myself. When he was talking, it was like hearing a piece of myself talk, though he was saying things that I wouldn't even say. And I thought, "God, this is an incredible experience." The observer part of me was watching the interaction between this man and myself." And the "me" part of it was incredulous about all this stuff that was going on.

He wasn't hard, ugly, and mean. He was soft and caring. He was embarrassed that things were the way they were. He said, "I called these children irrecuperable; and they are not." I could see how layer on layer...like my father, I could see it...fifty years of growing up under a Communist government with fear, and suspicion, and pain, and people being jailed in the middle of the night. You know like, they do...imprison people sometimes for things that people don't even know why they are in prison. It was really clear to me why he was suspicious...real clear to me why he would have closed-off his feelings to the children. He grew up under a repressive Communist government. People were jailed day and night for whatever. This is on the wane, but he still holds old feelings and suspicions from the past. He was given an orphanage to run with inadequate funding, inadequate supplies, with uneducated, untrained workers, and no food. I can understand, in order to stay emotionally intact in that kind of situation, sometimes a coping mechanism might be to cut-off or deny feeling.

If something is so painful in the human condition that you had to experience over a long period of time...it is possible to shut down to it. And it could be me...and given the allowance, if it could be me, it could be my father. He grew up in a really repressive home. The connection it made...I could understand on a deeper level...I could understand my father. I could see the healing process.

So I heard this unfeeling, uncaring, son-of-a-bitch, and I thought, "This man has a defense mechanism that's working for him because it is the only way he can survive in this horrible mess!" And then, it was like, okay, it just clicked, *(snapping her fingers twice)* okay, it's your father. Because my father is shut down emotionally in a lot of ways. He comes from the head. And the allowance I could make for him, the Romanian director, I now could make for my father. And I haven't been able to do that before...I haven't been able to do that at all. *(Christine took two very deep breaths and then moved into a long deep silence.)*

(Christine showed pictures of the children with whom she worked. These were children who were suffering from malnutrition, failure to thrive, cerebral palsy, and AIDS. She showed a picture of a child's legs that were malformed as a result of bundling, children who could not sit up and self-feed, a boy of eight who looked like he was four, a girl of twelve-and-a-half who had never been outside.)

One of the things that happened to me in my childhood was that my father was physically abusive, and my mother did a lot of standing around and watching it happen...probably she was afraid herself. In Romania, the nurses would take thick sticks and knock the hell out of those kids. Then the kids in turn would model that behavior. The nurses would delegate responsibility to a child to keep an entire room of children quiet via the stick. I saw this happening, and I said to myself, "Christine, you can either turn your back to this, like what happened to you, or you can do something about this while you are present." So I took the translator around with me, and every time I saw a child with a stick, I would ask the child to give me the stick. I then asked the translator to tell the child, "Children are for loving. They are not for beating." The child would then give me the stick, and I would break it. Then after a couple of days, something magic happened. Kids started to break sticks. And then they would take the sticks, run, and put them in the fire. It felt so good to have done it and not have been afraid that everybody would be upset at what I did.

(This gentle, but driving woman then fell into a deep, pensive silence.) It was real hard for me to come home. The part that made it hard to come home was having created...having the awareness of a family that had come together...whether it was working with children or working with people from another country...and leaving that. I know that I have people here to love me in my family and everything...yet it was hard. There was a finality. I don't readily have the option to call someone and say, "How are you doing?" This ended up raising issues of abandonment for me...which I am still in the process of healing.

A professional meeting in the West offers me the opportunity to go out and visit with my parents. My parents are now in their mid-seventies. I do not often get to go to my parents' home. The distance, time, and expense makes it difficult. Emotionally, it is also not easy for me to return. I called my parents to tell them that I was going to be in the area and would like to see them. They told me they were planning a fishing trip, but would cancel it for a couple of weeks. However, they called back the next day to say that the salmon would be running and they would not be available.

I asked the Universe, "Why, when I get to a certain part of talking about Romania, why do I get a constricted throat? Why is it still lingering? Why do I still have that longing?" The message came back really strong, "It is because of the wound of abandonment." It is like your parents; they have never been there! They were never there! Now you are almost fifty years old and you are still looking for that validation of your worth based on, "Are they going to be there for you?"

In Romania, I experienced what I wanted—a sense of family acceptance. "Well, thanks...that's what I needed." I was grateful for the experience I had. It was a real beautiful blessing, and leaving hurts.

The British team came in the week before we left. There were several different specialists that came with them, i.e. occupational therapists, nurses, etc. These people had also brought a lot of clothing. If we carried on with our agenda, we were doing massage, a feeding program,...then the things the British would have done would have had to wait. We could have said, "Fine, bring the clothing. Put it in that storage room. See you later. We have our own program." But, somehow it was like, "Take your agenda and set this part of your program aside, and how can we sit here and all work together?"

What then happened was that the clothing was distributed. The occupational therapist wrote a program and the massage therapist came in and did it. And the British nurse said, "Look at what is going on here with skin infection. While a woman in hotel management from the United States said, "Teach me how to do it." People began to say, "Here is my puzzle piece. Tell me how this can fit in with yours." This is how we worked. So no one's agenda was more important than anyone else's.

It doesn't always work this way here. We heard that at other orphanages there had been rivalry between teams. But it seemed that when people went over with a common heart, a common purpose, that became their highest priority. "What can be the most we can do here? How can we all work together to make it happen?" Then we were all there together—British, Irish, Norwegian, Romanian, American—and it all ran like clock work.

I made a number of decisions when I came back from Romania. I returned home to financial uncertainty. I recognized that I had been working myself to a frazzle before I left. I said to myself, "Screw it! I'm not going to do that." I decided that I wanted to spend time with my daughter. This was my daughter's last year at home before she left for college. I discussed my feelings with my family and received their support.

Regarding my parents, I decided, "I have confronted them several times, and because I did that, they moved even further away. So I decided that they may live another five years, I'll see them once a year. That's good. It is not that important. It will not be something between us that makes it happen. And if I need to heal that, I need to heal that here." *(Christine pointed to her heart.)*

I could sit and focus on the fact that they were not there for me, or I could sit and focus on knowing that they were doing the best they could...and then choose to focus on any other part of my experience with them that was good...because that is what I am going to take with me.

I have also decided that living a life intensely, or living it as if this moment is important, does not have to be confined to Romania. When I finally got that on an experiential level, I realized I could live life as intensely as I want anywhere I want. It is like the difference between working in an emergency room or a doctor's office. I can choose to do that, or I can take any one moment, and say, "I want this moment to be as real, as meaningful as I want to make it." I don't have to go back to Romania to have that moment. I can have it here. This awareness feels good, and it feels freeing.

Now that I am home, I find myself more aware of everyday situations. Rather than taking them for granted, I see choice-points, options. Being home has been an emotional time. It is pieces of my belief-system getting mirrored, and I have to decide: "How am I going to act? How am I going to live my life?" Sometimes, I wish I wasn't conscious. Before, I was unconscious, I wasn't aware of all that stuff. Then I became conscious of the options, and I can see this one say, "Work on me; work on me; work on me." How do I choose now? Or choose once again? And I have to do it again and again and again! *(Sigh).*

The ultimate answer there, in Romania, is to empower other people. Americans coming, or British coming and doing is like a Band-Aid. However, when you teach and empower other people to take care of themselves or bring them into an awareness of how, it is the same thing. Like, I have this awareness and that helps me to grow from where I am to some other place. And because I believe that, one of the things that I want to earn money for is to help that education…education of people in Romania, that "want-to-learn" that I personally know. In that way, I still feel connected.

I underwent two shocks in my journey. The first was "entry shock". When I arrived in Romania, it was like getting catapulted into the 1920's. There were horses and carts in the road. There were no diapers on children. Women were sweeping the sidewalks with brooms made out of sticks and twigs. That was like…way back when. Then I experienced "re-entry shock." That was really tough because I didn't want to leave.

In the very beginning I had a repressed feeling. Somewhere along the line there were little earthquakes, and the feelings came up. Then, I could feel that something was pretty far along the healing way because I don't have strong feelings about it anymore. This may look like I have repressed feelings, but I don't. I can feel them in a different way. Then it's as if it happened to a different person. Romania offered a beautiful measuring stick which said, "This doesn't really hurt anymore, and that feels good." As a result, I can deal with life from a totally different place than if I had repressed the feelings.

Where I am going with my work is not having to feel so much rests on me as a massage therapist. That my client may be seeing a psychotherapist, a physical therapist, or a minister. So I am a piece of a

collective puzzle. I do not have to do the entire job. The same thing
with teaching and learning. When someone is on my table, we are
interchanging in a healing process. They may bring things to me that I
am healing in myself or need healing in myself. These are things that I
already believed, but now I am more keenly aware of it.

We are now doing the best we can. Sometimes someone is on my
table, and they have issues that grate me. I remind myself, "This person is doing the best they can with what they have. And there is still
some part of me that I haven't accepted and need to work on."

*(Like peristaltic waves, Christine's memories come back to her.
The feelings become innervated, and the experiences feel real again.
The flashback of memory allowed sweet, past events to feel alive and
full again. Christine burst out into delightful laughter.)* It was wonderful to see changes happen in the children and the team of
volunteers I worked with.

DISCUSSION

SELF-ACTUALIZATION   Abe Maslow was a psychologist and father of
the human potential-movement. He studied self-actualizing people and
distinguished between two types of motivation. The first type of motivation he recognized was a reaction to a deficiency, like eating when
hungry. The second type was generated by a need to fulfill one's innate
potential. He called this "self-actualization." Christine went to
Romania out of a desire to share her skills and abilities with those
whom she believed had a need for them. In sharing herself this way,
she was self-actualizing. Maslow also coined the construct of "synergy." Synergy implies a social system where each component part
contributes its strength to create a unity which is greater than the sum
of its parts.

Christine actualized dormant parts of herself by extending beyond
her everyday experience. She brought a dynamism of self-awareness,
introspectiveness, and a metaphysical openness to the Universe, as
she asked her personal growth question, "Why else am I here?"
Christine is a self-actualizer.

When the Universe answered, Christine began to have a clearer
sense of who she was and why she was here. As Christine took an
assertive role in interacting with her Universe, she felt less alien and
alone. She created a niche where she belonged.

A GROWTH AGENDA   This unusual woman tackled problems with two
agendas. Christine's first agenda was the "obvious" task—a bodyworker helping children in the orphanage. And she left herself open for

another "deeper," latent task. As Christine asked the Universe "Why else am I here," on a right-brain creative level she made the statement, "I am here for another reason, and I am open to that reason." It is no accident that Christine found her answer continuously "unfolding like a flower."

FLEXIBILITY   This is a woman with unusual leadership qualities. She is not a leader because she sets a concrete task then deliberately and rigidly pursues it to its end. She is a leader because she sets a spiritual goal and then has the foresight, wisdom, and strength to adjust and accommodate her will to her environment in order to achieve her goal. Rather than superimposing her will onto others and losing a sense of her self-mission, Christine flexed while maintaining focus on her spiritual goals.

Christine brought all of herself to the task: past history, recent history, mind, spirit, action, awareness of the specific and global environments. Christine left home with a mind-set of "fitting in however I could fit in." She reprioritized her tasks as teams from other countries arrived, bringing materials and skills that were more immediately needed. While this may seem to be only logical, Christine knew that at other orphanages, teams were characterized more by "rivalry" than cooperation.

MUNDANE   Christine described her daily life as mundane. One might find it difficult to believe that this philosophical wife, mother, bodyworker, and teacher had a mundane life. Christine in her daily life often went from one task to another mechanically. This mechanical existence began to "dilute" her personal sense of clarity and purpose. This is not to say that there was no purpose and meaning to her life. It is just that Christine's awareness, clarity, and spirit had faded in the face of the stress and the dull routine of her days. Clarity of her significant and latent values was blurred against the background of the familiar. In contrast, her values and their implications came into sharp focus when Christine radically changed her environment.

INTUITIVE WISDOM   Christine made a snap-decision to go to Romania. She was somewhat surprised by the words coming out of her mouth, "I am going!" Christine's usual decision-making process was slower, more deliberate using rational, cognitive processes to arrive at her decisions. Christine did not have to figure anything out, write lists of "pros" and "cons," or check out what others thought. She intuitively and spontaneously knew that her background and interests matched this project. She also intuitively knew that this experience would offer her a key to achieving a new quality of life. Christine trusted her intuitive wisdom and discovered how she could actualize her vision.

NEAR-DEATH Christine characterized her experience of going to Romania as a near-death experience. In some ways her growth experience was a death experience. Her familiar, comfortable, sensible, and safe ways of perceiving her world died. Even her familiar language was of limited value in Romania.

The loss of familiar internal world structures, of perceptual frames, can be so frightening to many people that they are often stopped from engaging in growth events, from surrendering their chronic holding patterns. To surrender is tantamount to crying and never stopping, flying apart, going crazy, or dying. It is like Columbus' men fearing that they would sail so far west that they would fall off the edge of the known world and perish.

When there is no solid ground to support growth steps, such horrific endings are possible. Some people do "go over the edge," come apart at the seams, lose their senses, or engage in destructive behaviors with themselves or others in order to stop their pain or fright. Christine had undergone psychotherapy and received extensive bodywork in addition to her own bodywork training. She had been a facilitator for multiple handicapped children and adults. Christine took herself to the edge of her known world and made a leap of faith. The consequence of her decision was the opening up of a new level of experience, awareness, perception, knowing, and understanding for herself. Often when people refer to a near death experience they also imply a spiritual awareness or awakening that allows them to return with a new sense of life and purpose. Christine also had such a spiritual union.

A SPIRITUAL UNION Christine was able to integrate emotionally what she had formerly only known intellectually. This allowed her a new sense of relatedness to the people she met in Romania. She discovered an unknown strength inside of herself. She was able to model for others how one acts when she hears "every child crying being your own child." The authoritarian director of the Romanian orphanage became her brother. The abusive care-givers became her sisters. Beyond the here and now, from her spiritual depths, Christine was able to forgive the men who had sexually abused her. Even more significant, Christine was able to appreciate her parents' limitations. She transcended her feelings of abandonment as she released her expectations for them to be more than who they were or more than they were capable of becoming.

Christine went to Romania as a healer and found herself being healed. This woman struggled with her feelings of separateness and knew a new sense of "oneness." This allowed Christine not merely to identify her values, but to revel in the preciousness, power, and exhilaration of becoming fully alive as she overcame her mother's role model. As Christine actualized her personal values, she realized a spiritual union that was luminous. It was more real than anything she had experienced or could imagine. In this luminescent experience of the oneness of mankind, Christine felt the spiritual healing of her psychological wounds.

CATHARSIS   Christine was physically and sexually abused as a child. The scars of those events became psychological glasses through which Christine viewed the world. She could see through the eyes of her "inner child" and project onto men the images of those who had abused her.

Christine, an American volunteer in Romania, brought material gifts, her knowledge, skills, and enthusiasm. In addition, she provided her abilities as a team leader. One of her responsibilities in this capacity was to work with the director of the orphanage. Many who have been abused by an authority figure in their childhood may regress in the face of another authority figure, and, in this regression, dissociate or relinquish their power.

Christine did not bring herself to her role of team leader as a "wounded inner child." She did not tackle this task fearing hurt or rejection by an often-belligerent man. Instead, Christine recognized the outer trappings of these traits for what they were. She was able to look below the surface and see the essential, the defense mechanisms of a man responsible for tasks that were beyond his knowledge-base, skills, and available support. He was given the depressing job of taking care of sick, unwanted, underdeveloped children suffering from failure-to-thrive issues. This administrator was saddled with a poorly trained staff whose numbers were inadequate for the task they had to perform, and was insufficiently financed to boot. He operated in a political mind-set where, if his performance were unacceptable, he could disappear in the middle of the night never to be heard from again. He was given a thankless, impossible job and was expected to do it.

Christine was able to see the director's plight. She was able to see how the situation had affected him psychologically. Christine broached this man neither as a child frightened of him, nor as an adolescent using his faults as justification for rebellious behavior against him. She saw the poverty, the complexity, and the lack of genuine support for his situation. What "clicked" for Christine was that he needed his defenses to survive. As she realized this, she transcended her former role of abused child. This transcendence made her into a fully adult woman psychologically. In her realization, Christine empathized with the director and his plight. She remained an adult and dealt with him as an adult.

As a result of her transcendence, Christine is more likely to enter into future situations, not as the insecure, wounded "inner child" who would step out in a defensive posture, but as her self-confident adult. Christine also gained a spiritual sense of belonging to the Universe.

GENERALIZATION Christine recognized that the orphanage director's personality was, at least in part, dictated by conditions beyond himself. She was able to see that underneath his gruff exterior there was a gentle, caring man. From this observation, she generalized similarly that her indifferent, non-supportive father was a man trapped by his environment. He was as much a prisoner of his abusive style as he was a warden. Christine began to view her father as a man with his own personality dynamics and frailties. If there was animosity towards him or whomever had sexually violated her, she let it go. To hold onto that animosity would have made her a prisoner of her own anger. She chose not to live her life shackled by past scars.

TRANSCENDING THE NORM Often psychotherapy is a process intended to bring an individual to a place in her or his unconscious memory where some psychosocial trauma is stored. The awareness and emotion, which had previously been banished, is reclaimed and released. A new more effective "adult" perspective and solution can be created for the old problem. Ultimately, this solution will not merely be an expression or intellectual exercise utilized in a therapy office. It will be a dynamic integrated by the individual and applied to improve the quality and style of her or his entire life.

Christine's psychotherapeutic experiences helped her to understand the abuse that was inflicted upon her in the past. However, there was a portion of this life-wound that remained unhealed. This unhealed level interfered with her ability to forgive, let go, and move on fully. When she was in Romania, Christine encountered life experiences which deepened this healing.

Confronted at the orphanage by children being beaten with sticks by their nurses and older children, Christine was suddenly jerked back in her awareness to her own childhood. She identified with those abused children. She remembered her mother's passivity. She did not want to replicate the message received from her mother's abusive inaction that women are to be frightened and passive in the face of aggression.

Christine consciously recognized her moment-of-truth. She could replicate what happened to her by turning her back on the children she saw being abused, or she could take action. Christine chose to take constructive action. As Christine recognized her father's limitations and released both her unrealized expectations and any animosity for her father's failures, so she recognized her mother's limitations and forgave her. Christine internally transcended her mother's limitations and the wounds they left by creating her own therapeutic intervention. She obtained the support of her translator, and took action. In a punitive, male-dominated, Communist society, she provided a role model to the aggressive male children for the destruction of the weapons of child abuse. She replaced the abusive custom with a new ethos, her own ethos, "Children are for loving; they are not for beating." Christine did for those children what her parents had failed to do for her. In her action, Christine was as confirming and honoring of her needy, wounded, "inner child" as she was of the Romanian orphans.

TWO SHOCKS   Christine described two shocks that she encountered in her journey. The first was an "entry" shock when she arrived in Romania, a country that was technologically different than her own. The second shock Christine spoke of was "re-entry" shock. This shock related to leaving Romania where she felt a deep sense of family acceptance. It was hard to leave this environment and just as hard to return to an environment in which the luminescent quality of family, community, and Universal oneness did not exist.

Christine transcended her re-entry shock by "making a number of decisions." She determined to work less because she had been working herself to a "frazzle," and she wanted to be more available to her daughter who would soon be leaving for college.

Christine was not retraumatized when her elderly parents chose to pursue salmon fishing rather than to make contact with her. She decided that she had made sufficient attempts to develop a meaningful relationship with them. She realized and accepted that they were incapable of genuine, meaningful, loving contact. As she brought her sincerity to them, rather than moving closer, they moved further away. They could not tolerate her honesty or intimacy nor appreciate her strength. They could not respond to her efforts to make healing contact or express pride in her maturity.

Christine recognized the parent-wound she needed to heal was not with her parents; it was located within her heart. She could relate to her parents only to the degree they would allow, and she could remember those positive memories that she wanted to take with her. She could not have the loving parents that she wanted. Her parents had their own wounds and were incapable of behaving in loving, nurturing, and confirming ways. They were unable to transcend their own self-serving norm. This was a truth that she would have to live with. It is an extremely difficult life lesson for anyone to grapple with and emotionally accept.

Christine established her adult emotional self as a result of releasing her childhood expectations, animosities, and resentments toward her parents. Had she been unable to have a full emotional resolution with her dysfunctional parents, her ability to realize her adult emotional strength would have been truncated. She would have been emotionally constrained from being fully present to her talents, abilities, potentials, and relationships. Christine's personal transcendence was part of the impressive work that she accomplished in Romania.

TRANSCENDENCE   When people transcend a developmental impasse, it is evidenced by solving a specific presenting problem. Beyond the specific problem, the ability to solve problems in other unrelated areas will also be witnessed. This is a truth of surmounting developmental hurdles.

As difficult as it was to leave Romania, Christine realized that she did not have to be in a foreign country to feel fully alive. To overcome her "diluted" life experience, Christine had only to bring her awareness and intent to the moment, and she could experience life more fully. She could not realistically maintain contact with "her people" in Romania by phone. So, she dedicated herself to continuing to support the Romanians she knew in empowering themselves through education, and in taking care of themselves.

Christine brought back other healings from her trip. She decided that at home she needed to work with her clients as a member of a team. She no longer carried the belief that she had to help her clients entirely on her own. As a result of working with a team in Romania, Christine learned to rely on others. She needed to utilize and share the support of the other members on her team, the psychotherapists, physical therapists, and ministers. Christine would be "a piece of a collective puzzle."

Christine brought back yet another awareness regarding clients who pushed her buttons. She recognized that she must be patient, "They are doing the best they can with what they have." She also realized that she was confronting a new growth experience: her clients were becoming her "teachers." To find the answer to the irritation, rather than trying to change others, she must look within herself.

Her delightful laughter was another gift with which Christine returned as she reminisced over the joyful, growthful changes she was blessed to participate in and witness while in Romania.

SUMMARY

Christine went to Romania with an "obvious agenda"—to provide massage therapy to orphaned children. Beyond this altruistic task, her awareness and intentionality offered an invitation to Life to teach her. She offered this invitation by doing what she always did when she went to any workshop or growth event. Christine asked the questions, "Why else am I here?" "On what other level am I here?" This bodyworker carried with her the awareness that there are deeper levels to her life. Her task was to discover what they were.

Upon returning, Christine discovered that her entire experience had been an unfolding, "healing experience" of her past wounds. She determined that ultimately the best thing she could do for the Universe would be to heal herself. The deepest healing that may have occurred was being able to see beyond the gruff, mean, isolatory role played by the man who was the director of the orphanage. Christine was able to perceive the person beneath the dysfunctional role he played and forgive him. With this forgiveness, she received an inner healing. On a feeling level she was able to know her parents as people and to release the inner, reactive holding patterns that resulted from the dysfunctional role they played as parents. She was truly freed to move on from those past wounds. The humanitarian support that Christine offered as a representative of her community and country, and the economic contributions for the education of Romanian caregivers were immeasurable. Beyond the incalculable value of Christine's deeds, her model is an inspiration to anyone who opens her or himself to learn from her story.

CONCLUSION

CHARACTERISTICS OF BODYWORKERS   The twenty-five people interviewed in the preparation of this book can be best characterized as
soft-spoken, mild-mannered, and personally or spiritually committed
to their work. They tended to be intuitive and had an emotional-
somatic orientation. Many had difficulty putting their personal
thoughts and feelings into words. The clinician in me often wanted to
reach out and help them, but I did not permit myself to interfere. I
instead remained present for the bodyworkers, listening to, and at
times, clarifying their stories.

As a group, they were easy to be with. Empathic, they experientially understood the issues of abuse, and often, as a result of the
traumas of their own upbringing, were concerned about the traumas of
others. They had an intrinsic desire to provide support, nourishment,
and healing for their clients. The level of altruism and humanitarianism
they displayed was extraordinary. I derived a feeling of well-being just
being in their presence. For some, the results of their contacts with
clients seemed to border on the miraculous. At other times, the boundaries between a bodyworker's personal needs, and the needs of the
client became blurred. I could feel their unconscious inner wounds as
these professionals attempted to find healing for themselves vicari-
ously through contact with their clients. This blurring interfered with
both their business and their personal lives. When they encountered
adversity in their profession, many of these practitioners naturally
engaged in self-exploration in order to deal with the obstacles. In this
respect, these individuals were inspiring.

Interestingly, the participants in this study tend to isolate themselves professionally and to deal with their professional problems
privately. Often they accepted and internalized the psychological
stresses resulting from their work experiences and did not share troubling incidents with colleagues, friends, or spouses. While some of the
interviewees had sought counseling or psychological support to deal

319

with personal concerns, as a whole, they did not obtain consultation for professional issues or work conflicts.

As the professional encounters of twenty-five bodyworkers were examined, numerous themes arose. These themes capture issues that are likely to be present for bodywork practitioners as well as anyone who provides support, supervision, education, care, or direction for others. The frequency with which they occur in actual practice is unknown and would be important to investigate further. An overview of these themes follows.

MOTIVATION FOR BEGINNING AND CONTINUING IN THE PROFESSION
Clearly, interviews with the individuals in this book suggest that people are drawn to bodywork for various reasons. Their attraction may emerge from a rewarding or healing personal experience. Others seek a vocation which will allow them to provide support, help, or healing to others. Bodywork careers can be personally as well as professionally fulfilling because of the interpersonal contact with clients and the sense of participation in the process of relieving discomforts and improving health and well-being. Still others engage in bodywork training for the personal growth they may receive from "touch" training, but do not pursue this discipline as a career. Among those who do go on to practice professionally, once the basics of a bodywork discipline are learned, they adapt their skills to a variety of clients presenting a range of body and personality types. Many bodyworkers continue their education by learning new bodywork techniques or new disciplines which are then incorporated into their routines, entirely or in part. Over time, bodyworkers discover that a unique style begins to emerge, and with additional experience, they develop a professional routine.

ENCOUNTERING AND OVERCOMING OBSTACLES From time to time, the practitioner will encounter a client who presents a challenge or an obstacle that demands far more than an alternative technique or skill to overcome. Indeed, surmounting the obstacle requires that, in order to succeed, the bodyworker must confront her or his own sense of professional/personal identity. These professional events may produce an emotional reaction such as anxiety, worry, guilt, annoyance, anger, self-doubt, sleeplessness, depression, or even physical aches and pains. When the "obstacle" is not resolved, the emotional reactions tend to linger and can interfere with the practitioner's peace of mind. With sufficient intensity or frequency, these troubling events or obstacles produce work stress or burnout, which can lead to withdrawal from a particular client, from one's practice, or even from the profession itself.

Such obstacles emerge for beginning and seasoned professionals alike, and have nothing to do with the practitioner's technical skills or intellectual ability. These events may serve as torches, illuminating untraversed realms within the caverns of the bodyworker's own identity. By presenting obstacles, clients challenge the blind spots in their practitioner's psychosocial history. If the practitioner chooses to accept the challenge and press beyond the shadows of her or his present knowledge, the client becomes teacher. The practitioner's ability to accept these lessons seems to hinge on the interaction between her or his awareness of the significance of the moment, willingness to pursue the ambiguous, and her or his courage to confront her or his own psychological depths.

Overcoming obstacles provides several benefits. A bodyworker can develop a better understanding of the phenomena she or he encountered externally, with the client, and internally within her or himself. Lingering traumatic emotions may dissipate or even disappear, resulting in greater comfort for the bodyworker with her or his emotional self. As alienated parts of the personality are reintegrated, the bodyworker establishes new, stronger personality boundaries which provide an increased sense of self-esteem and personal integrity. She or he learns the psychological stance needed to work with a troubling client more effectively. Once the obstacle is transcended, the professional can function confidently, with a solid sense of her or his boundaries. Moreover, the practitioner gains a generalized capacity to cope with anyone, in either professional or personal life, presenting similar challenges. In short, confronting current professional problems facilitates the resolution of other conflicts—past, present, or future.

It became apparent that there can be synergistic interactions between work encounters and personal growth. Grappling with work-experience obstacles leads to personal growth, which in turn, can be translated into greater strength and depth in professional practice.

Unfortunately, for bright, but non-verbal bodyworkers, the growth potential of work challenges often goes unrealized, because experiences that are not translated into verbal expression often are not intellectually recognized, examined, or explored. The encounters remain unavailable for problem-solving and resolution. In this instance, a number of study participants experienced cathartic releases and healings of previously unresolved psychosocial wounds merely by sharing their experiences with an attentive, emotionally-present listener. Some interviewees, with no prompting, gained a meaningful perspective which provided not only the comfort of emotional release, but a transcendence of the familiar stance to a sharper, more active, better-integrated personal identity. When these events occurred, they were deeply gratifying for me. Clearly, had these participants not shared their stories, their wounds would have remained unconscious, festering, their effects unchallenged and unchanged.

The stories presented in this book were the first that came to the individual teller's awareness. Later other stories often emerged from many of the interviewees. Clearly, bodyworkers possess deep pools of professional experience. Each story that a bodyworker chooses to retrieve and explore offers the opportunity for additional depth of understanding and personal liberation.

What I came to appreciate during each interview is that work encounters are not simple, singular events, but rather a multiplicity of events. Practitioner and client meet on economic, somatic, social, psychological, medical, religious, spiritual, and perhaps even psychic realms. And these realms exist within, as well as between, each bodyworker and client. Consequently, the interviews were complex, with many themes and issues appearing simultaneously. Generally, one issue became the focal point around which the practitioner made some kind of realization and/or personal-professional decision. This epiphany, in turn, resulted in transcendence to a new perspective, permitting the bodyworker to assume a new juxtaposition between her or his personality and the work conflict she or he faced. This new stance was often accompanied by increased feelings of personal integration, professional mastery, and self-respect.

HELPING AND GIVING ADVICE As sensitive caring individuals, bodyworkers, as a group, are dedicated to helping others. Trying to heal clients of their illnesses or giving them advice to solve their problems may sound like a humanitarian endeavor. If the help or advice is actually desired, then it may be viewed as helpful. But if the desire to help is the agenda of the bodyworker alone, and not of the client, "help" may be given at the client's expense and may even be contraindicated.

Bodyworkers, like all individuals, are subject to unconsciously projecting their unresolved needs onto their clients, resulting in either rescue fantasies or countertransference. Based upon psychological misperception, those motivated to "help" others may press their clients to make changes which are, in reality, neither desired nor appreciated. The professionals, whose egos have become involved in their clients' making changes or feeling appreciative, have their own feelings hurt deeply when the clients fail to change or express appreciation for their "helpful" interventions. Countertransference may also induce bodywork practitioners to develop dual relationships such as friendships with clients. When these relationships are based upon the client's meeting some unfulfilled need in the bodyworker, feelings of hurt, anger, and rejection, as well as emotional trauma for both parties may ensue.

It is important for practitioners to understand that clients who complain about problems are not necessarily asking for help. This may be especially true for clients who chronically complain and constantly appear to make no significant changes in their life circumstances. Such clients may simply need to express their distress to a concerned, caring listener with a comforting touch.

While "helping" can have a paradoxical effect on any client, it may be most problematic for those troubled clients struggling with significant psychological problems, abuse survivors, or those suffering from illness, injury, pain, or near death. For these clients, the consequences of change, as well as the support to take successful action, may be beyond the client's capabilities. Pressing another to change, especially in the direction of one's own beliefs or wishes, or at one's own pace, can be psychologically damaging or traumatizing to the client as well as to the bodyworker-client relationship.

"Helping" may be appropriate when a client asks for help. One may also suggest to a client that obtaining professional help might be appropriate. After offering help, a bodyworker must assess if the suggestion is met with interest. "Helping" has not been appropriate when the client does not respond to the practitioner's efforts or when the bodyworker suddenly loses clients that she or he has attempted to help. In addition to traumatized or disgruntled clients, inappropriate help can result in an economic blow to one's practice. Helping may also be contraindicated for clients who are unwilling to take positive or constructive action in their lives, but instead want their bodywork professional to do it for them. Bodyworkers who seek to help may be comforted by remembering that the healing potential of bodywork itself, performed by a caring, emotionally present bodyworker, can be miraculous. One must be mindful that while a practitioner can be an important player on a "care team," they need not be the sole player. Others, too, have the capacity to help the client.

INSTRUCTORS Occasionally, bodywork practitioners acknowledged instructors who demonstrated psychological awareness and concern for the personal aspect of their students. Such individuals were sought in times of need. Most often, the bodyworkers in this study did not perceive their massage school instructors as aware of or knowledgeable about psychological phenomena. They did not approach these instructors for psychological consultation or utilize them as referral sources. Practitioners also reported that experiences of a psychological nature encountered in training classes were frequently ignored or trivialized by instructors. Often, instructors offered simplistic answers or rules, with little or no explanation, suggesting that students can ignore psychological material. Such academic role modeling fosters students' belief in a mindbody split and discourages them from recognizing or understanding the significance of psychological material revealed by the bodywork they perform. Such disregard reduces the students' ability to recognize when a referral may be appropriate. Interviewees reported, time and again, that such training practices left them unprepared to deal with the psychosocial realities of everyday practice.

Even worse, other emotionally blind-sighted, narcissistic, or self-serving educators attempted to meet their own insatiable ego needs at the expense of students whose status and/or unresolved dependency needs make them psychologically vulnerable. One such "advanced" instructor reportedly violated the sexual boundaries of several of his female students.

LIMIT SETTING To some degree, all the stories in this book are about setting limits. The issues with which these professionals struggled seem best characterized as part of the process of personality development. By setting limits, individuals establish the boundaries of their personalities. If the limits are too confining, one of two things may happen. First, experiences may be restricted to those confirming our existing beliefs, whether or not they are valid. In this instance, the practitioner demands that the client enter into the bodyworker's perception of reality as if it were the only one, the correct one, or the best one for everyone. Second, in the face of conflictual events, the experience may be rejected, resulting in failure to grow. On the other hand, when limits or boundaries are too loose, practitioners incorporate people without question and start to merge with the client's reality, losing their own sense of self.

Engaging in personality struggles is neither good nor bad. Rather, it indicates that we can actively use our experiences to fine-tune who we are. To some extent, professional challenges may be met with eager anticipation because they demand our attention, concentration, and problem-solving. In return, they offer opportunities for attaining increased wisdom, maturation, growth, power, and love.

PSI PHENOMENON PSI phenomena refer to extra-sensory experiences. Many people who enter the bodywork profession have somatic, intuitive personalities. They acquire information from an unfamiliar, unaccustomed sensory data source which in turn, leads them to form certain impressions, intuitions, or assumptions about others. Some practitioners, before entering the profession, may be unaware of their intuitive abilities. After developing a new sense, that of touch, they may become cognizant of awarenesses that are different, exciting, or even anxiety-provoking. By understanding the developing sensory process, PSI phenomena may become less personally troubling.

Nevertheless, an intuitive ability can be problematic, or even frightening, for many reasons. Individuals may perceive more than they want to know about others. The knowledge they derive may be unknown to the source. Having knowledge of others that they do not have about themselves, can feel either like an intrusion or an overwhelming responsibility. And some bodyworkers may be frustrated by an inability to discern whether they are perceiving a truth about another or merely projecting their own thoughts, beliefs, prejudices, feelings, hopes, etc. onto that person. Inaccurate intuitive impressions can present a hurtful and warped self-perception to a vulnerable client. Even when accurate, they can be traumatizing to a client who is not ready to hear or deal with the material. Verbalizations of intuitive impressions can be retraumatizing to an abuse survivor who lacks sufficient defenses or is unprepared to deal with the information. In general, it is unwise to share intuitive information.

SEXUALITY This issue encompasses the many sensations, feelings, and attitudes that bodywork professionals have about their our own sexuality *and that of others* and also relates to setting healthy limits regarding sexual issues. Certain situations that arise professionally may put bodyworkers in touch with memories of familial and social situations in their private lives, memories which may be fraught with anxiety, pain, conflict, punishment, or trauma. These old memories may blur the bodyworkers' clear sense of who they are currently in regard to their sexuality. In turn, professionals are confused as to how to deal with clients who raise their awareness of such incidents. If bodyworkers are sufficiently uncomfortable about their sexuality, they may repress it i.e., push the discomfort out of awareness, rather than confront it and/or obtain professional help. On one hand, repression may lead bodywork practitioners to seek personal gratification from professional contacts. On the other, bodyworkers may attempt to avoid the clients with whom the issue arises and anxiously hope that they never come back.

While professionals can overtly attempt to block from awareness personally troubling confrontations with clients, suppressed or repressed awarenesses do not go away. They are translated into somatic tension lodging in the body tissues, covertly robbing the practitioner of peace of mind and precision in work. In turn, the tension is somatically transferred to unknowing clients. Through touch, the mindbody status of the practitioner can negatively effect the client. And the opposite is also true. When bodywork professionals succeed in their identity achievement, they provide a healthy role model against which clients can form their own unique and healthy personal/sexual identities.

SIGNIFICANT PSYCHOLOGICAL PROBLEMS   Anyone can, and usually does, feel "down and out" from time to time. There is nothing abnormal about episodic symptoms such as anxiety, anger, sadness, or depression. However, when certain criteria of alterations of mood or personality are met, a collection of these symptoms may be sufficiently severe as to be called "significant" in nature. Many of the stories in this book concern clients with significant psychological problems. All bodyworkers can expect to encounter folks with such problems in their practices.

A problem is considered "significant" when four trends have been identified: the "down" times last longer than the "up" times, the "down" times outnumber the "up" times, the "downs" get lower and lower, and normal everyday functioning in work, interpersonal relationships, recreational activities, and self-perception is impaired. Significant psychological problems are also characterized by a lack of awareness that the problem even exists. In order to keep problems unconsciously submerged, the individual is likely to deny, become irritable and/or defensive if the troubling issues are broached. In order to avoid violating the client's unconscious defenses, bodywork professionals must exercise caution in working with clients who suffer from significant psychological problems.

These issues produce secondary problems for the affected people which are related to the influences the unconscious defenses have on perception, personality, and social functioning. Significant psychological problems also produce management concerns for the professionals who work with clients exhibiting them. These people may not be reasonable, reliable, or responsible. How do specific clients need to be treated and what behavioral limits need to be set? Some clients evoke strong feelings in the practitioner: impassioned desires to help, rescue, or save the client; anger over the client's lack of responsiveness or appreciation for the bodyworker's efforts. Clients can also trigger troubling memories from the bodyworker's own psychosocial history. A bodyworker who chooses to work with such clients must be patient with ambiguity, tolerate unresponsiveness and the unpredictable. It is highly recommended that practitioners be willing to seek consultation when necessary and be open to working with an interdisciplinary team.

Bodywork can be a helpful adjunct to the treatment of motivated individuals suffering from a wide range of significant psychological problems. It relieves tension, promotes a sense of well-being, and allows a person to feel touchable and acceptable. Bodywork can encourage cathartic releases, facilitate beneficial insights for the client, and reduce anxiety sufficiently for constructive problem-solving and subsequent corrective action to take place. And bodywork can also provide a supportive team approach to healing.

Progress with those clients who have significant psychological problems will be slow and even frustrating at times. This work can also be extremely rewarding, as step-by-step, these clients overcome barriers to their well-being, personal growth, and happiness. As body-workers provide their strength, support, and patience to the process, they too mature.

MEN   One of the most striking issues regarding men arose from the sampling process rather than from the content of the interviews. While twenty-five women were contacted in order to obtain twenty partici-pants, it was necessary to interview fourteen men in order to obtain the five desired stories. Most of the study participants, both male and female, were selected because of their involvement in some type of advanced education or professional growth. Therefore, they were pre-sumed to be willing, and able, to provide information relevant to personal/professional growth experiences. The disparity between the men and the women was notable. What was happening with the men that they were not as available as the women to explore growth issues?

Information from this project suggests that, compared to women, men are less willing to offer information about their personal-profes-sional work experiences and may be less aware of personal reactions to issues regarding their work. It also seems that they are less apt to take steps to advance their personal/professional growth as a result of work encounters. In contrast, it appears that, when faced with per-sonal challenge, women are the ones, by and large, who rise to the occasion.

From the stories presented reflecting men's issues, it appears that many men deflect challenge through denial, blame, distraction, or dodging behind an implacable, unresponsive image of strength. In short, men repress their emotional reactions. Psychological theory holds that if repression is present, there must also be unconscious fear of an awareness too painful or too frightening to contemplate. As a result, both the object of the fear and unconscious defense of repression are pushed out of awareness. Repression extracts a high price: large amounts of psychic energy must be devoted to maintaining the lack of awareness, energy that could be available for problem-solv-ing or other creative endeavors. One might argue that the abundance of available, creative, problem-solving energy in our society would be mind boggling, if not for such repression.

Even with an understanding that emotional repression may be normative for many men, in the bodywork profession certain occupa-tional "hazards" may interact with men's crippled emotional capacity and create problems for the practitioner and client alike. Warm, empathic, genuine, sexually responsible male bodyworkers may be subject to female clients' cathartic discharges. The professional's presence, sound, and touch may convey a form of therapeutic safety and security never before known by the client. In such an emotional oasis, a female client may be spontaneously catapulted into an unconscious well of unresolved emotional wounds. The safety of the environment allows the stagnant emotional magma to come gushing to the surface, purging the musculature of internalized feelings. Such emotional discharges, while cathartic for clients, can be overwhelming or even traumatic for men who are unfamiliar with, avoidant of, or lacking in understanding or appreciation of emotional "logic." If the male practitioner identifies psychologically with the client, he may believe that he would never want anyone to cause such distress in himself, and may feel guilty for "hurting" the client. If the bodyworker is out of contact with his own emotional process, the client's emotional discharge may be so powerful as to explode the emotional shackles of the bodyworker's own repressed memory, bringing forgotten, traumatic feelings to the surface. An emotionally naïve bodyworker may even become angered at the traumatized client who is releasing her distress precisely because of the undesired awareness it creates in him.

Getting in touch with forgotten truths can be painful for both client and bodyworker alike. If the psychological revelation is met with anxiety, fear, or repulsion, it may lead to retraumatization. If the process is approached with an attitude of understanding and acceptance, it can lead to healing, growth, and transcendence.

While an emotional release from a female client may be problematic, working with another male may be even more difficult. In our society, norms, which foster machismo, lead to emotional suppression, superficiality, and the denial of emotional expression in men. For the male client, maintaining the facade of "being tough" may take precedence over allowing an emotional catharsis or release.

Mutual competitiveness and resistance to feeling "one-down" may interfere with both the practitioner's and client's achieving a personal "one-up." Mutual understanding, supportiveness, and true camaraderie may be sacrificed to maintain socially stereotypical expectations of male-male relationships. Furthermore, concern over possible sexual excitement may lead to either the male bodyworker's or male client's "numbing" to awarenesses generated from the experience of genuine contact. This compromises the full benefits of bodywork. While a client may or may not be clear about the solidity of his emotional core, if a male bodywork practitioner chooses to work with other men, it is essential that he be comfortable with touch, free of preoccupation with sexual issues, and emotionally present for, and supportive of, another man's emotional release.

Male professionals may also become the object of "transference" with abused clients. As mentioned earlier, when a male bodyworker presents himself as concerned, supportive, empathic, and respectful of sexual boundaries, a client may feel sufficiently safe to allow otherwise-repressed memories to emerge. Even the practitioner's innocuous personality traits may trigger past memories of someone else who had similar traits, but was emotionally toxic. And normative male behaviors, and/or figures of speech, may be intrinsically, though unintentionally, demeaning to women.

It is also possible that a client's negative experience may not be a transference of unresolved past trauma onto the male bodyworker. Rather, the client may feel injured by current insensitive, displaced, hurtful, intrusive, or abusive behavior on the part of the practitioner. It behooves a professional bodyworker to clarify for her or himself what is occurring and to respond appropriately.

ABUSE Many of the stories presented related to clients who have been abused. Whether the abuse has been physical, sexual, or neglectful, bodywork can be therapeutic for a survivor. The survivor-client's self-body awareness may have been abandoned at an earlier stage of development because the individual perceived that body awareness allowed the "self" to suffer physical and/or emotional trauma. Touch from a well-grounded professional can help the client regain contact with her or his alienated body.

The bodywork relationship can also be therapeutic in the process of "desensitizing" the abused client. Desensitization diminishes the emotional effects of the original trauma as the abuse survivor experiences touch which is neither intrusive nor abusive. The client's internalized negative emotions can then be released. Repressed memories may be recaptured as the emotionally-braced muscles regain a fuller range of motion. This information can help a client to better understand what happened in the past and, in psychotherapy, to integrate an alienated part of her or his personality. The client can also discover that it is possible to be close and be touched and that touch can be pleasurable, nurturing, and healing rather than traumatic. The unresolved trauma can be "desensitized." These experiences, in the safety of the bodywork relationship, may then generalize to other contacts outside of the bodywork session, and the client can gain a new, solid, healthier sense of self-esteem.

For bodyworker professionals working with clients who have been abused, gaining and maintaining one's own boundaries is critically important. At best, the experience of working with an abuse survivor can be ungrounding. The situation becomes even more challenging when one is an abuse survivor oneself. Furthermore, if the abuse occurred during the practitioner's childhood, the effects are very likely compounded by the complications of growing-up within a dysfunctional family. Boundary-keeping becomes even more difficult.

Interactions between a client and an abused practitioner may magnify the problems of each. For either, if more stimulation than can be tolerated enters the perceptual field, unconscious defense mechanisms spring into action. Anxiety, personality diffusion, dissociation, and distorted identifications with the abused client, the perpetrator, or perhaps even a non-supportive parent, may signal that something is going awry in the professional bodywork relationship. Without sufficient support, these defensive reactions may become self-limiting or even self-destructive in nature.

If unattended, the issues of trauma and abuse do not just disappear. They tend to become increasingly problematic. Professional work with a psychotherapist skilled in this area is of paramount importance for both the bodyworker and the client. If the demands and distress of working with an abused client exceed a practitioner's coping ability, she or he must decide whether to limit one's practice, obtain professional support to overcome the discomfort, and/or refer the client to anther bodyworker.

DEATH, DYING, ILLNESS, AND INJURY Several bodyworkers' stories involved clients who were touched by illness or death. Like other voyages, death, dying, illness, and injury are journeys into the unknown. Journeys, even those into unfamiliar territory, which are shared with a well-grounded, trustworthy companion, lose their fright or terror-potential. In times of such distress, social support has the potential to change the quality of each precious moment of the sufferer's life. Such support can bring about a sense of well-being and peace, in spite of the critical condition of death, dying, illness, or injury. Having this type of companionship at such a time may be a blessing known by very few.

Practitioners working with clients traversing these realms will experience strain, depending on the intensity of the client's level of distress and the bodyworker's vulnerability to it. This strain, or wounding, may bypass the bodyworker's attention on a day-to-day basis. In time, however, the wounding or strain takes its toll; fatigue, which unattended, can result in total burnout.

Because of the gravity of confronting death, dying, illness, and injury, bodyworkers need to truly appreciate the side-effects of their chosen field. From time to time, a practitioner must provide her or himself with a "mental health checkup" to measure the degree of strain or wounding encountered and take steps to provide for revitalization.

Such a checkup should include an exploration of the effect that working with critical clients has had on oneself, provide for emotional expression, and invite consideration of whether contact with critical patients has touched upon any personal experiences or memories of death, dying, illness, or injury of a significant family member, friend, or associate. The bodywork professional should also explore whether an earlier loss was a motivating factor in the bodyworker's choice to go into a helping profession. Indeed, if there is a link, it is essential for the professional to learn how to keep the personal from complicating and compromising the professional.

When working with critical patients, it is always helpful to work as part of a team of professionals. A team offers diversification of specialty areas, knowledge-bases, and problem-solving skills. It also provides opportunities for increased observation, monitoring, and feedback. Finally, a team approach allows for mutual support, the sharing of responsibility, and relief from stress. For bodyworkers choosing to traverse such challenging realms with their clients, team work is the method of choice.

BURNOUT   Before being elicited by this study, the majority of stories presented had gone untold. Indeed, until the question of professional struggle and/or personal growth had been posed, many interviewees had not translated the events into words. This implies that, for these bodyworkers, the encounters existed in an unexpressed, unresolved fashion within their bodies.

The significance of these internalized struggles remained within the bodywork practitioners in the form of psychophysical stress creating psychophysical toxins. These toxins inhibit professional performance, limit personal functioning, and, in some cases, even interfere with the practitioner's physical health and well-being. Because clients come for bodywork specifically to feel better by expelling stress from their bodies, practitioners are constantly bombarded with clients' psychophysical toxins. Whether or not either the bodyworker or the client appreciates the nexus, there is a mind-society-body connectedness. Bodyworkers extract psychosocial toxins held in somatic form from their clients. By default, a bodyworker hears, touches, and may even intuit her or his clients' stresses. However skilled in her or his own psychological understanding, the bodyworker, especially one who is more sensitive, cannot participate in this cleansing function without being effected by the process.

Bodywork practitioners may fail to recognize the stresses and strains to which their work subjects them because of unconscious childhood and/or adulthood demands to assume a helping role, played-out in professional practice. Unawareness of emotional and psychological aspects of practice may have even been learned in professional training. Lack of awareness may also result from the professional's preoccupation with the technical nature of her or his work. Further complicating the work of the bodywork practitioner may be family members who do not understand their bodyworker partners, what they believe in, or what they are trying to accomplish in their chosen profession and do not support them. Even society-at-large does not want to recognize or appreciate the work bodyworkers do to relieve and undo the wounding society itself inflicts upon its members.

CULTURAL BACKGROUND The growth and development of the individual bodyworker, as well as the profession as a whole, does not occur in a vacuum. There is a cultural background providing both shape and form to this unfolding. Contemporary American society is struggling to find solutions to the issue of burgeoning utilization of health care services, its costs, and the limits of available funding. It also is struggling to determine who may benefit personally from these services and who will handsomely profit economically from them. Selling "health care" delivery contracts to the lowest bidders in the form of "managed care" is the industrial answer favored for reducing costs. As the scarce care-dollar is diverted from direct care delivery to financial support of a new class of "care managers," the funding available for delivery of treatment is even further diminished.

This health-care scenario places a premium on rapid diagnosis and utilizes the least expensive remedy as the treatment-of-choice. In this "production-line" process the patient's identity is further truncated and becomes merely the diagnosis of her or his disease or injury. Health care providers are forced by third-party micro-managers to tailor their perspectives and treatment to conform to a "brief," less expensive model. Professionals' energy and contact time with patients have already been reduced. Newer clinicians are being trained in an arena which caters to these new industrial norms. At one point in time, the industry ideal was to treat the "whole patient." This focus has been supplanted by "problem-focused" treatment. The fact that a presenting problem may exist in a larger psychosocial context having etiological significance is lost to expediency and cost-containment. The ultimate remedies to many ailments may lie in the realm of "life management" of the patient. This approach does not readily lend to the cost containment or "brief model." A major danger of cut-rate "health care" is that it demands more of its practitioners while providing them with less. Just such a situation arose when a couple in the throes of a divorce called asking for marital therapy. The couple suffered from poor communication skills and decades of unresolved conflict and wounding. They had seen a psychiatrist many months earlier; he placed the husband on an antidepressant. The husband admitted that he did feel calmer while he was taking an antidepressant. He added that it did not alter the conflicts the couple was having. At some point, the husband's physician determined that he no longer needed medication. After discontinuing his antidepressant, the intensity of his agitation returned and the couple's problems remained unchanged. When it works, Prozac can provide an excellent buffer for distressing feelings of depression. However, as the husband discovered, Prozac cannot magically resolve marital conflicts.

In spite of the intensity of their conflicts, the couple was highly motivated for treatment. The prognosis was good. After calling the patient's insurance company to authorize outpatient psychotherapy for the couple, I was informed that the insurance company would grant three psychiatric sessions without a co-payment from the clients, but it would provide no payment for my psychological consultation. In other words, this couple's insurance would pay to buffer the symptoms of their problems, but it would provide no payment to resolve the problems.

When people obtain insurance, they do not usually know in advance what type of coverage they will need. Nor do they have the expertise to know which policies should be carried for different conditions. And many people who enjoy insurance coverage from their place of employment may have no choice as to the type of policy they carry or what the policy will cover. In one recent encounter, I attempted to obtain additional funding for ongoing treatment for an anorexic adolescent. A micro-manager, running into the limits of her own company's policy, reported to me, "The parents never should have bought this policy!" In another instance, a micromanager for a major insurance company was asked for additional sessions to support an alcoholic client: "We specialize in short-term, problem-focused treatment. She will have to find community support." Well, I am a community support! What the micromanager meant was that this client would have to find no-cost services from the community which would not drain the resources *and profits!* from her company. This micromanager was changing a psychotherapist—*me*—from a primary care-giver into an administrative gate-keeper. When I requested authorization for supportive psychotherapy services for a woman who had just been raped, another micromanager callously indicated that her "subscriber's policy did not include services from a psychologist." When pressed about the need for her company to take ethical action on behalf of this victimized woman, the administrator agreed to find a nurse who could talk to the "subscriber." Tragically, both cost containment and profit maximization are served while patients are lost along the way.

With third-party payers controlling treatment in the illness business as well as walking away with the profits, some care-providers are eliminating the managed-care middleman by directly selling their own "care" packages to large businesses. Many fine and dedicated health care practitioners are finding it more and more difficult to practice their life's work in an externally "managed," highly competitive *though not necessarily humanitarian* "caring" atmosphere. Finding their work oppressive as defined and dictated by a central office administrator, some professionals are making the difficult decision to take early retirement or seek employment in less politically stressful work arenas. This reduction in the number of caring providers further challenges the climate of the health delivery field, making it less responsive to and supportive of the individual patient.

Even within the field of psychology, there is dissension and division regarding the appropriate and ethical course of psychological treatment. One school of therapy, the cognitive-behavioral approach, espouses a "brief, problem-focused therapy" model. For obvious reasons, such an orientation is favored by managed care corporations. While problem-focused therapy may resolve many simple, straight-forward problems, it does not explore the full, personal significance *the meaning* of the problem, allow for release of feelings, or explore the pros and cons of the various alternatives to prevent its recurrence. It does not teach clients how to deal with their whole "selves"—their feelings as well as thoughts and behaviors—in everyday life experiences. It does not allow for the time needed to undo lifetime patterns of holding, resistance, or repression.

Beyond the immediate issues of the techniques of solving a particular problem, many psychotherapists believe that the relationship they develop with their clients is a powerful teaching tool. These therapists teach invaluable interpersonal skills through modeling and by providing the client with an experience of being in a responsible, caring relationship. Psychotherapists who are sufficiently psychologically mature to provide such a unique relationship, enable the client to understand her or himself and to become self-accepting as their feelings, thoughts, and behavior become integrated. Individuals who have not known genuine caring from their own family backgrounds or personal experiences may find it impossible to experience these qualities with others. The school of therapy which focuses on the techniques of brief problem resolution may ignore the critically important relationship variables in treatment. This is particularly troubling because there is a sizable scientific body of research to support the hypothesis that what makes an effective therapist is not the theoretical orientation or therapeutic techniques utilized, but rather the level of professional maturity possessed by the therapist. In contrast, there are other theoretical orientations in psychology which believe in nurturing the feelings, utilizing a developmental process, considering existential meaning, and enhancing the quality of the professional therapeutic relationship. They believe that each and every one of these issues must be considered when treating a patient. They recognize the importance of professional support for those who are otherwise socially and psychologically isolated and do not have the benefits of caring family or supportive friends to deal with the stress of life. These approaches to psychotherapy require more time and provide important on-going support for clients suffering from chronic problems or illnesses. Therapists embracing this philosophical stance appreciate the time necessary to develop the safe, trusting relationship which is essential in overcoming the effects of a dysfunctional family-of-origin, chronic life stressors, or problematic addictions and dependencies. In addition, these therapists serve as role models for those who need to learn how a caring person can be present and provide continuing support and direction for those undergoing phase-of-life changes. This approach to treatment perceives the legitimacy of conferring with a psychologist for individuals who do not suffer from gross psychopathology, but desire consultation with a mature, psychologically knowledgeable professional who can help them fulfill their human potential by exploring existential issues such as: Who am I? Why am I here? What are my values? And what is the meaning of my life?

Precisely because mind and body are one, physical illnesses of "heart," as well as psychological illness of the "mind," may result when these emotional, developmental, value-laden, issues remain unresolved. These illnesses-of-heart, in turn contribute to the rising costs of medical health care. Indeed, resolving these issues psychologically in the short term, may be far more cost-effective than addressing them medically in the long term. Physicians and insurance companies know all too well, that heart disease frequently is preceded, as well as followed, by depression and that the patient's prognosis is better if depression can be ameliorated. In this case, psychological treatment directly impacts the need for health care utilization. Although specific problem-focused resolution may be the most appropriate intervention for many dilemmas, it is problematic when the industry fails to appreciate the value of different approaches in addressing various problems. Instead it limits the entire field of psychological practitioners to one politically or economically favored treatment modality.

In addition to external health-care influence, political/economic factors within the bodywork profession itself may limit practitioners' awareness of psychological factors in themselves as well as in their clients. As the popularity of alternative forms of health care proliferates, so do the number of new bodywork schools. Institutional competition and survival of a given program call for the reduction of expenses. Rather than expanding curriculum, limited revenues may allow only the essentials of bodywork education be provided. Many training facilities focus less and less on personal experiences in the training of bodyworkers. These new practitioners are, consequently, unprepared to recognize and address psychological issues in bodywork practice.

The high stress-level of contemporary life increases the need for mindbody support. Services of those providing mindbody integration as well as stress management will become increasingly significant in the prevention and amelioration of illness. As a more knowledgeable, health-conscious public becomes aware of the significance of the mindbody connection, its need for attention, and the deficits in traditional health care, society will take a more concentrated look at alternative avenues for delivering support. There will be an ever-increasing societal value of the supportive presence of those whose work comes as much from their hearts as from their heads, and a decreasing societal homage to "the bottom line." The calling cards of such practitioners will be their personal availability arising from a genuine caring, rather than from providing the maximum number of yearly authorized sessions. These professionals will provide continuity of care by being available in good times as well as in bad *not just while a significant level of pathology is present,* enriching the quality of their clients' lives.

FINAL THOUGHTS As I concluded the interviews for this study, what became ever clearer to me is that we do not enter into the world with a completely formed identity; achieving personal or professional identity is a process. We enter life with the potential to survive on many levels. We may survive via the fight-or-flight instinct, a basic or primitive strategy. Or, we can survive by using our capacity for highly complex problem-solving. In this instance we examine our experiences, glean meaning from our observations, generate response alternatives, select the best one, and take meaningful action.

We have no choice as to the environment into which we are born. We are often preprogrammed by our original environment to believe that what we learn from our family and our community is the best or the only life-path available to us. Normally, we follow this narrow path through life, allowing our fears and doubts to direct us toward paths of dependency, avoidance, denial, pretense, projection, or aggression.

It is possible that certain life experiences may catch our aware-ness and touch us in such a way that we realize that we have choices as to how we respond. At these critical choice-points we have a num-ber of alternatives. By continuing to do what we were told, simply because we were told to do it, we foreclose the opportunity to develop a sense of our self or identity. Or we may take action that is devoid of conviction and sincerity, moving from one alternative to another. Finally, by facing, accepting, and grappling with our imperfection, without judgment, shame, or blame, we choose to develop our sense of personal identity. In this instance we recognize that obstacles, mis-takes, and even failures are life's curriculum for growth. By choosing to embrace life's lessons, we confront the obstacles from without, and within, as we strive for a more complete sense of self-identity achieve-ment. Above and beyond what was given to us as we came into the world, our identity and the shape of our personality is molded as a con-sequence of our interactions with our environment.

Work is one of the many arenas in which we are confronted with life challenges. If work encounters are perceived merely as technical obstacles, issues of personal growth never emerge. Approaching work in this manner only allows a person to become more technically profi-cient. If we bring ourselves fully to these challenges, we develop not only as workers improving our role performance, but also as individu-als. We become more solid people. If we permit a dialogue between our personal side and our worker side, we create vocational paths that are ever more comfortable and more personally fulfilling.

Personal-professional growth issues that a bodyworker encoun-ters can help the practitioner detoxify her or his psychosocial identity and allow transcendence of the norm of personal and social denial. As bodywork professionals achieve greater strength through the process of growth and the quality of their presence and touch, they filter back well-being and health, not only to their clients and themselves, but also to society as a whole. From this dialogue, addressing professionally troubling encounters, bodyworkers' personal-professional growth, and the healing of society at large, what emerges is beyond technique—the hidden dimensions of bodywork.

BIBLIOGRAPHY

Alberti, R. E., & Emmons, M. L. (1975). *Your perfect right*. San Luis Obispo: Impact.

Barnard, K. E., & Brazelton, T. B. (Eds.), (1990). *Touch: the foundation of experience*. Madison: International University Press.

Bass, E. & Davis, L. (1988). *The courage to heal*. New York: Harper & Row.

Bassoff, E. S. (1991). *Mothering ourselves*. New York: Penguin Books.

Beattie, M. B., (1987). *Codependent no more*. San Francisco: Harper & Row.

Berry, C. R. (1993). *Your body never lies*. Berkeley: Page Mill Press.

Borysenko, J. (1987). *Minding the body, mending the mind*. New York: Bantam New Age.

Bradshaw, J. (1990). *Home coming*. New York: Bantam.

Dychtwald, K. (1986). *Bodymind*. New York: Putnam Books.

Edwards, D. & Gil, E. (1986). *Breaking the cycle*. Los Angeles: Association for Advanced Training.

Eisler, R. (1988). *The chalice and the blade*. New York: Harper Collins.

Erikson, E. H. (1963). *Childhood and society*. New York: Norton.

Fieve, R. R. (1981). *Moodswing*. New York: Bantam Books.

Ford, C. W. (1989). *Where healing waters meet*. Barrytown: Station Hill.

Forward, S. (1989). *Toxic parents*. New York: Bantam Books.

Friedman, J., Boumil, M. M., & Taylor, B. E. (1992). *Sexual harassment*. Deerfield Beach: Health Communications.

Gil, E. (1988). *Treatment of adult survivors*. Walnut Creek: Launch Press.

Goldenson, R. M. (1984). *Longman dictionary of psychology and psychiatry*. New York: Longman.

Grof, S. & Grof, C. (1989). *Spiritual emergency*. New York: St. Martin's Press.

Hancock, E. (1989). *The girl within*. New York: Ballantine Books.

Hay, L. L. (1984). *Heal your body*. Carson: Hay House.

Hanna, T. (1987). *The body of life.* New York: Knopf.

Hasting, A. (1991). *With the tongues of men and angels.* Fort Worth: Holt, Rinehart and Winston.

Hollis, J. (1993). *The middle passage.* Toronto: University of Toronto Press.

Hunter, M. & Struve, J. (1998). *The ethical use of touch in psychotherapy.* Thousand Oaks: Sage Publications.

Juhan, D. (1987). *Job's body.* Barrytown: Station Hill.

Kelly, C. R. (1974). *Education in feeling and purpose.* Santa Monica: The Radix Institute.

Kepner, J. I. (1987). *Body process.* New York: Gardner Press.

Kepner, J. I. (1992). *Healing tasks in the psychotherapy of adult survivors of childhood abuse.* Cleveland: The Gestalt Institute of Cleveland Press.

Kreisman, J. J. & Straus, H. (1989). *I hate you—don't leave me.* New York: Avon Books.

Kurtz, R. & Prestera, H. (1976). *The body reveals.* New York: Harper & Row.

Kurtz, R. (1990). *Body-centered psychotherapy.* Mendocino: LifeRhythm.

Lasch, C. (1979). *The culture of narcissism.* New York: Warner Books.

McNeely, D. A. (1987). *Touching.* Toronto: University of Toronto Press.

Maslow, A. H. (1968). *Toward a psychology of being.* New York: Van Nostrand Reinhold.

Masterson, J.F. (1988). *The search for the real self.* New York: The Free Press.

Miller, A. (1990). *Banished knowledge.* New York: Doubleday.

Miller, A. (1981). *The drama of the gifted child.* New York: Basic Books.

Missildine, W. H. (1963). *Your inner child of the past.* New York: Pocket Books.

Montagu, A. (1986). *Touching.* New York: Harper & Row.

Peterson, K. C., Prout, M. F., & Schwartz, R. A. (1991). *Post-traumatic stress disorder.* New York: Plenum Press.

Polster, E. & Polster, M. (1973). *Gestalt therapy integrated.* New York: Random House.

Rosenberg, J. L., Rand, M. L. & Asay, D. (1989). *Body, self, soul.* Atlanta: Humanic Limited.

Smith, E.W.L., Clance, P.R., & Imes, S. (Eds.), *Touch in psychotherapy.* New York: Guilford Press.

Tannen, D. (1990). *Your just don't understand.* New York: Ballantine Books.

Tart, C. T. (1989). *Open Mind, discriminating mind.* New York: Harper Collins.

Trager, M. & Cathy Guadagno, C. (1987). *Trager mentastics.* Barrytown: Station Hill Press.

Truax, C. B., & Mitchell, K. M. (1971). Research on certain therapist interpersonal skills in relation to process and out come. In Bergin, A. E., & Garfield, S. L. (Eds.), *Handbook of Psychotherapy and behavioral change* (pp. 299-344). New York: John Wiley & Sons.

Upledger, J. E. & Vredevoogd, J.D. (1983). Craniosacral therapy. Seattle: Eastland Press.

Upledger, J. E. (1991). *Your inner physician and you.* Berkeley: North Atlantic Books.

Vaeger-von Birgelen, C. (1996). *Off the hook.* New York: Plenum Press.

Wagner, E. J. (1992). *Sexual harassment in the workplace.* New York: AMACOM.

Whitfield, C. L. (1989). *Healing the child within.* Dearfield Beach: Health Communications.

Whitfield, C. L. (1993). *Boundaries and relationships.* Deerfield Beach: Health Communications.

Zinker, J. C. (1977). *Creative process in gestalt therapy.* New York: Brunner/Mazel.

INDEX

We would like to hear from you. If you have comments about the book, your experience with the book, or growth events that may have emerged for you as a result of reading this book, please feel free to write to:

BLHY Growth Publications, Inc.
2521 Far Hills Avenue
Dayton, OH 45419

Additional copies of this book can be obtained through BookMasters: by phone, 1 800 245-6553; or by E-mail, order@bookmaster.com. Please refer to the Code: CHDB.